NL

L

BOLLINGEN SERIES XXXIII

HUGO von HOFMANNSTHAL

SELECTED
PROSE

Translated by Mary Hottinger
and Tania & James Stern

Introduction by HERMANN BROCH

BOLLINGEN SERIES XXXIII

PANTHEON BOOKS

THIS IS THE THIRTY-THIRD IN A SERIES OF WORKS
SPONSORED BY AND PUBLISHED FOR
BOLLINGEN FOUNDATION

Library of Congress Catalogue Card No. 52–8758

SET, PRINTED AND BOUND IN THE U. S. A.
BY KINGSPORT PRESS, INC., KINGSPORT, TENN.
DESIGNED BY ANDOR BRAUN

The translation of *Andreas,* by Mary Hottinger, is a comprehensive revision by her of her translation published in 1936 by J. M. Dent and Sons, Ltd., London, to whom acknowledgment is made. Mrs. Hottinger also translated the extract from *The Woman without a Shadow* and the tales in part 6. Tania and James Stern translated the selections in parts 2, 3, 5, and 7; "Twilight and Nocturnal Storm," in part 4; and the introduction by Hermann Broch. The collected works of Hugo von Hofmannsthal, in German, are published by S. Fischer Verlag, Frankfurt a/M, Germany.

Contents

Contents

4

5

6

7

Introduction

ALMOST all of Hugo von Hofmannsthal's lyrical work (including the poems and the short dramas in verse) springs from one decade of his youth, the years 1890–99. The lyric period is outlasted on the one hand by the epic, supplanted on the other by the dramatic. The former starts off in 1894 with the *Tale of the Six-Hundred-and-Seventy-Second Night* and leads to two climaxes—to the novel-fragment *Andreas*, begun about 1912, and to the great symbolic narrative *The Woman without a Shadow*, published in 1919 as an eleventh-hour prose work along with the opera libretto of the same name. The dramatic period, on the other hand, whose starting point we may consider to be the First Act of *The Mines of Falun* (1899), continues uninterrupted until the poet's death in 1929. Along with these poetic activities, however, there runs his work in the essay, which, far from faltering, continues to grow in dimension; accompanying Hofmannsthal on his entire literary career, which began in his seventeenth year, this production was to be his constant medium of self-contemplation and self-interpretation, his philosophical diary in the course of existence.

THE ESTRANGEMENT FROM LYRICISM: "THE LETTER OF LORD CHANDOS"

For a born dramatist to abandon his narrative production or to confine it to the short story, founded on situations and as such related to the drama, is not rare—as has been demonstrated by Kleist, Hebbel, Grillparzer, as well as by Shaw and Wilde. It is equally comprehensible that with born story-tellers like Zola, Gorki, Hamsun, Thomas Mann, Joyce, the reverse took place. But for a born lyric poet to abandon the poem form in favour of epic prose and in favour of the stage remains all but unparalleled in literary history. And yet such is the case of Hugo von Hofmannsthal. He renounced lyricism when barely past his twenty-fifth year, thus at a time when poetic power is as a rule beginning fully to develop.

"Precocity spells early decline" is a very superficial generalization explaining nothing; it is particularly inappropriate to Hofmannsthal, who never, even in his first poems, wrote poetry typical of youth. What is usually of paramount importance to young people—the subjective reaction of the "I"—is to the young Hofmannsthal of little concern. Even in the earliest poems, regardless of their being written in the first person (which, incidentally, rarely occurs), the "I" is concealed, the lyrical statement is shifted to the object, an attempt is made to cull it from that which is seen, felt, and experienced while excluding actual seeing, feeling, experiencing: in short, any element of subjectivity. For, omitting any specific "confessional poetry" (*Bekenntnis-Lyrik*), he embarks at once on a "poetry of objective insight" (*Erkenntnis-Lyrik*), something the "normal" poet achieves, at best, after long years of growing and maturing, as a final phase. A final phase, of course, can also continue to grow and develop indefinitely. Not that Hofmannsthal's poetry had, with the first leap, reached a "goal," nor was it the allegedly too sudden leap and even less the exhaustion after the leap: other and considerably deeper-seated reasons inhibited further development. It can be maintained that inhibition and incentive are strangely identical in Hofmannsthal's development and that both must be sought in the

[x]

phenomenon of his most striking self-effacement—his "I"-sup-
pression.

In this connection we may recall a sentence, as strange
as it is memorable, from the *Book of Friends:* "Plasticity develops not through observation, but through identification."
This is a word of advice to the artist, and it implies: As long
as objects are to you merely an antithesis to your "I," you will
never grasp their real essence, and no amount of intensive
observation, description, or copying will help you to do so.
You may succeed, however, if you are able to divest yourself
of your "I" by projecting it into the object so that the object
can begin to speak in your stead. For you yourself, a single
individual facing a single object, have only your subjective
impressions, have thus like the animal-soul hardly a language,
at best mere sounds of terror and delight, of warning and en-
ticement, at most exclamations such as *Oh!* and *Ah!;* whereas
real language perpetuates not only the momentary impression
of objects but their essence, hence requiring a far more intimate, richer, more subtle relationship with them than animals
have. And this second immediacy (as we may call it, since
insight springs therefrom) is achieved exclusively by the surrender of the "I" to the object. He, however, who is satisfied
with subjective exclamations is no artist, no poet: confession
is nothing, insight is everything.

For Hofmannsthal, consequently, insight is complete identification with the object: the artist who is able to intensify his
intuition, as is his task, beyond that of everyday life, to the
point of complete identification with the world and everything in it, hears its specific language. He hears the language
of objects, gives it human expression, and thereby enriches our
language. Or more precisely, he senses the pre-established harmony between the "I" and the world, between the language,
concept-bearing and concept-borne, and the objects described

by it, so that he grasps them all, singly or united, from within their true existence; for he perceives in them all their *tat tvam asi* like an echo. That is mysticism. And even though with Hofmannsthal it may be confined predominantly to the artistic domain, it would be an empty assumption if it did not enable us to inquire after the proof of its evidence. Hofmannsthal gives the answer. Not that he actually refers to his historical sources, the philosophies of India, of Heraclitus, Leibniz, Böhme—no, his evidence is not acquired by reading: he refers to moments of poetic ecstasy, to those moments he describes as "exaltation," since it is in them that at one blow and under obliteration of the "I" the wholeness of existence is perceived, or rather in wondrous long-known familiarity re-perceived, an absolute recollection of a pre-experience, a total recall whose origin (not to be confused with the physiological memory of generations) manifests itself unequivocally as a metaphysical "pre-existence" of mankind. It is the phase wherein man has been endowed with complete identification of the "I" with the non-"I" (facing him as the world), the phase wherein he has received once for all the divine gift of harmony of object, idea, and word—in short, the basis of all world intuition, all insight and all language.

To find the way back to complete identification, back to pre-existence, reveals itself thus—and this is actually Hindu philosophy—as the ultimate ecstasy of man, probably the greatest spiritual height he can attain. And since this complete identification with his object has been made the artist's task, indeed his moral task, his work must be its expression, its image, its symbol; when these conditions are fulfilled the work becomes itself ecstasy and thus acquires that specific quality we term "beauty." And it is therefore the artist who realizes the well-nigh insurmountable difficulties that hamper the fulfilment of the task of identification. For of what elements does this non-"I" consist, this exterior world wherewith the "I" is supposed to identify itself? Firstly, the world is in constant motion; secondly, and this is far more disturbing: all means of expression (linguistic or otherwise) given to man to describe the world are part of that world; and thus, thirdly, with each act of identification a portion of the "I" enters the non-"I," changing and enriching the non-"I" so that a new act of identification becomes a necessity. Instead of a static object the artist deals with a highly fluctuating one, and rather than a single act of identification a whole chain is required; we are familiar with the first links in these chains, for they are the simple metaphors which belong to the prime prerequisites of poetry. But since they are bound to be insufficient there is born out of them a whole chain of symbol creations, of symbol-symbolizations, that have to hug reality more and more closely in order finally to produce—at least according to the idea—in the given sector of reality a total symbol of the world, the *tat tvam asi* of art.

However, in order to achieve this feat, the chains must at last, somewhere, be broken off; otherwise there would exist only work in progress and never a completed work of art. But when does the moment of completion arrive? How is this moment recognized? It is just the lyrical poem—in strange parallel to the joke—which undertakes an extremely bold irrational shortening of the chains, and presumably it is the lyrical content inherent in each work of art that is responsible for its act of completion. True, the term "lyric" does not offer an objective or precise criterion, nor even a subjective one, the less so since what is at stake is not only the secret of conciseness and economy, but also that of artistic exuberance. As beauty cannot be its own critical yardstick, where then is the criterion of achieved perfection? It was in connection with music, which already possesses its codifying rules, that man discovered the criterion of the medium, the criterion of the means of expression. From the medium he hoped—provided identification was radically channelled toward it with increasing perfection, like a correctly constructed fugue—that it would, as form, as language in itself, disclose the completing of a work of art: hence the primary mysticism of intuition is joined by a second one, that of form, of language and its perfection. Already alluded to by the Romanticists, although still overlaid by faith- (and other) mysticisms, the new principle emerges unequivocally with Baudelaire and henceforth dominates all poetry of the second half of the nineteenth century, setting a style for the novel from Flaubert to Proust, and becoming an absolute dogma for the entire symbolist school down to Mallarmé and George—a dogma so absolute and autonomous that their disciples considered in all seriousness investing it with the character of a new world religion serving exclusively the ideal of "beauty."

At this moment serious art steps over the borderline to the ridiculous and art begins turning its own marble into cardboard imitations. And of this danger Hofmannsthal's eminent critical mind was thoroughly aware. In the beginning, no doubt, he had been convinced that the goal of poetic insight could best be served by means of aesthetic perfection: all the more so since the basic emotional shock he had received at the first flaring up of the pre-existential memory and its artistic symbols—a shock he probably experienced more profoundly than anyone else—still continued to affect him. Yet if there were anyone who regarded insight not just as a façade but as the core of aesthetic perfection, it was he, to whom the "depth hidden on the surface" was of constant concern. He recognized the dangers of pan-aestheticism: the idea of a work of art whose universality should by a wealth of symbols finally produce All-cognizance appeared to him condemned to remain a thrust into the void; for the "beautiful," even if surrounded by the nimbus of religiosity, can never be raised to the level of the absolute, and therefore must remain incapable of transmitting insight. Herewith Hofmannsthal renounces pan-aestheticism (and incidentally George too), and it is a far more fundamental renunciation than any other based on naturalistic reasoning (frequent at that time). It indicates that he who tries to supplant a genuine religiosity with an aesthetic one serves a false god and promotes all the insanity and evil which invariably and inevitably emerge from any pseudo-religiosity.

The outbreak of insanity and how this condition grows is described by Hofmannsthal in "The Letter of Lord Chandos."

Lord Chandos, a young country squire of the Elizabethan epoch, in whom, however, we easily recognize the fully educated Oxford graduate and gentleman aesthete of our day, writes to his paternal friend, Lord Chancellor Bacon, the keenest thinker of his time. He describes, albeit with the discreet self-effacement imposed by his education and breeding, a most terrifying experience: at one blow he has lost the mystical intuitive unity of "I," expression and object: his "I" has been brought abruptly to a state of hermetic isolation, isolated in an abundant world to which he no longer finds any access and whose objects no longer mean anything to him, let alone their names: world and objects have overwhelmed him, as it were, in a negative way by withdrawing from him. What reveals itself here is not contrition, not the condition of a man cast into nothingness—no, it is the state of utmost imperfection and therefore utmost disgust: it is disgust with objects because they are unattainable; disgust with the word, which, filled with utter disparity, can no longer reach an object; disgust with his own existence, which has lost its power of insight and as a result its self-fulfilment as well. Man has been defeated by the aggression of objects (an aggression which the essay "The Irony of Things" describes in a slightly different light) and the required but now unachievable radical identification with objects; this act of most perfect love has been supplanted by love-defeat, by life-impotence itself, by the disgust it generates.

Hofmannsthal very wisely did not put the Lord Chancellor in the embarrassing position of having to answer this letter, for what could a Bacon, who was no Shakespeare—different, of course, had he been one—have done about such an outburst of anguish? To his sober sense of reality, supported by faith, insight was simply insight; and that this could ever break down, indeed, that this breakdown of the human act of creation could also endanger the divine act (and this was the deepest fear in the Chandos Letter), this he would have considered an utterly incomprehensible blasphemy. In accordance with the ideas of his time he would have seen in it a sure sign of being possessed by the devil—the inevitable pyre, therefore, for his young friend as well as for the poet Hofmannsthal himself. And had he been familiar with modern psychology, he would have spoken of schizophrenia, explaining that presumably every poet is threatened with a split in his personality and tries to protect himself from this threat by plunging into his work, into which he projects all his splits in order to abreact with the help of such sublimation his fear of schizophrenia—a somewhat devious reasoning, after all, for a Lord Chancellor of Queen Elizabeth.

Nevertheless, every human soul, particularly that of the artist, above all that of a poet, is subjected to splits: nowhere is the paradoxical character of the process of poetic creation (a true paradoxy of the infinite) as clearly visible as in the phenomenon of the split whereby poetry is as much destroyed as it is fructified. The Chandos Letter describes the extreme case of utter annihilation, since here man, incapable of identification, unable to bridge the tension between perceiving and the perceived, is completely at the mercy of the unperceivable existence, of objects, their impalpable hostility, their incomprehensibility, their irony. But the despair over this condition, as the young Chandos expresses it, reveals the paradoxical-fertile content of the process, that is to say the identification of the subject with an object incapable of the act of identification. In other words, the act of identification is performed with its own opposite—without which it would have been impossible for Hofmannsthal to describe Chandos's despair. But this, just this, is the dialectical structure of the creative process: no matter whether, as here, identification and non-identification are brought into a synthesis or whether this happens to another pair of opposites, we always see the reflection of the primary contrasts, and this (to the regret of the Freudian school) is certainly not, or is at most in a very metaphorical sense, the sexual contrast; rather is it that of the "I" and the non-"I," of being-"I" and being-the-world, both, thanks to the psychic split, the domicile of man and the fount of his poetic creation. For it is from this tension between the "I" and the world that poetic energy springs forth, undivided at its source yet forked into lyrical and dramatic expression, both equally indispensable to it—one projecting the outer world to the inside, the other projecting the inside to the outer world, as a result of mutual conditioning. With all this, however, the function of the psychic split is not yet exhausted: it not only allows us to experience the contrast (of the "I") to the world, to experience the aggression and irony of the world as well as of objects (thus rendering all this tangible and soluble)—no, it is also the prerequisite for any kind of self-observation. And out of the despair-bearing awareness of man's own failure arises that self-irony wherewith poetry—no other art medium is to the same degree capable of this—looks so to speak over its own shoulder, increasingly doubting itself, doubting its inherent truth, its social significance, and actually expressing these doubts. Poetry is a dream, but one that is continually growing aware of its own dreaming, and for that reason can grow into a dream-smile. And just because the element of irony is so definitely a function as well as a result of a split, we must assume that it reaches back to the beginnings of poetry, perhaps back to the laughter of the gods, and cannot be confined to the Romanticists, in spite of the eminent place they gave it in their instrumentarium.

As often as the poet succeeds—and otherwise he wouldn't be one—in making his splits fruitful, in grasping a piece of reality by mastering all his antinomies, in capturing with his symbol-chains the world whole or in parts, or even in perpetuating it by a total symbol from which radiates a recognizable harmonious unity, he will experience that "exaltation" whereby, for Hofmannsthal, ecstatic moments of highest fulfilment of values were characterized. Nor can any irony weaken such ecstatic bliss, rather will it be enhanced by the knowledge embodied in irony. What happens in the Chandos Letter, however, has scarcely anything to do with irony. Here we are shown a young man for whom the "I" and non-"I" have lost all connection, since for him the symbol-chains have sundered even before the forging of the first link: nothing remains to him but the mere split itself, so that all his life-values are extinct. He is in a state opposite to ecstasy, in a state of panic, the deepest abyss of man. When describing this condition, Hofmannsthal must himself have been in the last stages of life-panic. How, then, could he write at all? How can muteness be abreacted with the aid of speech, how blindness with the aid of sight? That a poet invents murders and identifies himself with the murderers to rid himself of his own homicidal tendencies is conceivable, and one can imagine that Goethe, after Werther's death, had once for all conquered any suicidal tendencies of his own. No less conceivable is the fact that wherever a poet fails to incorporate his emotions completely into his literary work, and thus to neutralize them in actual life, the fate of his protagonists will become his own: this is what happened to Strindberg. But that a poet—and this is the case of Chandos—can extract from a panic that must have been his own the ecstasy that follows each successful achievement, this borders on the inconceivable. In so far as this work is to be taken as an expression of a real experience, the paradox here seems to have veered round into the antinomic.

No doubt the Chandos Letter must have been preceded by an exceedingly severe emotional shock, and it was only natural that it called for abreaction. It was presumably no less severe an experience than that which Hofmannsthal—at the time little more than a boy—underwent at the beginning of his poetic career, when this shock revealed to him the miracle of identification between the "I" and objects. Now, all of a sudden, the reverse had occurred: in his struggle with the problem of symbols there suddenly arose the possibility that he might henceforth be unable to effect identification, and this carried with it a taboo on poetic production. This was a catastrophic discovery, and it would not have been surprising had it been answered by an immediate cessation of all poetic activity. Nevertheless, this did not happen; the command to remain silent, despite the accompanying emotional shock, was apparently less categorical than the earlier command which had forced him into raising the poetic voice. For, if the beginning of the poetic creation had occurred like a dream, alarmingly beatific yet overwhelming, irrepressible, and emerging directly from darkest depths, the new experience was equally alarming though no longer beatific, but instead sombrous, taking place in considerably more awake, more conscious zones, shot through by a variety of rational ideas and considerations: the summons to renounce poetic activities was no dream-challenge to which the entire person had to submit with his every fibre—no, it was rather a moral precept appealing to the conscience and consequently to free will, hence permitting a rational understanding and perhaps even a refutation. It was not an unconditional command; true, it released all ideas of panic but not panic itself, and although it represented sufficient emotional shock, the attempt to abreact into work could be risked. The attempt proved but a partial success, possibly because a Renaissance vignette—which, after all, is just what the Chandos Letter is —was insufficient for so powerful a theme. A compromise had to be made: the ban on production was confined to poetry itself, while all other work could be carried on.

In this compromise, the naming of things—the "christening task" of poetry—is at stake. For, of all branches of literature, it is pre-eminently the one allied to verse which has proved itself suitable to such a task. This is an assertion, of course, to be taken *cum grano salis,* for we can contrast a Shakespeare, a Dante, a Goethe, with great prose writers of the calibre of a Cervantes (not to mention those of lesser stature); but so far as the assertion holds good it lends to lyricism, to the poetic art *pur sang,* a special significance, and folk poetry is not the last to have a share in it: language creation occurs where new layers of reality and insight are opened up, and this can happen only from the "I," from its solitude, from its piety, in short from its lyrical centre. Poems that meet the challenge of this condition—and they are not few in the long line of occidental poetry from Sappho to Lorca—are adopted without further ado by popular art and transfigured into the anonymous. Such honour, on the other hand, has to this day never fallen to the works of aestheticism and its decorative art, simply because no splendour of words, accompanied by artistic achievement no matter how high, is sufficient to penetrate into new domains—with the result that the reverse, perhaps, also holds good: failing the discovery of new planes of reality, be it in the natural or supernatural sphere, there is no lyricism—at best but a derivative one. And thus it is here in this realm that the artist must search incessantly for criteria of aesthetic perfection, must demand in peculiar mock-humility the complete absorption of the subject by the aesthetic object, whereas popular poetry (taken in a wider sense) masters the lyrical shortening of symbol-chains in a natural way, in such mysterious simplicity that all the identification-mysticism of the aestheticists pales by comparison and disappears. Genuine religiosity *versus* adulation of beauty, search for the essential *versus* joy in the gesture, true humility in piety *versus* spiritual pride—that is the difference. Hofmannsthal's young nobleman falls into panic-stricken despair because he is an aesthete and in his overweening vanity can no longer find a way out. Had a truly humble and pious man been struck by the Chandos catastrophe, it would have made him even more pious and his silence would have been contrition, would have caused a search for still deeper realities.

We may assume that all this played quite a relevant part in Hofmannsthal's creative work. The Chandos Letter may be considered as the first result of his break with aestheticism, the second being his turning to folk art, the striving for a genuine rather than a specious humility. But can such a transformation be brought about according to preconceived plan? Hofmannsthal was well aware that folk art allows for no imitation and that with the imitation of folk lyricism the artist falls into the trivial. How then assert himself as a poet in spite of it? He solved this problem by inventing a supplementary theory: the return to the popular may be achieved by gaining moral influence over the masses. As a result, intelligibility is imperative and consequently the poem with its inevitable esoteric element is excluded from the outset. But in the narrative and above all on the stage this goal seems to be attainable. And perhaps the success of the theatre may be taken as a criterion of perfection for which aestheticism has searched in vain.

THE NARRATIVE WORK

Hofmannsthal's narrative work comprises, distinctly, two groups of production: on the one hand the fairytales belonging primarily to his youth, but resumed once more about 1919 with *The Woman without a Shadow;* on the other hand the stories in more realistic form. The latter group contains *A Tale of the Cavalry* (1898), the novellas *Bassompierre* (1900) and *Lucidor* (1910), and the very remarkable attempt "Twilight and Nocturnal Storm" (1911). This group culminates in the novel *Andreas,* written in 1912 and 1913 but never finished; to it the earlier fragment "Contarin," as a kind of atmospheric preliminary sketch, also belongs.

At the time of the first World War James Joyce was working on his *Ulysses,* which he had started in 1908 (in 1914 *Dubliners* appeared, and in 1916 the *Portrait*). Why the allusion to this contemporaneousness? Why not point to Proust, no less a contemporary, whom many consider a distant relative of Hofmannsthal? No, surprisingly enough, the parallel to Joyce is the more conclusive. Could the reason be that the early lyrical poetry of both men was so bound to tradition? Or was it the similarity between Hofmannsthal's theory of pre-existence and Joyce's historical philosophy adopted from Vico? These are surface analogies. It would seem more significant that Joyce, too, probably had his Chandos experience, for the atomization of expression that he undertook in his prose work with intent to form from its phrase-fragments and word-particles a new and more genuine expression of reality suggests a downright fury and disgust, a disgust with the outworn inadequate language, with its clichés, frozen both in vocabulary and syntax. And this suspicion is strengthened when we observe that the mysticism of art, language, and perfection, common to both poets, and almost to them alone, led them to the problem of the infinite symbol-chains and symbol-symbolizations.

In its moment of highest grace music sometimes succeeds in creating world-symbols out of nothingness; everywhere else they are created out of the reservoir of memory so that, newly created, they may be stored in it again. Both Joyce and Hofmannsthal moved on to the specific art-form of memory—that is, to the narrative, hence to that of the novel. Here, however, a fundamental difference can be noted. Joyce was endowed above all with an auditive, Hofmannsthal with a visual memory; hence with the one the symbol-chains took the form of echo and counter-echo, with the other the form of a succession of images in infinite reflection and counter-reflection; here the novel becomes visual space, there sound space. Both methods are legitimate; nevertheless, their potentiality is by no means equal. For the visual impression can be transposed into the auditive—this, too, is one of the miracles of great music, of its power to create (not imitate) a cosmos—whereas the auditive can hardly be expressed adequately in the visual. Though this, of course, is a purely technical limitation, it was certainly a contributing factor when Hofmannsthal laid aside, unfinished, his narrative masterpiece *Andreas*. It was reserved for the infinitely more rational Joyce—the poetry of his youth shows how much more sparsely, more contrivedly, hence how much less poetically, his associations occurred—to become the master of the modern novel and to open up for it (not only in the technical sense) completely new avenues of expression. Is this one more manifestation of the contrast between a poetry of confession and one of insight? Does the former thus prove itself again more productive? If music in its ultimate greatness—take Bach

—can be conceived as deepest self-confession, then painting is the most penetrating objective insight; and it would therefore be justifiable to postulate that Joyce the musician aimed from the beginning—most clearly in the *Portrait*—at confessional writing.

Does visuality then produce "I"-suppression or—and this is more likely—does the "I"-suppressing artist, inimical to confession, feel the urge toward visuality? On leafing through Hofmannsthal's poems, on opening at random his diary-like letters, one sees on every page evidence of his visual memory and is continually surprised by the manifold diversity—a diversity that can easily compete with Joyce's auditive memory, trained in twenty languages. Anything that ever delighted the young man's eye, images of landscape through which he had wandered, images of towns and villages and their gardens, but also (and not least) theatre scenes and sets that had already formed the deepest impressions in the child—all this is saturated with colour and plastically retained; truly everything is there, only the living human being as such is missing. And if he is, as an exception, admitted, then he is usually an actor and therefore denatured to a mere puppet, almost as though the self-suppressing author felt bound to be as reticent about his fellow man. In one of Hofmannsthal's spiritual ancestors, in Adalbert Stifter, certainly the greatest prose-writer of Austrian post-classicism and perhaps the greatest depicter of landscape in German literature, this tendency is if possible even more pronounced. Whether insight or confession, both rest here exclusively in the landscape, and within it man is nought but a prop, nought but—in the truest sense of the word—an optical figure, a non-living being whose shadow-existence follows some abstract moralizing, some idealistically romanticized conventions, and knows no genuine human desire, thus (in Freudian terms) is moved continually by a sort of Super-Ego but never by the Id. In this connection two facts emerge; firstly, that aestheticism is not conquered by moralizing but merely shifted to a sidetrack, and secondly, that by it the life-totality required of the great novel of world literature can never be achieved. Hofmannsthal, by his often unsuccessful effort to free himself from an art which by its visuality serves purely aesthetic purposes, was aware—and his Poet in *The Little Theatre of the World* bears witness to this—that this form of art falls short in all problems where the intrinsic human substance is at stake; consequently he discovered that the approach to these problems lay in enveloping the human being in the landscape's immortality. He created a new type of man, a man completely under the spell of the landscape's magic, and with his protagonist Andreas he succeeded in the most magnificent manner. Nevertheless, even the most glorious magic succeeds only within the magic hour; the moment this has passed and the clock strikes one—which happens here (and even more so with Stifter) as soon as the book is closed—the landscape, it's true, remains, but the magic figures disappear. For they possess almost no human existence of their own, much less that street existence, as we may call it, with which characters like Robinson Crusoe, Gulliver, Rastignac, Oblomov, Saccard, Alyosha, and even Madame Bovary have engraved themselves into the memory of mankind, remaining all but independent of the book and filled, for that very reason, with well-nigh mythical overtones. They all come close to the totality of the human image whose manifold dimensionality engulfs the Id as well as the Super-Ego, the magic and mystical as well as the fully conscious and metaphysical. And exactly the same range is peculiar to Joyce's method, which—growing clear from a certain distance—achieves in a pointillistic and apparently contourless manner, with the help of its auditive particles, utmost concreteness for Bloom, Dedalus, and Earwicker; aiming beyond this, however, at mythical moorings, not only by the form of the work itself, no, even more so—as though to discover the source of language—by advancing the auditive symbols to those deepest regions wherein murmurs the dream and through it time immemorial.

Nevertheless, neither Bloom nor Dedalus nor Earwicker are mythological characters. For the modern myth, which so many poets are eager to create, does not exist; there exists only something which could actually be described as counter-myth: myth, after all, is cosmogony, is description of those primordial powers which menace and destroy man, and oppose their symbolic figures with hero-symbols no less promethean, which reveal how man conquers the apparently unconquerable and is capable of living on earth. None of this is still pertinent today, or rather, mythological rationality has been superseded by the scientific rationality which now in its turn has to describe with indeed sharper rational symbols the primeval powers and the possibility of their defeat. And even if the most primal anxiety continues to live unchanged in man; indeed, even if it clings to its inherited forms, the fear-inspiring element has, without his being fully aware of it, been shifted and no longer lies in primitive nature, lies instead—strangely enough—in nature tamed into civilization, lies in man himself, from whom suddenly, again myth-demanding, or rather demanding the counter-myth, the untamed, the untameable, rises anew. Machine-jungle, concrete-jungle, civilization-jungle—whether it will be possible to tame them once more by the old heroic means is debatable; at the moment they represent a situation as ghastly as it is unheroic, and the new heroes with their dictatorial blood-lust make them even more unheroic, more ghastly. It is a situation of utter helplessness and Kafka, not Joyce, did it justice; in Kafka we find the germ of an adequate counter-myth in whose instrumentarium hero-symbols, father- and even mother-symbols, become non-essential or even completely superfluous because he is concerned with the symbolization of helplessness itself, in short, that of the child. Hofmannsthal, on the other hand, thanks to a poetic knowledge of the irrational closer to Kafka than to Joyce, sensed this, too. Could he have freed himself from the calamitous stage-costumes which, with their liveried footmen, etc., followed him everywhere as permanent obstacles, the counter-mythical force of a piece of prose like "Nocturnal Storm," written some time before Kafka's first publications, would have become lucid and fertile. And the same holds all the more true for *Andreas*.

So far as one can speak of a myth-construction in Hofmannsthal's work, it stands under the symbol of the voyage, or more exactly under that of the river whose waves carry men as though in a dream from birth to death, from the source to the mouth, from the prehistoric rock piled into mountains and the weighty dynamism of glacial slopes down to the might and eternal calm of the sea—its beginning and end immutable nature, keeping immemorial time visibly present, infinitely more present for the visual type of man than would be the resounding and murmuring of dreams. Yet, halfway down the road, in the plains cut across by hurrying streams, the traveller comes upon fortified yet gaily decorated cities and well-tilled country, upon culture, beautiful in itself as well as in its creations, truly rivalling nature by its mystical creative power, indeed, surpassing it, for here in the region of the spirit and of art and purifying civilization man sheds his stupor. Here for the first time he is able to free nature from its primordial danger and to draw it into the magic circle of newly won beauty, so that he, no longer a will-less driven creature, becomes henceforth by virtue of such new receptiveness to nature the helmsman of life's journey, beholding before him the last port as his homeland:

> *Wasser stürzt, uns zu verschlingen,*
> *Rollt der Fels, uns zu erschlagen,*
> *Kommen schon auf starken Schwingen*
> *Vögel her, uns fortzutragen.*
>
> *Aber unten liegt ein Land,*
> *Früchte spiegelnd ohne Ende*
> *In den alterslosen Seen.*
>
> *Marmorstirn und Brunnenrand*
> *Steigt aus blumigem Gelände,*
> *Und die leichten Winde wehn.*

(Water plunges to engulf us, the cliff rolls to strike us dead, already on strong pinions birds come to carry us away. But below lies a land mirroring fruits without end in its ageless lakes. Brow of marble and well-coping rise from the flowery plains, and the light winds blow.)

Here the twenty-four-year-old poet strikes the keynote of the theme that was to become his lasting one, the theme of the mythical voyage. Still trusting in beauty, he did not yet recognize that nature, having been rendered harmless by culture and elevated to beauty, had in turn bequeathed to culture, as a permanent Greek gift, the sinister, the menacing. Heir to this gift is the uncreative man of civilization, the mystery-estranged, mystery-hostile "lower classes" of the cities, the civilization-mob in whose non-Being smoulders immemorial time strangely warped and distorted, mocking with the ghastly mimic laughter of malignity. Thus everything is full of polar ambiguity and the mythical voyage to the mouth of the river can become simultaneously a "bad descent," a desertion of the zones of the Super-Ego, a slipping into the Id, a self-abandonment to the most anonymous entanglement and for this very reason to the anonymously shameless, to the bestial pre-human —eternal temptation for man, for his mania for shedding the humane qualities bestowed on him—so that freed of shame he can relapse into the primal state, fall back into the condition of the primordial child.

Mountain landscape as primeval nature, the Valley of the Po as the sphere of blessed civilization—both represented for Hofmannsthal (in whose veins flowed, among other blood, that of the Austrian peasant and the Lombard patrician) a twofold native land, and it may be that it was this he had in mind when he began to write *Andreas*. In fact, however, it became the book of the mythical voyage and its content is the double descent: on the one hand that from the mountain world to Mediterranean culture, on the other that from the upper sphere of clarity to the lower depth of confusion. It is the story of the young Herr von Ferschengelder, from rococo Vienna, who is sent by his parents to Venice for the purpose of broadening his education, and who thereby embarks on a journey of increasing enchantment and an almost solemn perilousness. The journey leads at first into the Carinthian Alps, straight into the first, however brief enchantment with landscape. It enfolds Andreas in lovely simplicity, and at the old farm bearing the coat of arms of the noble peasant family of Finazzer he finds their daughter Romana, a rural Austrian Ophelia—unforgettable yet to be fled, yet to be extinguished in the enchantment, the oblivion, of Venice which promptly and inevitably falls upon the new arrival. Here in the neverending maze of alleys and canals, a reflected image of every intrigue, every possible human entanglement, he gets caught in a net of reflections and counter-reflections, in a thicket of psychic identifications and antagonisms, in a spiritual masquerade packed with erotic depths and superficialities. Into what kind of watertown filled with beauty and mud had fate brought him? It is salt water, yet not sea—could the life voyage, youth and age seemingly blended, be coming so soon to an end in this glitter of threatening ambiguity? Here everything is clear-seeing scepticism yet dream, while yonder with Romana Finazzer everything was both dreaming illusion and reality in the gushing of the clear mountain streams. Does Andreas seek the one or the other?

The completed fragment of the novel, describing only the Finazzer adventure and the days of arrival in Venice, does not answer these questions, but from the preliminary sketches and Notes for the general synopsis, the fact clearly emerges that Andreas moves in Venice on forbidden ground. The Notes consist of hundreds of allusions to situations, pieces of dialogue, witty epigrams, and between them sharp flashes of lightning which characterize and outline the human beings, though also revealing in their sharpness, of course, that they are pseudo-contours, since no "I" is established. For example: "What attracts him in Andreas: that he is so open to influences from others; the life of others is present in him in purity and strength. . . . Andreas is . . . the geometrical locus of the destinies of others." And as a result the "lower" lives also gain power over him in their vulgarity, first in the person of the servant Gotthilff, whose diabolism had necessitated his leaving the Finazzer farm; and one may conclude from the drafts that the iridescent city might bring about a repetition of the sinister element in an extremely intensified form. But, in this merging of characters, this flowing of the evil into the good, is not the path being prepared for the status of the primordial child? In the Notes, unclear to whom it refers, we find the following: "Relatedness. Alone with the child, the child looks up: 'Out of the substance, which I may not seek—for I have that substance—all the heavens and hells of all religions have arisen—to cast them away would be gross darkness.—The child's look: links me to what is simply there.' . . . Only the cataclysm reveals supreme ecstasy."

Introduction

These are mystical words and, although they stammer, they are rational in comparison with what they are meant to express—with the mythical fear that shudders when faced with primal substance and yet longs for it because it is the primal abode of the cataclysm. Myth cannot abide the rationality inherent in any description; Kafka does not describe, Hofmannsthal cannot resist it, for no amount of magic, however plausibly described, is capable of lifting landscape and the visual into the multidimensional. In the rational sphere Hofmannsthal undoubtedly knows about the mythical solution ("I should like to die reconciled to my childhood"); but even with the water motif, so important for the mythical voyage that he resumes it in the death of the Knight of Malta, the noblest figure in the book (he "hears water flowing, desires to conjure up all water he has ever heard flow"), he remains confined to the level of description. For Andreas himself it is decided only that he—upstream and without having found "self-confidence"—is to set out on his return journey, bringing home nothing but this very small increase of knowledge: "with Romana . . . it might be my heaven." And even that is a subjunctive.

With *Andreas* Hofmannsthal had set for his narrative production a pinnacle whose height he had underestimated; he abandoned the ascent because, having started out with chiefly visual but otherwise insufficient equipment, he would have felt bound to make use of autobiographical elements (which had already accumulated in the preliminary sketches for the novel)—and this was incompatible with his need for "I"-suppression: more important to him than completion and publication was personal self-interpretation, self-contemplation, self-education, which had been his concern in writing poetry from the beginning—with the result that he was always ready to resign himself to the fragmentary.

All the same, a poet never utterly abandons a theme he has
not truly mastered, and just as in the phylogenetic total development of poetry the fairytale emerges from the myth, so in
Hofmannsthal's ontogenesis *Andreas,* with its tendency to
myth, was followed by the fairytale of *The Woman without a Shadow,* save that here, contrary to the general rule,
the structure of the main theme is not adhered to, but is in-
verted: while the theme of the child remains, it is transposed
into the problem of parenthood. A fairy princess, so the story
goes, falls violently in love with the Emperor of the South-
Eastern Islands and becomes his happy wife; she lives, however, under a terrible curse because, not yet being quite terres-
trial, she will have to return to the realm of the spirits (to
which she is still bound) unless she succeeds in becoming a
mother within twelve months, thereby acquiring a human
shadow. Meanwhile the Emperor (still unsuspecting and
merely amorous) is threatened with being turned to stone. In
direst distress, driven by the fact that time is running out, she,
in the guise of a poor woman, elopes from the palace with her
fairy nurse, whose plan it is to induce the beautiful, wicked
wife of Barak the dyer, with the aid of promises, money, and
magic power, to sell her shadow. But when the two women
arrive at the home of the dyer's wife, the deal is thwarted by
one obstacle after another, and the Empress is forced to realize
that only by serving mankind can she gain her own human
soul, her shadow, and her children. She realizes that to achieve
these ends utter readiness to sacrifice, to die, to renounce is
necessary, realizes the necessity while carrying it out, and in
so doing already shares in her own redemption as well as that
of the Emperor, the dyer, and his wife. In spite of its oriental
pomp, this is a simple, almost puritanically moralizing fable
—all puritanism, whether Christian or Jewish, permits only
that love and marriage which are blessed by children—and

at first no resemblance to *Andreas* can be detected. But has not the fairy daughter who wishes to acquire a human soul the status of the child? And is not the Emperor, under the threat of being turned to stone for failing to develop, in the same position? Indeed, does not the same hold true for the dyer and his wife, however good he, however wicked she may be, both of them living in a state of stupor? Their very problem of parenthood makes child-symbols of all these characters. Their immaturity is quite as obvious as that of the young Andreas, and if they are ever to grow into that maturity which is the essence of the father- and mother-symbol, they would have to aim at that self-identity which—a reappearance of the Chandos problem—issues from the identification of the Self with existence: in *Andreas* it is alluded to (with the hope of a possible solution) as self-education to love, and seen from this vantage point myth (even attempted myth) and fairytale draw considerably closer to one another.

In other words, whether in myth or fairytale, we are shown the immature and (in contrast to the heroic childlike Parzival) the unheroic childlike Being, a Being whose psyche is infinitely split, to whom a dominating system of values is no longer granted, and who consequently—most significant characteristic of modern times—has to obey infinite systems of values; a Being overwhelmed by commands and consequently frightened into infantile confusion. Even where heroic traits appear, as in *A Tale of the Cavalry,* they are determined by the split and are merely passive. Hofmannsthal experienced this psychic split as an "evil," actually urban, enchantment and—aiming at the popular—opposed it with the landscape enchantment as a "good" one, a "normal" one, almost as a flight into a safe normality, which prescribes the bearing of children and permits a simple social life. For that, too, is enchantment.

All this—enchantment and moralizing, nostalgia for the

Orient and for that threshold of the Orient, Venice, as well as nostalgia for a secure bourgeois life—all this had become with him so permanently established a theme because it was clearly associated with the first impressions of fairytales received in the well-protected nursery. And no doubt its god-parents were the fairytales of the *Thousand and One Nights* as well as those of the Grimms and Andersen. The form of the fairytale, moreover, was especially well suited to Hofmannsthal's talent and limitations, not least those of visuality and "I"-suppression. Especially the oriental fairytale, with its carpet-like ornamental charm, is visual in the extreme, for its figures have no individuality, are not "I"-borne, "I"-bearing characters, but without exception visually conceived types: they are "the" Caliph, "the" Vizir, "the" young son of a merchant, "the" water-carrier; they are weightless, transparent, shadowless glass marionettes; they are homunculi, and the hand of the story-teller, seizing their wires, though it may move them to a most miraculous pseudo-visibility and pseudo-life, cannot overcome the lack of shadow and weight, the unreality of the marionette stage—the visual method of fairytales being an unalterable fact. It is a highly un-Homeric, almost anti-Homeric method since it recognizes no duty to produce proof, and thus it also remains unproven that the Empress, by virtue of moral and miraculous social conduct and of a by no means unbourgeois fairy-respectability, has really gained her shadow and her motherhood and has fought her way through to self-identity. Measured by the logical precision of the myth, the pattern of the fairytale tends towards a general noncommittal quality, a general diffusiveness, in which the individual statement does not go beyond a vague, empty, at best magical assertion: man's tragic path of purification, a fundamental theme of myth, bequeathed to all great works of poetry—for instance *Faust*—is no longer to be found in the fairytale, perhaps because this is a late form; if its pseudo-purifications are to be convincing it requires a second enchantment, that of music—eternal example: *The Magic Flute.*

Hofmannsthal's fairytales are final manifestations of a late art form. In all evolutions of intellectual history there are large and small waves, and the fairytale, although itself a late form, has once upon a time—as long as it was on the lips of the people—had its period of youth. At that time it was of a beguiling simplicity. Final forms, however, require extreme technical skill; they are products of late and (as today) of latest cultures, and they all strike us like the mastering of a Chandos experience: the stream of symbols, no doubt, has begun to flow again, but the natural direct connection between association, linguistic expression, symbol, and object has not been restored; a certain freezing of symbols has taken place, and in order to keep communication comprehensible and flexible, more and more symbols must be brought into play, further intensifying with their superabundance the process of freezing, since—and this is the transition from symbol to allegory—they would no longer be at all comprehensible were they not ordered into an established and consequently allegorical canon, the opposite extreme to direct communicability. And because this is a process of paralysis, an homunculoid, lifeless quality clings to allegory, by which it is exposed to the danger of petrification as well as to that of evaporation. But is not the Empress also threatened by evaporation, the Emperor by petrification? Hofmannsthal's special method and its application become at a stroke visible in *The Woman without a Shadow.* In the central chapter of the narrative, the Unborn, his future children, appear to the Emperor, summoning him to fatherhood—to creativeness. The scene takes place in the subterranean splendour of a cave, in the womb of the earth, which incidentally is reminiscent of *The Mines of Falun.* But Hofmannsthal's symbolism extends further, for creative power implies also the evoking of names, the evoking of the essential out of the *hinc et nunc* of objects. The unborn little Princess spreading before her father the carpet of the world and on it every living creature, says of her weaving: "I do not see what is, nor do I see what is not, but I see that which always is, and thus I weave." To this sphere, of course, the Emperor has no access; his forebodings still slumber in the unawakened realm of desire, and although he stands on the threshold of illumination the work of divine creation evades him, so that he grows silent while beginning slowly to turn to stone. And thus once more Hofmannsthal renders symbolic (an absolutely Joycean trick) the allegorizing process, renders symbolic by means of the content his own means of representation. And in this way with renewed artistry he breaks through the merely allegorical, merely artificial, merely intermediate, and gains for it a new immediacy, a beautiful simplicity without which the fairytale would be no fairytale.

Nevertheless, *The Woman without a Shadow* is an artificial fairytale rooted in no popular myth whatever, and even though Hofmannsthal counted it among his most important works—for, reaching a summit of his narrative art, he had mastered anew the Chandos experience and wrought the highest technical accomplishment, something cherished by every artist—he was aware that he had created a baroque structure which, without Gothic antecedents, had to float suspended in the air. Had he not seen this so clearly, he would not have felt obliged to resume the childhood theme for the third time, giving it a final form: this he did in the drama *The Tower*.

THE ESTRANGEMENT FROM THE EPIC: THE ESSAYS

With *The Woman without a Shadow* Hofmannsthal takes leave of the epic in order to turn henceforth exclusively to writing for the stage. Even before the first World War he had reached a period of quite unusual fecundity with such plays as *Oedipus and the Sphinx, Cristina's Journey Home, Everyman, Rosenkavalier, Ariadne*—all appearing in amazingly quick succession. Even the prose written during this epoch casts glances at the theatre; the story *Lucidor* (1911) bears the significant subtitle "Characters for an Unwritten Comedy" and ends with the even more significant words: "Life may create the dialogue which followed, comedy might imitate it, but a story cannot."

This is a thoroughly incorrect statement, at least one without a claim to general validity. For Hofmannsthal himself, of course, it was true enough; it is even one of the clues by which we can find an explanation for the sparseness of his narrative and the fertility of his dramatic production. For this statement, after all, is nothing but an unrestrained admission of his lack of auditivity! Is not the stage therefore the obvious medium of expression for the poet of the visual? For him who frequently reduces the human being to a mere prop in the general picture, is not the theatre the natural, indeed, the necessary medium by which to root his characters if not in the earth itself, at least in that world which is the stage? Is not precisely the stage, moreover, the instrument best suited to his urge for "I"-suppression, since it allows him, in fact absolutely compels him, to disappear completely behind the performance? In the *Book of Friends* we find the strange line, "The beautiful, even in art, is inconceivable without chastity." This is the pronouncement of a man who restrains himself from furnishing a novel with even the slightest autobiographical features, the pronouncement of a discreetness which esteems the subjective and the private so highly that, on the one hand, it has to be defended as inviolable and, on the other, it must not be forced on any fellow human being. It is also the pronouncement of a deep masculine modesty which shrinks from any of that tempting, shameless exhibitionism that lurks in the execution of all art; it is a pronouncement of Hugo von Hofmannsthal. Is it not then sheer good fortune that the man of the theatre, the exhibitionist *par excellence,* so to speak the expert on exhibitionism, stands beside him ready to take over? True, the professional exhibitionism of the actor, the singer, the dancer, is in the final analysis equally frightening (less so the comparatively natural kind displayed by the actress, the ballerina or diva); but it is beyond the borderline of responsibility, and what lies on this side of the line, the author's life, his voice, his gesture, remains in anonymity. All the inhibitions which the need for "I"-suppression imposes on a poet of the visual are removed from his shoulders by the stage; here his productivity can expand without inhibition—doesn't this make him a born dramatist?

The fallacy of this question is obvious. Even though the stage meets the "I"-suppression of the visual poet half-way, it does not relieve him of his other difficulties, in fact it faces him in addition—this can be sensed even in Goethe's drama— with its own particular difficulties. The depicter of landscape, for instance, reduces the human being to part of the setting, and this has its scenic analogy in the "stock role," hence in that stage character which lives only by virtue of sharp characterization, not by virtue of its inner psychical, dramatic, and hence drama-creating conflicts. For the true dramatist the stock role is confined to the use of the interlude and curtain-raiser scenes, to peripheral characters, not rarely to the servants of the protagonists, in general to the people of the "lower classes" with their dialect and mime, of whom Shakespeare's jesters will always remain the prime example. The poet of the visual, on the other hand, knows of little else but stock parts and since for this reason he is hard put to it to invent original conflicts, he is inclined to fall back upon existing themes which he then peoples with stock characters—to which even the protagonists are often reduced. Just this—at least until 1919—was Hofmannsthal's dramatic technique; since it corresponded to his visuality he handled it to perfection, occasionally extending it (above all in *Bassompierre*) to the narrative field: his stock characters are filled with penetrating self- and world-interpretations elucidating the phenomenon of their own Being as well as that of the life around them, but their wisdom is that of opera arias and banderols. Their impetus, in any case, comes exclusively from a given situation. For in comedy as well as in opera, especially in comic opera—all based on given situations—the stock character is sufficient, and following this principle Hofmannsthal wrote not only the most beautiful modern opera librettos (who can forget a Marschallin or a Baron Ochs?) but also evolved his own comedy style, bringing it (later on) in *The Man Who Was Difficult* to an undisputed climax of virtuosity, to a virtuosity all the more masterly since here in a specific stock character, that of Count Kari, "I"-suppression itself is made the centre of the play and its inherent masculine modesty is confronted most brilliantly with stage-exhibitionism. However, whether opera or comedy, their virtue is born out of a dilemma of visuality, and this could not satisfy a Hofmannsthal. So in his period of most untroubled productivity and easiest success, he not only threw himself into the labour of *Andreas,* but when this likewise did not satisfy him, dared to approach the drama once more from a completely different angle. It was, much later, in *The Tower* that he tried, by divesting himself of the techniques hitherto employed, to break through the stock qualities and to close the antinomy that yawned between confessional poetry and "I"-suppression.

Everything truly human takes place in the sphere of antinomies; the animal, sometimes envied by man on this account, knows nothing of it. And the less animal-like man becomes, the more is he torn by antinomies, growing nevertheless all the richer thereby if he succeeds in reconciling them: it is out of mastered antinomies that human harmony is composed, its quiet ecstasy being ultimate happiness on this earth. Just for this reason antinomy and harmony are the foundation pillars whereon the drama rests; just for this reason it is able to exert a more immediate purifying influence than any other art-form; and it is just because of it that the drama represents (especially when its harmony-structure fits into folk tradition) what is known as national poetry. Goethe, not really a national poet in this narrower sense, at least not as a dramatist, did nevertheless rise to national dignity because his mastering of antinomies, by which his soul was torn more violently than that of any other, enabled him to arrive at the most powerful, the complete harmony of existence. In self-confession his "I" dissolved into all cosmic worlds, and in his world-insight his "I" was revealed, here as there gaining self-identity out of conflict. Since his youth Hofmannsthal's gaze had been turned toward Goethe, not Schiller (the "real" national poet), certainly not toward Hölderlin either, even less toward Mallarmé and George; only from Goethe's example could he expect any solution of his own basic antinomy—confessional poetry together with "I"-suppression. And it was from Goethe that he learned that poetry, if it is to lead man to purification and self-identification, has to cast itself into the abyss of his antinomies, in complete contrast to philosophy, which hovers on the brink of the abyss and, without risking the leap, remains satisfied with the mere analysis of the observed.

Hofmannsthal was not a "non-leaper"; he was an inhibited leaper. He was, so to speak, in a permanent state of being ready to leap; his starting run, impressive as it was in *Andreas,* led to the actual leap only in *The Tower*: only there did he triumph over his shrinking back from the precipice; he had always held an intermediate position, so characteristic of him, on the extreme brink of the abyss; and although on the one hand he may have been depressed by a frustrated desire to create, he was on the other hand inspired—just because of this position of his—to a mastery of the philosophic essay hardly equalled in the German language. For everything that hindered him in the purely poetic domain lost its inhibiting aspect in the essay, indeed it actually worked to his advantage. Even the aestheticism of his youth, even the mysticism of language and perfection, took a positive turn in the realm of the essay since it is a realm of the simple rational statement; and therefore all tendency toward pomp had to be subordinated to simplicity and rationality. The same holds true for the flood of associations and memory-images whose symbol-chains and symbol-symbolizations remained indomitable in Hofmannsthal's novel to the point of destructiveness, whereas in the essay they function unequivocally as a constructive element. Because Hofmannsthal—in accordance with his whole nature —had no ambitions in the sphere of the theoretical, he was permitted to loosen up the essay by incorporating these series of images, and thence there issued an original, a unique form of presentation which is more closely related to lyricism than to philosophy. Is it the precursor of a new philosophy which draws from poetry the courage to leap into the abyss of antinomies, and thereby to venture new insights into existence? It is perfectly possible that Hofmannsthal sensed something of this kind, but here too his almost anti-revolutionary aversion to the leap becomes noticeable; he shrank not only from the abyss of antinomies as such but also from his own forebodings, whose abysmal depths he did not even wish to be aware of. One has but to read "Colours," an essay bordering on the ontological, to realize that, though it shrinks from transgressing the customary boundaries of philosophy, it is—and has every claim to be called—a prose of confession.

To express it somewhat paradoxically: disregarding *The Tower,* Hofmannsthal arrived at confessional poetry only outside the poetic sphere. But can this poetry in a realm outside itself still achieve what it is meant to achieve as confession, that which is expected of it? Can self-identification occur at all when the leap into the abyss of antinomies has not been attempted? Or can one expect the images rising in infinite wealth from the immense essayistic work to make up for the unfulfilled venture of the leap? In their totality these essays describe a vast ellipse of landscape which, rich in heroic culture and heroic Nature, stretching from northern Italy to southern Bohemia and encompassing the Austrian Alps, has its focuses in Venice and Vienna. It represents the mirror for Hofmannsthal's Austrian-ness (or more correctly, his Old Austrian-ness); although at first sight this seems to be a purely geographical localization, it takes little to discover that the history-bound attachment to the native land is here but the starting point for something more essential. For, deeply involved in Austrian culture, open to it at every pore, contributing to it, continuously taking a share in its preservation, Hofmannsthal experienced unceasingly the anonymity of culture-forming factors, the anonymity of the folk song, of the rural wood-carvers, of the many builders who had helped shape the landscape; and the more absorbed he became in this development the more did this unfolding of culture appear to him as a natural process. Is not poetry, too, a product of nature, just as is the language in which it grows? Is not the creation of culture part of man's innermost nature? Does the way in which human endeavour—most evident, perhaps, in architecture—grows into landscape in order to be reabsorbed by it not prove that this endeavour was part of that nature from the beginning? Who can draw the line here? The Hapsburg empire was the outcome of wars and Acts of State and yet it seems (independent of those political, collateral mechanisms) to have grown from a pre-existence rooted in its soil in order to live there an everlasting post-existential life. And it seems equally incomprehensible that Venice once upon a time was actually built by pile-sinkers, masons, and roofers. Here again has there not been a spiritual existence created and guarded by nature? The artificial flows into the natural, but this in turn into the artificial, and no matter whether it be stage or so-called reality, the planes of actuality cut across one another, leaving man to wander between ever-changing, dreamlike stage-settings which, derived from an anonymous somewhere, have nevertheless been erected by himself. He wanders, stripped of his "I," yet recognizing it everywhere: man's reality lies in the anonymous, and whatever he creates becomes real only when he, like the folk artist, has plunged into anonymity, returned to nature, cast off all homunculoid qualities, and recovered his shadow. The native land, the native city, the native landscape were the ever-present elements of Hofmannsthal's sentiments, and, by serving them, his essays assumed the character of a confession—so much so, in fact, that the leap into the abyss of antinomy was no longer felt to be a compulsion.

However, plausible as this may sound, things are by no means so simple. In a piece of prose filled with nostalgia, "A Memory of Beautiful Days"—a title that could stand for the body of Hofmannsthal's essays—he describes how after an extensive walk in a very receptive state of mind through a Venetian evening he is visited at night by the demonic-delightful desire to remember and to create poetry, thus showing how the poetic act springs directly from the impression of surroundings, from landscape and mood, how it completely fills and yet extinguishes the "I," a magical receiving and rendering of the scene, a magic wherein the "I" entirely dissolves and disappears into anonymity. This, of course, is considerably more complex than the simple reference to his country and its native art, but it was (and was described by Hofmannsthal himself as such) undoubtedly the method whereby he tried to accommodate both "I"-confession and "I"-suppression: the allusions to the theories of his youth, which demanded an absorption of the subject in the object, are obvious. It is even more striking that the self-identification that should issue from such "I"-confession refers to a preparatory phase, a phase preceding the act of confession, a strangely primitive phase preparing for the poetic act (impressions of a stroll and the compulsion to remember, both psychologically conceived), and it was all the more a preparatory phase since "I"-extinction here leads only as far as anonymity, thus stopping short at the mystical threshold where begins not only the frightful region of pantheistic chatter but also the sombre realm of utter contrition—the former rightly despised by Hofmannsthal, the latter inaccessible to him.

Hofmannsthal's creative powers are, in the main, strangely bound to this preparatory phase; in this phase his essays reach their perfection, so that it is precisely here that they assume the character of poetry—poetry in essay form. True, the complete identity of world-insight and "I"-confession does not spring from a universal and hence "I"-revealing affirmation of the world, as it did with Goethe—no, rather in analogy to him (surely not in imitation) it is here achieved on a narrower basis, namely in the framework of a predominantly visual landscape-confession more or less rooted in the native land. But just this is the poetic and, odd as it may sound, mythical framework of the essay, for however and wherever genuine poetry becomes apparent there also shimmers a ray of its primordial beginning, a ray of the myth.

And actually there are several essays by Hofmannsthal that have this shimmer. One of them (written around 1910) is the triptych "Moments in Greece." The first of the three is a monastery- and shepherd-idyll, but what an idyll! The passage of the clouds is arrested, and out of the great silence resounds primordial Greece, the Immutable that existed before Homer made it speak, the heavenly stillness of an eternally awakening soul, today as for ever. The second section, "The Wanderer," describes the meeting with a sinister figure on the stony slopes of Parnassus and represents the essential mythical vision of the triptych; this Wanderer is an outcast from civilization—significantly enough, a German—a man cast back into the inchoate wilderness. Industrial civilization, retrogressed into unchained Nature, tears society out of joint: thus he, "debased into a beastlike, frightened being," encircled by every mythical threat, haunted by mythical fear, has lost his way, has become an erring child filled with adult anxiety, helpless rage, and the craving to destroy the world and himself. The most gruesome confrontation of the world of antiquity with that of modern man! After this climax the third section, "The Statues," forms the epilogue, a glorified and glorifying one, for here we have the mysticism succeeding each myth and the theology issuing therefrom, the rational revelation: "If the unattainable feeds on my innermost being and the Eternal builds out of me its eternity, what then still stands between me and the Deity?" Hofmannsthal achieves here his mythical aim more lucidly, more concisely, more powerfully than in his poetry and novels, not by any means because he had chosen *the* mythical landscape (he achieves similar effects in other places as well, for instance in his fairytale-like description of Fez) but because here the difference between landscape and mere props entirely disappears and the human being dissolves completely in the landscape, the landscape completely in the human being. In their mutual identity they represent a reduced image of that powerful unity which fills the myth when it fuses Nature and man to the point of being indistinguishable, anticipating the totality of culture which is man's nature: it is merely a reduced reflection in a mirror, merely the phase preceding poetry, and nevertheless—in Hofmannsthal's hands the essay becomes just this—a phase preceding myth or more correctly preceding the myth of the future.

"All fantasy in which you intensely participate is myth; in myth everything has a double and counter meaning: Death = Life, Snake-fight = Love-embrace. Hence in myth everything is balanced." These words are in the *Book of Friends,* and they announce the constancy of problems which gave Hofmannsthal's life and work an unswerving, obstinate direction: he was concerned steadily with the position of man in the cosmos, with the ethical balance which must be established between "I" and existence, if human life is to become really unified. Hofmannsthal's life (with all his Austrian suppleness) is irrevocably all one piece, his continuous development even more so. His work as essayist proves this; it shows not only the homogeneity of the symbol-groups which belong to and themselves make up the constancy of problems; it also shows how they progressively (and in this connection avoiding any allegorism) unfold more and more freely and how their style mirrors the growth of the whole personality. In 1896, at the age of twenty-three, he writes, about a book of prose sketches by the Viennese writer Peter Altenberg, "the little book is governed by mysterious powers as the delicate magnet is governed by enormous forces lying in the Unknown." And in 1929, in an essay on the Lessing bicentenary—one of his last and most beautiful—he resumes the same metaphor and says of Lessing that he is "a swinging rod of steel fixed to a base of granite: Reason." And although Hofmannsthal himself was less granitic, less rational than the northern German, both passages are self-confession—the first one, of 1896, anticipating his own crystallization, the other, of 1929, confirming it, yet in the difference of the two styles revealing the enormously rich inner growth over the span of his life.

December, 1950

HERMANN BROCH

1

ANDREAS

Oh quante sono incantatrici, oh quanti
Incantator tra noi, che non si sanno!

The Wonderful Mistress

"THIS is a fine thing," thought young Herr Andreas von Ferschengelder, on September 17, 1778, for his boatman had unloaded his trunk on to the stone steps and pushed off again. "What am I to do now? The fellow goes off and leaves me standing here, there is no such thing as a coach in Venice, so much I know, and as for a porter, why should one ever come to such a God-forsaken place? I can speak their language—what good will that do me? They'll do what they like with me all the same. How do I speak to utter strangers asleep in their beds? Shall I knock on their doors and say, 'Good morning, neighbour'?" He knew he would do no such thing. Meanwhile steps were ringing on the stone pavement, sharp and clear in the morning stillness; some time passed until he heard them close by, then a man in a domino emerged from an alley, caught his cloak about him with both hands, and made straight across the square. Andreas took a step forward and bowed. The domino raised his hat, and with it the half-mask fixed to the inside. There was a trustworthy look about the man; to judge from his bearing and manners, he belonged to the best society. Andreas was anxious to hurry; it seemed unmannerly to detain a gentleman on his way home at such an hour. He hastily explained that he was a foreigner, from Vienna; just arrived from the mainland by way of Villach and Gorizia; then, realizing that all this information was superfluous, he was overcome by embarrassment and stood stammering Italian.

The stranger approached with a most civil gesture, saying that he was entirely at Andreas's service. With this movement, his domino had fallen apart in front, and Andreas could see that the courteous gentleman had nothing on under his cloak but his shirt, shoes without buckles, and garterless stockings that left his calves half bare. He at once begged the stranger not to remain standing in the chilly morning air —he would soon find somebody to direct him to an inn or a lodging-house. Wrapping his cloak tighter about his hips, the mask assured Andreas that he was in no hurry. Andreas was deeply mortified to think that the other now knew he had seen his strange dishabille; his silly remark about the chilly morning air made him hot with shame, so that he too, unthinkingly, threw his travelling cloak open, while the Venetian most obligingly assured him that he was particularly glad to be of service to a subject of the Queen-Empress Maria Theresa, especially as he had already been on terms of great friendship with several Austrians, among others Baron Reischach, Colonel of the Imperial Pandours, and Count Esterhazy. These famous names, pronounced so casually by the stranger in front of him, inspired Andreas with the utmost confidence. True, he himself knew such great gentlemen by name only, or at most by sight, for he belonged to the minor, or bagatelle, nobility.

When the mask declared that he had what the foreign cavalier needed quite close at hand, Andreas was beyond declining. When they were already on their way, he asked casually what part of the town they were in, and was told, "San Samuele." And the family to which he was being taken was that of a patrician, a count, who happened to have his elder daughter's room to let, for she had been living away from home for some time. Meanwhile, they had arrived at a very high house in a very narrow lane; it looked distinguished enough, but extremely dilapidated, for there was no glass in the boarded windows. The mask knocked at the door and called several names; an old woman looked down from a high window to ask what they wanted; there was a rapid parley between the two. The Count himself was already out, the mask explained to Andreas; he always went out at this time in the morning to buy what was needed in the kitchen. But the Countess was at home, so they could settle about the room and then send for the luggage, which they had left behind.

The bolt on the door was withdrawn, and they entered a small courtyard, full of washing hung out to dry, and mounted a steep flight of stone steps hollowed out like bowls with age. Andreas did not like the look of the house, and it seemed odd that the Count should be out so early for the kitchen shopping, but the thought that he was being introduced by a friend of the Freiherr von Reischach and of Count Esterhazy cast a bright light over everything and kept despondency at bay.

At the top, the steps gave on to a fairly large room, with the fireplace at one end and an alcove at the other. At the single window, a half-grown girl was sitting on a low chair, while a woman, no longer young but still handsome, was endeavouring to build up the child's beautiful hair into a very elaborate headdress. As Andreas and his guide entered the room and removed their hats, the child, with a scream, darted into the inner room, and Andreas caught sight of a thin face with dark, charmingly arched eyebrows. The mask turned to the Countess, whom he addressed as "Cousin," and presented his young friend and protégé.

There was a short colloquy, and the lady named a price

for the room, which Andreas agreed to without demur. He would have dearly liked to know whether it was a room that looked on to the street or one that faced the courtyard (for his heart sank at the thought of spending his time in Venice in such a room), and whether the house was in the town or the outskirts. But he found no opportunity for his question; the conversation between the two others showed no sign of coming to an end, while the young creature who had vanished swung the door to and fro and cried with spirit that Zorzi must be got out of bed at once, for he was lying upstairs in bed with the colic. Then the Countess told the gentlemen to go up, the boys would soon turn the useless creature out. He would leave at once, and so make room for the newcomer's luggage. She apologized for not going with them, but she had her hands full with getting Zustina ready to pay lottery visits with her. All the patrons on the list had to be visited that very day before evening.

Again Andreas would have liked to know what all this talk about patrons and the lottery meant, but as his guide, with a vigorous nod of approval, seemed to take the matter for granted, he was again prevented from asking, and they followed two half-grown boys, who were obviously twins, up the steep wooden staircase to Signorina Nina's room.

At the door the boys stopped, and when a faint groan was heard, they looked at each other with their quick, bright squirrel's eyes and seemed highly delighted. The curtains of the bed were drawn back; a pale young man was lying on it. A wooden table by the wall and a chair were covered with dirty brushes and pots of paint; a palette hung on the wall, facing a bright, very pretty mirror. Otherwise, the place was empty.

"Are you better?" asked the boys.

"Better," groaned the man in the bed.

"So we can take away the stone?"

"Yes, take it away."

"When you have the colic, you must lay a stone on your stomach, then it gets better," announced one of the boys, while the one nearest the sick man rolled away the stone, which their combined strength could hardly have lifted.

It was painful to Andreas to see a sick man thus turned out of bed on his account. He stepped to the window and threw wide the half-open shutter: there was water below, sunny ripples were lapping round the brightly coloured steps of a very big building opposite, casting a quivering reflection, a mesh of dancing rings, on a wall. He leaned out; there was another house, then another, then the lane opened on to a big, broad canal lying full in the sunshine. A balcony projected from the corner house, with an oleander on it, its branches swaying in the wind: on the other side, cloths and rugs were hanging out of airy windows. Opposite, on the other side of the great waterway, there stood a palace with fine stone figures in niches.

He stepped back into the room; the man in the domino had vanished, the young man had risen and was superintending the boys, who were busy clearing away pots of paint and dirty brushes from the only table and chair in the room. He was pale and a little unkempt, but handsome; there was nothing ill-favoured in his face except for a wry twist in his underlip which gave him a shifty look.

"Did you notice"—he turned to Andreas—"that he had nothing on under his domino but his shirt? Even the buckles cut off his shoes. I suppose you know what that means? He's a desperate gambler. What else could it mean? You should have seen him yesterday. An embroidered coat, a flowered waistcoat, two watches with trinkets, a snuff-box, rings on every finger, fine silver shoe-buckles. The scoundrel!" He laughed, but his laugh was not pleasant. "You'll have a comfortable room here. If you need anything else, call on me. I can show you a coffee-house close by where you'll be well served if I introduce you. You can write your letters there, see your friends, and settle your business—except for what you generally deal with behind locked doors."

Here he laughed again, and the two boys relished the joke, laughing out loud as they struggled with all their might to drag the heavy stone out of the room; there was a family likeness between them and their sister downstairs.

"If you have any business that needs an honest man," the artist went on, "I shall be honoured if you will entrust it to me. If I am not at hand, see that you get a Friuli man; they are the only safe messengers. You'll find some of them on the Rialto and in any of the big squares. You can tell them by their country costume. They are trusty and close, they remember names, and can even recognize a mask by his walk and his shoe-buckles. If you want anything from over there, ask me. I'm the scene-painter there, and can go about the place as I like."

Andreas understood that he was referring to the grey building opposite, with the brightly coloured stone steps leading down from the door to the water, which had looked too big for an ordinary house and too mean for a palace.

"I mean the San Samuele theatre. I thought you knew that long ago. As I said, I am the scene-painter, your landlady is one of the attendants, and the old man is a candle-snuffer."

"Who?"

"Count Prampero, your landlord. Who else should it be? First the daughter was an actress, she got them all in—not the girl you saw—the elder, Nina. She's worth while. I'll take you to see her this afternoon. The little one is coming out next carnival. The boys run errands. But now I must go and look for your luggage."

Andreas, left alone, threw back the shutters and fixed them. The hasp of one was broken: he made up his mind to have it seen to at once. Then he put all the remaining paint-pots and tins outside the door and, with a linen rag he found lying under the bed, scoured the paint spots off his table till it shone clean. Then he carried the paint-stained rag out of the room, looked for a corner to hide it in, and discovered a twig broom, with which he swept out his room. When he had finished he put the pretty little mirror straight, drew the bed-curtains, and sat down on the single chair at the foot of the bed, his face towards the window. The kindly breeze came in, stroking his young face with a faint smell of seaweed and sea freshness.

He thought of his parents and of the letter he would have to write to them in the coffee-house. He resolved to write something in this fashion:

"Kind and honoured parents,

"I have arrived safely in Venice. I have taken a cheerful, very clean and airy room with a noble family who happen to have it to let. The room looks on to the street, but instead of the earth, there is water below, and the people go about in gondolas, or, if they are poor, in great barges rather like the Danube ferry-boats. These boats take the place of porters, so that I shall be very quiet. There is no cracking of whips or shouting."

He thought he might mention that there were messengers in Venice so clever that they could recognize a mask by his gait and shoe-buckles. That would please his father, who was an eager collector of the oddities of foreign lands and customs. He was in doubt whether to say he was living quite close to a theatre. In Vienna that had been his dearest wish.

Many years ago, when he was ten or twelve years old, he had two friends who lived in the Blue Freihaus in the Wieden, on the same staircase in that fourth courtyard where the "regular theatre" was housed in a barn. He remembered how wonderful it was to be visiting them towards evening, and to see the scenery carried out, a canvas with a magic garden, a bit of a tavern inside, the murmur of the crowd, the candle-snuffers, the *mandoletti* sellers. More poignant than all the rest, the confused hum of the instruments tuning up—to this day the memory brought a pang. The floor of the stage was uneven, the curtain too short in places. Jackboots came and went. Between the neck of a bass fiddle and the head of a fiddler, he once saw a sky-blue shoe, embroidered with tinsel. The sky-blue shoe was more wonderful than all the rest. Later, a being stood there with the shoe on—it belonged to her, was one with her blue and silver gown; she was a princess, dangers surrounded her, an enchanted wood closed round her, voices sounded from the branches, monkeys came rolling fruit along from which lovely children sprang, shining. The princess sang, Harlequin was at her side, yet far, far away from her. All that was beautiful, but it was not the two-edged sword which had pierced his soul, from tenderest delight and unutterable longing to tears, awe, and ecstasy, when the blue shoe stood empty beneath the curtain.

He made up his mind not to mention that the theatre was so near, nor even the strange costume of the gentleman who had brought him to the house. He would have had to say that the man was a gambler who had played away everything, down to his shirt, or else go out of his way to conceal that part of the story. He would not, of course, be able to tell about Esterhazy, which would have pleased his mother. He was quite willing to mention the rent, two sequins a month—it was not much, considering his means. But what was the good of that, seeing that he had, in one night, by a single act of folly, lost half his journey money? That was a thing he would never be able to confess to his parents, so what was the good of boasting about his thrift? He was ashamed in his own eyes and shrank from the memory of the three calamitous days in Carinthia, but the face of the rascally servant already stood before him, and, whether he would or no, he needs must recall it all in every minute particular from the beginning: once a day, morning or evening, it would all come back to him.

ONCE again, he was at the "Sword" in Villach after a hard day's travelling, and was just going up to bed when, on the very staircase, a man stood offering himself as servant or courier. He: He needed nobody, was travelling alone, looked after his horse himself during the day, and the ostler could do so at night. The other would not leave him, went sidling upstairs with him, step by step, as far as his room, then stepped into the doorway and half across the threshold, so that Andreas could not shut the door: it was not fitting for a young gentleman of quality to travel without a servant; it would look paltry down in Italy, they were infernally nice on that point. As for him, he had done little else all his life but ride abroad with young gentlemen—his last was Baron Attems auf Petzenstein, and before him, the Canon, Count Lodron—Herr von Ferschengelder must know them. He had ridden on ahead as courier, ordered everything, arranged everything, till the Count was speechless with amazement, "he had never travelled so cheap," and their quarters were of the best, and he spoke Flemish and Romansh and Italian, of course, as fluently as you please, and knew about all kinds of money, and the ways of innkeepers and postilions—nobody could beat him there; all they could say was: "There's no getting at your gentleman, he's in good hands." And he knew all about buying a horse, so that he could get the better of any horse-dealer, even the Hungarians, who were the most knowing, let alone the Germans and Italians. And as for personal service, he was valet and barber and perruquier, coachman and huntsman, beater and loader, knew all about hounds and guns, correspondence, reading aloud and writing billets in all languages, and could serve as an interpreter, or, as the Turks say, dragoman. It was a wonder that a man like him was out of a place, and indeed, the Baron auf Petzenstein had wanted his brother to take him *à tout prix,* but he had taken it into his head to be servant to Herr von Ferschengelder—not for the wages—that was of no matter to him. But to serve a young gentleman making his first tour, to win his affection and esteem, that was the thing for him. What he had set his heart on was trust, that was the reward a servant like him looked for. He wanted kindliness and confidence, not money. That was why he had not been able to bear the life in the Imperial Cavalry, where there was nothing but talebearing and the stick—no trust. And here he passed his tongue over his moist, thick lip like a cat.

At this point Andreas stopped him, saying that while he thanked him for his obliging offer, he did not mean to hire a servant at the moment. Later, perhaps, in Venice, he might hire a man, and he made as if to shut the door, but he had already said too much. That last little flourish—for he had never thought of hiring a footman in Venice—took its revenge. For now the other felt in the uncertainty of his tone who was the real master in the dispute, and blocked the door with his foot, and Andreas could never make out later how it was that the ruffian, as if the matter were settled between them, at once began to speak of his mount—there would be a bargain that day the like of which would never come their way again. That very night a horse-dealer was passing through the town; he knew him from his time with the Canon—not a Turk, for once. The man had a little Hungarian horse to sell which might have been made for him. Once he got that between his legs, it would be doing the high step inside of a week. The bay was priced, he thought, at ninety gulden for anyone else, but seventy for him. That was because of the big horse-deal he had put through for the Canon, but the bargain would have to be settled that very day before midnight, for the dealer was an early riser. So please would His Honour give him the money at once out of his waist-belt, or should he go down and fetch his portmanteau or his saddle, for he would have his capital sewn up there—a gentleman like him would only carry the bare necessary on him.

When the wretch spoke of money, his face took on a loathsome look; under the impudent, dirty blue eyes, little wrinkles twitched in his freckled skin like ripples on water. He came close up to Andreas, and a smell of brandy was wafted from the thick, moist, protruding lips. Then Andreas pushed him out over the threshold, and the fellow, feeling the young man's strength, said no more. But again Andreas said a word too much, for he felt some compunction at treating the intruder so ungently. Count Lodron would never have been so rough, he thought, or laid his hands on him. So he added, partly by way of dismissal, that he was too tired at the moment, they could think about it next morning. In any case, nothing had been settled between them.

He meant to leave the next morning without further discussion as early as possible. But in that way he merely twisted the rope for his own neck, for in the morning, before it was even light and Andreas was awake, there was the fellow already standing at the door, saying that he had already saved five gulden cash for His Honour, had bought the horse—a beauty—from the dealer for sixty-five gulden, it was standing down in the courtyard, and every gulden under sixty-five Herr von Ferschengelder should lose when he got rid of the horse in Venice was to be struck off his own wages.

Andreas, looking out of the window, still only half awake, saw a lean but spirited little horse standing down in the courtyard. Then the conceit seized him that it would be, after all, a very different matter to ride into towns and inns with a servant riding behind him. He could lose nothing on the horse—it was certainly a bargain. The bull-necked, freckled fellow looked burly and sharp-witted, nothing worse, and if Baron auf Petzenstein and Count Lodron had had him in their service, there must be something in him. For in his parents' house in the Spiegelgasse, Andreas had breathed in with the air of Vienna a boundless awe of persons of rank, and what happened in that higher world was gospel.

So there was Andreas with his servant riding behind him, carrying his portmanteau, before he even knew or wanted it. The first day everything went well, and yet it seemed dull and dreary to Andreas as it passed, and he would have preferred not to live through it again. But it was no use wishing.

Andreas had intended to ride to Spittal, and then through the Tyrol, but the servant talked him into turning left and staying in the province of Carinthia. The roads, he declared, were much better there, and the inns without their like, and life far merrier than among the blockheads in the Tyrol. The Carinthian maids and millers' daughters had a way with them, and the roundest, firmest bosoms in all Germany— there was a saying about them, and many a song. Didn't Herr von Ferschengelder know that?

Andreas made no answer; he shivered hot and cold beside the fellow, who was not so much older than he—five years at most. If he had known that Andreas had never seen, let alone touched, a naked woman, some coarse jeer would have been forthcoming, or talk such as Andreas could not even imagine, but then he would have torn him from his horse and set upon him in a fury—he felt it, and the blood throbbed in his eyes.

They rode in silence through a wide valley; it was a rainy day, grassy hill-slopes rose right and left, with here and there a farm, a hayrick, and woods high above on which the clouds lay sluggishly. After dinner Gotthilff grew talkative—had the young master taken a look at the landlady? She was nothing much now, but in '69—that was nine years ago, when he was sixteen years old—he had had that woman every night for a month. Then it had been well worth while. She had had black hair down to below the hollows of her knees. And he urged on his little horse and rode quite close to Andreas, till Andreas had to warn him not to ride him down—his chestnut could not stand it. In the end she got something to remember him by, it had served her right. At the time he had been with a countess's waiting-woman, as pretty as a picture, and the landlady had smelt a rat; she had pined away with jealousy, and grew as hollow-eyed as a sick dog. At that time he had been courier to Count Porzia—it was his first place, and a fine surprise it had been for all Carinthia that the Count had made him his huntsman at sixteen, and confidential servant into the bargain.

But the Count knew very well what he was doing, and whom he could trust, and he had good need of somebody who could keep his mouth shut, for the Count had more love-affairs than teeth in his head, and many a married man had sworn to kill him, gentlemen and farmers too, and millers and huntsmen. Just then the Count was carrying on with the young Countess Pormberg—she was as lovesick as a vixen, but she was no less in love with the Count than her maid, a fair-haired Slovene, was in love with him, Gotthilff. And when her husband had had the shoot in Pormberg the Countess had stolen to Count Porzia's stand, crawling along on all fours, and meanwhile the Count had given him his piece and told him to shoot for him, so that nobody should notice, and nobody had noticed, for he was just as good a shot as the Count. And once, with buckshot, he had brought down a fine buck at nearly forty paces, through undergrowth: he had caught a glimpse of its shoulder in the dusk. Then the animal had collapsed under his fire, but at the same time a woeful cry had come out of the thicket—it sounded like a woman, but directly afterwards all was still again, as though the wounded woman had held her mouth shut with her own hand. Of course he could not leave his stand then, but the next day he had paid a visit to the landlady and had found her abed with wound-fever. And he had been smart enough to find out that she had been driven into the wood by jealousy, because she thought the waiting-woman was out with him and that she would find them in the undergrowth together. He had split his sides with laughing, to think she had got something to remember him by, and from his own hand, and all the same could not upbraid him with it, but had to submit to his jeers, and spicy ones they were, and hold her tongue to everybody and lie herself out of it by saying that she had fallen on the scythe and cut herself over the knee.

Andreas pressed on, the other too; his face, close behind Andreas's, was red with wild, shameless lust, like that of a fox in rut. Andreas asked whether the Countess was still alive. Oh, she? She had made many a man happy and still looked no more than twenty-five. There was many a story he could tell about her, and for that matter, the ladies in the big houses here, if you knew how to take them, would give their whole hand and all the rest with it, where a country-woman would only give her finger. He was riding close beside Andreas now, instead of behind, but Andreas paid no heed. The wretch was as loathsome to him as a spider; yet he was but twenty-two, and his thoughts were wandering. He might, he dreamed, be arriving himself at Pormberg Castle that evening, an expected guest along with other guests. It is evening—the shoot is over, he was the best shot; whenever he fired something fell. The lovely Countess was at his side as he fired, her eyes playing with him as he with the life of the wild creatures. Now they are alone—an utterly solitary room, he alone with the Countess, walls a fathom thick, in deadly silence. He is appalled to find that she is no longer a countess, but a woman, nor is he the young chevalier—and there is nothing gallant or honourable about it, nor any beauty either, but a frenzy, a murdering in the dark. The ruffian is beside him, his mouth wide open, emptying his gun on a woman who has crept up to him in her night-dress. He has started back to the dining-room with the Countess, back to the decent gaiety there—he wrenched back his wandering thoughts and felt that he had pulled up, and at the same moment his servant's nag stumbled. The man cursed and swore, as if the rider ahead were not his master, but a man he had fed swine with all his life. Andreas let it pass. He felt a great lassitude, the broad valley looked endless under the sagging clouds. He wished it were all over, that he were older and had children of his own, and that it was his son who was riding to Venice, but a different man from him, a fine fellow, and that the world was clean and kindly, like Sunday morning with the bells ringing.

The next day the road mounted. The valley narrowed,

steeper slopes, here and there on a height a church or a few houses, far below them a rushing torrent. The clouds were on the move, now and then a shaft of sunlight shot down to the river, where, among willows and hazels, the stones gleamed livid, the water green. Then gloom again, and gentle rain. A hundred paces farther on the new-bought horse fell lame, its eyes were glazed, its head aged; it looked a different animal. Gotthilff broke out that it was small wonder, when the horses were tired in the legs and a man pulled up his beast on the road in the twilight, without a by-your-leave, so that the man behind could not help stumbling. He had never seen anyone ride so; in the cavalry he would have been put in irons for it.

Again Andreas let it pass; the fellow knows something about horses, he said to himself, he thinks he is responsible for the horse, that's what maddens him. But he wouldn't have taken that tone with the Baron auf Petzenstein. It serves me right. There's something about a great gentleman that a lackey respects. There's nothing of the kind about me: if I tried to put it on, it wouldn't suit me. I'll take him along with me till Saturday, then I shall sell the horse, though I lose half the money, and pay him off; a man like that will find ten places for one he loses, but he needs a firmer hand than mine.

Soon they were riding at a foot-pace; the horse's head looked thin and jaded, and Gotthilff's face bloated and angry. He pointed to a big farm in front of them, to the side of the road—there they would stop: "I'm not going to ride a dead-lame beast a step further."

THE HOMESTEAD was more than substantial. A square stone wall ran round it, with a stout turret at each corner; the gate was framed in stone, with a coat of arms above. Andreas thought it must be a gentleman's seat. They dismounted, Gotthilff took the two horses—he had to pull rather than lead the bay through the gate. The courtyard was empty except for a fine big cock on a dunghill, surrounded by hens; on the other side a little stream of water flowed from the fountain and made its way out under the wall, among nettles and briars; ducklings were swimming on it. There was a tiny chapel, with flowers on trellises against it. And all this was inside the wall. The path leading across the farmyard was flagged, the horses' hoofs clattered on it. It led straight through the house under a huge vaulted archway. The stables must be behind the house.

Then farm-hands appeared, with a young maid, followed by the farmer himself, a tall man, not much over forty, but still slender, and his face was beautiful. A stable was allotted to the strangers, Andreas was shown to a pleasant room in the upper storey, and it was all done after the fashion of those comfortable houses where even the unexpected guest is at home. The farmer glanced at the little bay, went up to it and looked between its forelegs, but said nothing. The two strangers were bidden to table at once.

The room was massively arched, with a huge crucifix on the wall and the table in the corner, with the meal already standing on it. The men and maids sat spoon in hand; at the head of the table there sat the farmer's wife, a tall woman with a candid face, though not so handsome and serene as her husband; beside her the daughter, as tall as her mother, yet still a child, with her mother's regular features, but flashing with joy at every breath, like her father's.

With the memory of the meal that followed Andreas struggled as with a mouthful of horror that he must swallow whether he would or no. The farmer and his family so kindly, so trustful, the whole company so decent, mannerly, and unsuspicious, the grace so beautifully spoken by the farmer, the wife attentive to her guest as if he had been her son, the men and maids neither bold nor bashful, and between master and man the same frank kindliness. But there sat Gotthilff, like a bull in the young corn, insolent and patronizing to his master, lewd and overbearing with the servants, guzzling, showing off, bragging. Andreas's gorge rose at the lengths he could go to and still laugh; the brazenness of the man's shameless silliness was agony to him. He felt as if every one of the servants, and the farmer and his wife too, were lodged in his own heart. The farmer's brow seemed to grow so still, and his wife's face pale and hard—he longed to get up and give Gotthilff what he deserved, beating his face with his fists till he should collapse, bleeding, and have to be carried out feet foremost.

At last the meal came to an end, grace was said—at any rate he at once ordered the ruffian off to the stable to see to the sick horse but first to carry the portmanteau and valise up to his room, and in so peremptory a tone that the man looked at him amazed, and, although with a grimace and a scowl, immediately betook himself out of the room. Andreas went upstairs—thought he would go and have a look at the horse, thought better of it, to avoid seeing Gotthilff—was standing in the archway—a door was ajar in it. The girl Romana appeared and asked him where he was going. He: He didn't know how to kill the time; besides, he ought to have a look at the horse to find out whether they would be able to leave the next day. She: "Do you have to kill it? It passes quickly enough for me. It often frightens me." Had he been in the village? The church was really beautiful; she would show it to him. Then when they came back, he could have a look at the horse; his man had been poulticing it with fresh cow-dung.

Then they went out at the back of the farmyard; between the byre and the wall was a path, and beside one of the corner turrets a little gate led into the open. On the narrow footpath leading up through the fields they talked freely; she asked whether his parents were still alive—whether he had brothers and sisters. She was sorry for him there, being so much alone. She had two brothers; there would have been nine of them if six had not died. They were all little innocents in Paradise. Her brothers were woodcutting up in the convent wood. It was a merry life in the woodcutters' hut: they had a maid with them too. She was to go herself next year—her parents had promised.

Meanwhile they had reached the village. The church stood off the road, they entered, whispered. Romana showed him everything: a shrine with a knuckle of St. Radegunda in a gold casket, the pulpit with chubby-cheeked angels blowing silver trumpets, her seat, and her parents' and brothers', in the front pew, and, at the side of the pew, a metal shield, on which there stood "Prerogative of the Finazzers." Then he knew her name.

They left the church on the other side and went into the churchyard. Romana moved about the graves as if she were at home. She led Andreas to a grave with a number of crosses on it, one behind the other. "Here lie my little sisters and brothers, God keep their souls," she said, and bent to pull up a weed or two from among the lovely flowers. Then she took a little holy-water stoup from the foremost cross. "I must fill it again, the birds are always perching here and upsetting it." Meanwhile Andreas was reading the names; there were the innocent boys, Egidius, Achaz, and Romuald Finazzer, the innocent girl Sabina, and the innocent twins Mansuet and Bibiana. Andreas was moved with inward awe to think they had had to depart so young—not one had been on earth for even so much as a year, and one had lived only one summer and one autumn. He thought of the warm-blooded, happy face of the father, and understood why the mother's regular features were harder and paler. Then Romana came back from the church with the holy water in her hand, reverently careful not to spill a drop. Thus gravely intent she was indeed a child; but unconsciously, and in her beauty and stature, she was already a woman. "There's none but my kin hereabout," she said, looking with radiant brown eyes over the graves. She felt happy here, as she felt happy sitting between her father and mother at table, and lifting her spoon to her shapely mouth. She followed Andreas's eyes: her look could be as steady as an animal's, and, as it were, carry the look of another as it wandered.

Built into the church wall behind the Finazzer graves there was a big, reddish tombstone, with the figure of a knight on it, armed cap-à-pie, helm in arm, a little dog at his feet, with its paws touching a scutcheon. She showed him the little dog, the squirrel with the crown between its paws, and crowned itself, as a crest.

"That is our ancestor," said Romana. "He was a knight, and came over from the Italian Tyrol."

"So you are gentry, and the arms painted over the sun-dial on the house are yours?" said Andreas.

"Why, yes," said Romana with a nod. "It is all painted in the book at home that is called The Roll of Carinthian Nobles. It goes back to the time of Emperor Maximilian I. I can show it to you if you like."

At home she showed him the book, with a childish delight in all the handsome crests. The wings, leaping bucks, eagles, cocks, and a green man—nothing escaped her, but her own crest was the finest, the little squirrel with the crown in its paws—it was not the most beautiful, but she loved it best. She turned over the pages for him, leaving him time to look. "Look! Look!" she cried at each page. "That fish looks as fierce as a fresh-caught trout—what a hideous buck!"

Then she fetched another book: the pains of hell were pictured there, the tortures of the damned arranged under the seven deadly sins, all engraved on copper. She explained the pictures to Andreas, and how each punishment precisely fitted its sin. She knew everything and said everything, frankly and artlessly, and Andreas felt as if he were looking into a crystal holding the whole world, but it was innocent and pure.

They were sitting side by side in the big room on the window-seat running round the embrasure; then Romana stopped and listened, as if she could hear through the wall. "The goats are home. Come and look at them." She took Andreas by the hand, the goatherd put down the milking-pail, the goats came crowding round it, all trying to get their swollen udders in: there were fifty of them, and the goat boy was completely beleaguered. She pointed out the most vicious and the quietest of them, the one with the longest hair and the best milker. The goats knew her too, and came running to her. Over by the wall there was a grassy spot. Hardly had the girl lain nimbly down when a goat was standing over her to let her drink, and struggled to stay there till she had sucked, but Romana sprang behind a barrow, drawing Andreas by the hand. The goat could not find the way, and bleated piteously after her.

Meanwhile Romana and Andreas climbed the spiral staircase of the turret looking towards the mountains. At its top there was a little round room, where an eagle was huddled up on a perch. Across its stony face and lifeless eyes a light flashed, it raised its wings in faint joy, and hopped aside. Romana sat down beside it and laid her hand on its neck. Her grandfather had brought it home, she said, when it was barely fledged. For as to clearing out eyries, he had not his like for that. He never did much else, but often he would ride far away, climb about, track down the eyrie somewhere in the rocks, rouse the country-folk, the cowherds and huntsmen, and make them tie the longest ladders together or let him down on ropes almost out of sight. He was good at that, and at marrying handsome women. He had married four of them, and as each died took a still handsomer one, and every time a kinswoman, for he said there was nothing like Finazzer blood. When he had caught the eagle he was already fifty-four, and had hung for nine hours at the end of four church ladders over a most frightful precipice, but directly afterwards, he had gone courting his handsomest wife. She was a young cousin's widow, she had always wanted him and had never looked at any one but him, was almost glad when her husband was killed—by a runaway ox, that was—though she already had a little girl by him and was far gone with child at the time. And so her father and mother were half-sister and half-brother, her mother a year older than her father, and that was why they were so dear to each other, because they were of one blood and had been brought up together. When her father rode away to Spittal or over into the Tyrol to buy cattle, even if it were only for a night or two, her mother could hardly let him go; she cried every time, clung to him, kissed his mouth and hands, and could not stop waving, and watching him out of sight, and calling down blessings on him. And that was how she was going to live with her husband—she would not have it any other way.

Meanwhile they had crossed the yard. Beside the gate, inside the wall, there was a wooden bench; she drew him towards it and told him to sit down beside her. Andreas marvelled to hear the girl tell him everything, as frankly as if he had been her brother. Meanwhile evening had drawn on—on the one hand the grey clouds had sunk down over the mountains, on the other was a piercing clearness and purity, with a few golden cloudlets scattered over the sky, the whole sky was in movement, the puddle with the quacking ducks a spray of fire and gold, the ivy on the chapel wall like emerald; a tit or robin glided out of the green gloom and fluttered with a sweet sound in the shimmering air. Romana's lips were loveliest of all: they were shining, transparent crimson, and her eager, innocent talk flowed between them like fiery air carrying her soul, while from the brown eyes came a flash at every word.

Suddenly, over in the house, Andreas saw her mother standing in an embrasure in the upper story and looking down at them. He told Romana. Through the leaded window the woman's face looked sad and stern; he thought they ought to get up and go into the house, her mother might need her, or she did not like them sitting there together. Romana merely gave a frank and happy nod, and drew him by the hand. He was to stay where he was. The mother nodded back and went away. Andreas could hardly understand; the only attitude he knew towards parents and elders was constraint and fear: he could not imagine the mother finding such freedom anything but displeasing, even though she might not say so. He did not sit down again, but said he must have a look at the horse.

When they entered the stable the young maid was crouching by the fire, her hair hanging in wisps over her flushed cheeks, the servant more on than beside her. She seemed to be brewing something in an iron pot.

"Shall I go for more saltpetre, Mr. Sergeant?" asked the slut, tittering as if it were some great secret. When the ruffian saw Andreas with Romana behind him he scrambled into a

more decent posture. Andreas ordered him to take the portmanteau, which was still lying in the straw, up to his room,
and the valise with it.

"All in good time," said Gotthilff. "I must finish here
first. That's a draught to make a sick horse sound and a
sound dog sick." As he said this he turned to Andreas with
a most insolent look.

"What's the matter with the horse?" said Andreas, taking
a step towards the stall, but he halted before the second step,
realizing that he knew nothing about it, and the bay looked
the picture of misery.

"What should be the matter? Tomorrow it will be all
right. Then off we go," replied the fellow, and turned back
to the fire, with a snigger.

Andreas took the portmanteau, pretending he had forgotten his order to the servant. He pondered whether he was
pretending to himself, to the fellow, or to Romana. She followed him upstairs. He left the door open behind him, threw
the portmanteau down; the girl came in carrying the valise,
and laid it on the table.

"That's my grandmother's bed. She bore her children in
it. Look how beautifully it is painted, but my mother and
father's bed is much finer, and still bigger. It has St. James and
St. Stephen painted at the head, and lovely wreaths of flowers
at the foot. This is shorter, because my grandmother was not
a big woman. I doubt if it will be long enough for you, it's
so short. We're of a height. Let's try whether we can sleep
in it full length. It's no sleep at all to sleep all doubled up.
Mine is long and broad. There's room enough for two in it."

Nimbly she swung her big, light limbs on to the bed and
lay full length in it, the tips of her toes touching a moulding
at the foot of the bed. Andreas was bending over her. She
lay as joyous and innocent under him as she had lain under

the goat. Andreas looked at her half-open mouth, she stretched out her arms, and drew him gently to her, so that his lips touched hers. He straightened himself—it flashed through his mind that this was the first kiss of his life. She let him go, then gently drew him to her again, and took and gave another kiss, and then, in the same way, a third and fourth. The door swung in the wind—it seemed to Andreas that somebody had looked in. He went to the door and out into the passage—it was empty. Romana followed close behind, he went downstairs without a word, and she followed him, quite buoyant and free.

Downstairs her father was standing telling the foreman how to bring in the part of the aftergrowth which had dried first. She ran confidingly to him and leaned against him. Standing beside the great child, the handsome man might have been her betrothed.

Andreas went towards the stable as if he had important business there. The servant came hastily out of the gloom, nearly ran into him, cried "Hallo there!" as though he had not recognized his master, and at once talk spurted from his moist mouth. The maid—that was a fine girl for you, she was busy helping him to cure the horse. She didn't come from here either: she came from the valley, and could do what she liked with the farmer folk. But the master needed no telling; he knew pretty well what he was about: he had got a young and pretty one. Well, well, that was the way in Carinthia—that was life! For by the time they were fifteen every maid had had her man, and the farmer's daughter was just as willing to leave her door unbolted as the dairymaid, one today, another tomorrow, so that everybody got his chance. There was a fire in Andreas's breast which leapt to his throat, but not a word left his lips. He longed to strike the fellow across the mouth—what prevented him? The other felt it,

and recoiled a step. But Andreas's mind was elsewhere. His
eyeballs quivered. He saw Romana sitting in the dark on her
virgin bed, in her nightgown, her feet drawn up under her,
watching the door. She had shown him her door and the
empty room beside it, and it all rolled past his eyes like mountain mist. He did not want to pursue the thought—strove to
turn away from it. Without more ado, he turned his back on
the wretch, beaten again.

At the evening meal, a feeling he had never known overcame Andreas; everything had fallen apart, the shadows and
the light, the faces and the hands. The farmer stretched out
his hand towards him for the cider jug. Andreas was startled
to the depths of his being, as if the hand of judgment were
groping for his heart-strings. At the other end of the table
the maid was cackling her "Mr. Sergeant." "Who is this 'Sergeant'?" demanded Andreas angrily. His voice sounded strange,
like a dreamer talking in his sleep. From far away the servant
glared at him, white and unkempt—sullen.

Later, Andreas was alone in his room. He was standing
by the table fidgeting with his portmanteau—there was a
tinder-box there, but he needed no light, the moon shone
bright through the window, the whole room stood out clear
in black and white. He was listening to the noises in the
house, he had taken off his riding-boots—he did not know
what he was waiting for. And yet he knew, and suddenly
found himself standing in the passage outside a bedroom
door. He held his breath. Two people, lying in bed, were
talking in a low, confiding tone. His senses were quickened,
he could hear the farmer's wife plaiting her hair as she spoke
and the house-dog moving about down in the yard, eating
something. "Who can be feeding the dog at this time of
night?" something in him wondered. And at the same time he
felt as if he must return to his boyhood, when he still slept in

the little room next his parents and overheard them talking in
the evening through the wardrobe whether he would or no.
Even now he did not want to eavesdrop, yet he heard all the
same, but through what he heard he could hear his parents
talking—they were certainly older than the farmer and his
wife, yet not much—ten years maybe. "Is that so much?" he
thought. "Are they so much nearer death—worn out? For every word they say could be left unsaid; one speaks, the other
replies, and real life is over. But those two in there are as confiding and warm-hearted as a newly married couple."

Suddenly he started as if an icy drop had fallen straight
on to his heart. They were speaking of him and the girl, but
even in that they found no harm. Whatever the child might
do, said the wife, she let her have her way, because the girl
would never do wrong behind her back. She was too frank
and open; she got that from him, for he had always been a
fiery friend and a happy-hearted man, and now, by God's
goodness, the girl had grown like that too. No, said the husband, she got that from her; she was her mother's child, and
so she could not be deceitful or underhand.—But now here
she was, an old woman, with a daughter already running
after a strange man, and the time would soon come when he
would be ashamed to treat her like a lover.—No, God save
him, she was always the same to him—nay more, always
dearer, and these eighteen years he had not rued it for one
hour.—No, nor had she, not for an hour. He was the only
thing she cared for; and, his pleasant voice replied, he cared
only for her and the children; they were one with her, those
that were left, and the others too. And that old couple the
river had swept away in the April floods might be counted
happy. They had floated away on a bed together, holding each
other's hands, it had dragged them down into the rapids, and
their white hair had shone like silver under the willows. And

that was what God gave to His chosen. That was beyond wishing and praying for.

Meanwhile the room had grown quite still. There was the sound of gentle movement in the beds, and he thought he heard the two kissing. He tried to move away but did not dare, the silence was so perfect. It came heavily home to him that things had not been so beautiful between his parents— no such fond closeness between them, although each was proud of the other and although, in public, they stood firmly side by side, and jealously guarded each other's honour and dignity. He could not make out what it was that his parents lacked. Then the two in the room began to say the Lord's Prayer together, and Andreas stole away.

Now more than ever he felt drawn to Romana's room, irresistibly, yet differently from before, everything stood out clear in black and white. He said to himself: One day this will be my house, my wife, then I shall lie beside her talking about our children. He was sure now that she was waiting for him, just as he was going to her, for many innocent, glowing embraces, and a secret betrothal.

With quick, sure steps he approached the door: it was ajar, and yielded noiselessly to his pressure. He felt that she was sitting awake in the dark, aglow with expectation. He was already in the middle of the room when he noticed that she did not move. Her breath came and went so soundlessly that he had to hold his own as he strained to listen, not knowing whether she was awake or asleep. His shadow lay as if rooted to the floor; in his impatience he all but whispered her name, to wake her with kisses if no answer came—then he felt as if a cold knife had pierced him. In another bed, over which a cupboard cast black shadow, another sleeper stirred, sighed, turned over. The head came near the moonlight— white-streaked hair. It was the old maidservant, the nurse.

Then he had to go; between each step and the next, time stretched endlessly. Crestfallen, as in a dream, he crept along the long moonlit corridor to his room.

He felt more at ease, more at home, than ever before in his life. He looked out over the back courtyard; the full moon was hanging over the stable, the night was crystal clear. The dog was standing in the full moonlight, its head strangely drawn to one side, and in this posture was turning round and round on itself. The creature seemed to be suffering horribly —perhaps it was old and very near death. Andreas was seized with dull pain; a sadness beyond all measure possessed him to see the animal suffering when he was so happy, as though the sight were a warning of the approaching death of his father.

He left the window. He could think of his Romana again, but now more truly and solemnly, because he had just thought of his parents in that way. He was soon undressed and in bed, and in his imagination was writing to his parents. Thoughts poured in upon him, every argument that came into his mind was unanswerable, they had never had such a letter from him. They must feel that he was no longer a boy, but a man. If he had been a daughter instead of a son—he began somewhat casually—they would long ago have known the joy, while still hale, of embracing their grandchildren and seeing their children's children growing up. Because of him they had had to wait too long for that joy; it was one of the purest joys of life, and in a way itself the renewal of life. His parents had never had much joy from him—the thought was as vivid as if they were dead and he must lay himself upon them to warm them with his body. They had sent him on a costly journey to a foreign country. Why? To see foreign peoples, to observe foreign customs, to polish his manners. But all these things were means, means to one end. How much better it would be if that supreme end, which was nothing more nor less than his life's happiness, could be attained by one resolute step! Now, by God's sudden guidance, he had found the girl, the life-mate, to make that happiness secure. From now on he had only one aim—side by side with her, to content his parents by his own content.

The letter he wrote in his imagination far surpassed this poor abstract; the most moving words came unsought, a chain of beautiful phrases formed of itself. He spoke of the fine estate of the Finazzer family, and of their ancient and noble descent, without boasting, but in a way which really pleased him. If he had had a pen and inkwell at hand, he would have jumped out of bed and had the letter written at a sitting. But then fatigue began to dissolve the beautiful chain, other visions mingled with his revery, and all brought horror and dread.

It might have been a little past midnight. He sank from one troubled and ugly dream into another. All the humiliations he had ever endured in his life, all the pain and fear he had ever known, came over him again. Once again he had to pass through all the confused and false situations of his life as a child and boy. And Romana fled before him, strangely dressed, half peasant, half lady, barefoot under her pleated black brocade skirt, and it was in Vienna, in the crowded Spiegelgasse, quite close to his parents' home. He had to follow her, in dread, and yet, in dread, conceal his hurried pursuit. She forced her way through the crowd, turned her face to him—it was expressionless and distorted. As she sped on, her clothes were torn in disorder from her body. Suddenly she vanished in an entry, and he after her, as far as he could with his left foot, which dragged intolerably and kept catching between the paving stones. Now at last he was in the entry, but he had to move slowly, and here no horrible encounter was spared him. A look that he had

feared more than any other as a boy, the look of his first cate-
chist, shot through him, and the dreaded little podgy hand
seized him. The loathsome face of a boy who had told him
on the back staircase in the twilight what he did not want to
hear, was pressed close to his cheek, and as he struggled to
push it away, lying in front of the door through which he
had to follow Romana was a creature which moved after
him: it was the cat whose back he had once broken with a
cart shaft, and which had taken so long to die. So it was not
dead, after all these years! Creeping like a snake with its
broken back, it came towards him, and panic seized him as
it looked at him. There was no help for it. He had to step
over it. With unspeakable torment he raised his left foot
over the creature, whose back writhed up and down unceasingly—when the look of the cat's upturned face struck him
from below, the roundness of the cat's face from a head at
once cat and dog, with a ghastly expression of sensual gratification and death agony—he opened his mouth to scream—
a scream issued from the house: he had to make his way
through the wardrobe, which was full of his parents' clothes.
The screams from within grew more horrible, as though a
living creature were being butchered by a murderer. It was
Romana, and he could not help her. There were too many
worn-out clothes, the clothes of many years, which had not
been given away. Dripping with sweat, he pushed his way
through . . .

He was lying in bed, his heart pounding. It was already
half dawn, but not yet day. The house was astir, doors were
banging, from the courtyard came a noise of hurrying steps
and loud voices. Then the screams arose again which had
torn his dreaming soul from the depths of his dream to the
livid light. It was the piercing weeping and wailing of a
woman's voice—a shrill complaint ceaselessly rising and fall-

ing. Andreas leapt out of bed and dressed, but he felt like a condemned criminal awakened by the call of the hangman: he was still too much in his dream—it was as if he had committed some dreadful deed, and now it was all coming to light.

He ran downstairs in the direction of the voice ringing so dreadfully through the house. Thinking it might be Romana, his blood froze. Then he knew that no such sounds could come from her though she were being burned alive in martyrdom.

Downstairs on the ground floor, a little passage leading sideways was crowded with farm hands and maids staring in at the open door of a room. Andreas joined them and they made way for him. On the threshold of the room he stopped. Smoke and a stench of burning rose towards him. A half-naked woman was tied to the bed-post, and it was from her mouth that there came the ceaseless, piercing complaints or curses, such as the damned in hell might utter, which had penetrated to the depths of Andreas's dream. The farmer was busying himself about the raving creature; his wife, half dressed, beside him; with his pocket-knife the steward was cutting the knotted rope which bound her ankles to the bed. The cords from her hands and a gag lay on the floor. The head maid was pouring water from a jug on to the smouldering mattress and the charred posts at the head of the bed, and stamping out the glowing sparks in the straw and twigs piled up beside the bed.

Then Andreas recognized in the screaming woman bound there the young maid who had been carrying on with his servant the day before, and a frightful foreboding made his blood run cold. The screaming subsided. In the comforting presence of the farmer and his wife, the half-demented woman was growing quieter. Twitching, she lay across the knees of the head maid, who wrapped her up in a horse-rug. She began to answer the farmer's questions; her swollen face took on a human expression, but every answer turned to a soul-rending shriek, which forced its way from her distended mouth and rang through the house. Had the man stunned her with a blow, or in some other way, and then gagged her? asked the farmer. What kind of poison had been mixed for the dog? Had a long or short time passed till she had torn the gag out of her mouth? But the woman could say nothing but scream with horror for a just God to hear her: tied her up he had, made up the fire under her very eyes, and bolted her in from the outside, grinned in at her through the window and taunted her in her deadly fear. And all this mixed with imploring prayers to forgive her her grievous sin. No name was spoken, but Andreas knew only too well whom they were speaking about. As though he had seen what he had come to see, he passed like a sleepwalker through the crowd of farm hands and maids, who silently made way for him; behind them all, cowering in a doorway, stood Romana, half dressed, barefoot and trembling—almost as I saw her in my dream, something in him said. When she became aware of him her face took on an expression of boundless horror.

He went into the stables; a young stable-boy followed him, perhaps suspicious. The stall where Andreas's chestnut had stood the day before was empty; the bay stood in its misery. The tall young lad, who had an honest face, looked at Andreas, who forced himself to ask, "Did he take anything else with him?"

"It doesn't seem so for the moment," said the stable-boy. "A few of us are after him, but his horse is certainly the faster, and he's had as much as two hours' start."

Andreas said nothing. His horse was gone, and with it more than half his journey money, which was sewn into the saddle. But that seemed little compared to the shame of standing thus before the farmer's people, into whose house he had brought the horror. The saying "Like master, like man" came into his mind, and then, like a lightning flash, the saying reversed, so that he stood as if drenched with blood before the honest face of the lad.

"The horse there was stolen from us too," said the stable-boy, pointing to the bay. "The master recognized it at once, but he didn't want to say anything about it at first."

Andreas made no answer. He went upstairs, and without counting what money he had left, he took out as much as he thought would repay Finazzer for his stolen property. As he had no idea what a horse like the bay might fetch among the country folk, he put into his pocket as much as he had paid for it in Villach to make sure. Then he stood lost in thought for a long time by the table in his room, and at last went downstairs to settle the matter.

He had to wait before he could speak to the farmer, for the three men who had ridden in pursuit had just come back, and were reporting what they had seen and what they had found out from the shepherds and wayfarers they had met; but there was little likelihood of laying hands on the scoundrel. The farmer was kind and composed, Andreas all the more embarrassed.

"Then do you want to keep the horse and buy it from me a second time? For I'm sure you've paid for it honestly."

Andreas said no.

"If not, how can I take your money? You have brought back my stolen property; besides, through you I know there is a slut in the stable, so that I can get her out of the house and into the hands of the law before she does more mischief. You are an inexperienced young gentleman, and our Lord had His hand visibly over you. The maid has confessed that when she was with the ruffian she saw a brand on his shoulder, and she thinks that if he had not caught her looking at it, for he turned as white as chalk when he did, he would not have used her so savagely. Thank your Maker that He has preserved you from spending a night in the woods with a runaway murderer. If you mean to go on to Italy, as you said yesterday, there is a carrier passing here this evening. He will take you to Villach, and from there you will find an opportunity of travelling down to Venice any day."

THE CARRIER did not arrive till the following evening, and so Andreas spent two more days at the Finazzer farm. It was painful to him to be on the farmer's hands after such an affair: he felt like a prisoner. He crept about the house, the people went about their work, nobody heeded him. Through a window he saw in the distance the farmer mount and ride away; he had no further sight of the wife. He went out of the house and up the fields behind the farm. The clouds were hanging low over the valley, the whole world was dreary and heavy, and as desolate as the end of time. Not knowing where to go, he sat down on a stack of wood. He tried to imagine other weather, but it seemed to him as if this valley could never look otherwise. "And yet I was so happy here yesterday," he said. He tried to recall Romana's face, but could not, and gave up the attempt. "Such a thing could only happen to you," he heard his father's voice saying, as sharp and clear as if it were outside him. He stood up, took a few heavy steps, the voice repeated what it had said. He stood still again, trying to protest. "Why do I believe it myself?" he brooded, and with dragging feet went slowly up the path; yet it was dreadful to him because he had been that way yesterday. Not that he had any thought of Romana: it was only the intolerably keen feeling of yesterday, of the afternoon hour, which had been followed by the evening, the night, and this morning hour. "Why do I know myself that it had to happen to me?" he brooded on, looking up now and then at the misty, wooded slopes beyond, as a prisoner looks up at the walls of his cell.

Sunk in these sombre musings, he began to count up his expenses for the four days' journey from Vienna to Villach, which now seemed exorbitant, then the money for the second horse and the stolen sum. Then he worked out what was left from Austrian into Venetian money: in sequins it seemed scanty enough, but in doubloons so beggarly that he stopped, daunted, and wondered whether to turn back or travel on. In his present state of mind he would have turned back, but his parents would never have forgiven him; so much money had been squandered for absolutely nothing. He felt that his parents were not really concerned with him and his happiness, but only with outward show and what people would say. The faces of friends and relations rose before him; among them some were malicious and bloated, some indifferent, some even kindly, but there was not one the sight of which warmed his heart.

He thought of his grandfather Ferschengelder, who had borne his own name Andreas, and of how once he had tramped off from his father's farm down the Danube towards Vienna with nothing but a silver groat tied up in his hand-kerchief, and of how he had risen to be an Imperial Lackey-in-Ordinary, with a title. He had been a handsome man, and Andreas had his stature, though none of his bearing. He re-membered how they had taunted him for being so unlike his grandfather, the pride of the family, and taking after his Uncle Leopold, who had been cruel to animals as a child, and had grown up to be a man of violence, who wasted his substance, could not preserve the honour of the family, and had brought nothing but grief and trouble on those who had had to do with him.

His Uncle Leopold's burly figure rose before him, his red face and bulging eyes. He saw him lying on his deathbed, the arms of the Ferschengelders on a wooden scutcheon at his feet. Through one door, flung open by a servant, came the childless, legitimate wife, a della Spina by birth, with a hand-kerchief in her beautiful, high-born hand; through the other half-open door slipped in the other, illegitimate wife, the round-faced peasant woman with the pretty double chin, her six children holding hands behind her and gazing anxiously past their mother at their dead, noble father. And as is the way with those in sorrow and darkness, in memory Andreas envied the dead man.

Turning back to the farm, he began again to reckon by how much the portion of the Ferschengelders had dwindled; he counted up how much of their present income was being sacrificed to his journey, and fell a prey to morbid imaginings. At the dinner-table he found his place set, but today, at the head of the table, the old, white-haired maid sat and served. Not only the farmer was absent, but his wife and Romana too. Andreas felt that he had always known it would be so, that he would not see Romana again. He ate in silence, the servants talked to each other, but none let fall a word about the event of the night. It only transpired that the farmer had ridden to Villach to see the magistrate. The steward, as he stood up, said to Andreas across the table that the farmer had left a message for him: the carrier might possibly not pass that way until the next day. In that case, Andreas might be so good as to stay on and accept what hospitality he had to offer.

It was a cheerless, still afternoon. Andreas longed for a breath of wind. The mist had rolled together into clouds, big and small; they hung motionless, as if from everlasting to everlasting. Once again he mounted the path leading towards the village. The thought of going downhill was repugnant to him; he could not have borne the return uphill with the Finazzer farm ahead. He knew no road on the other side of the valley. If he only had a companion—a farm dog or some other animal! "But that is a thing I can never have again," he said to himself.

The only thought that came into his mind was torment. He saw himself as a twelve-year-old boy, saw the little stray dog following his every step. The humility with which it adopted him, the first being it met, as its master, the joy, the bliss with which it moved if he so much as looked at it were past understanding. If it thought its master was angry, it would roll on its back, draw up its little legs anxiously, yield itself utterly, with an indescribable expression in its upturned eyes. One day Andreas saw it facing a big dog in the posture he thought it took for him alone, to soothe his anger and win back his love. His blood rose, he called the dog to him. Ten paces off it became aware of his angry look. And it came creeping on, its eyes fixed on Andreas's face. He taunted it for a low, cowardly beast, and under his taunts it crept closer and closer. It seemed to him that he raised his foot and struck the creature's spine with his heel. The dog gave a yelp of pain and collapsed, still wagging its tail. He swung round and went away. The dog crawled after him; its back was broken, yet it crept after its master like a snake, its back giving at every step. At last he stopped; the little dog fixed its eyes on him, wagged its tail, and died. He was not sure whether he had done the thing or not—but it came out of him. And that was how the infinite came home to him. The memory was torture, yet he felt a wave of homesickness for the twelve-year-old Andreas who had done it. Everything seemed good that was not here, everything worth living that was not the present. Below him he saw a Capuchin tramping along the road; before a crucifix he knelt. How serene his untrammelled soul must be! In thought Andreas took refuge in the figure till it passed out of sight at a bend in the road. Then he was alone again.

He could not bear the valley; he climbed up to the wood. He felt better among the tree-trunks. Damp twigs struck his face, he bounded forward, rotting branches crackled under him on the ground. He measured his bounds so that with each he was hidden behind massive tree-trunks: there were old maples and beeches still standing among the pines, and he hid behind each of them, then bounded on, until he had escaped from himself, as from a prison. He leapt on—he knew nothing of himself save the moment. Now he thought he was Uncle Leopold pursuing a peasant girl like a faun in the forest, now that he was a criminal and murderer like Gotthilff, with the sheriff's men after him. But he contrived to elude them—fell on his knees before the Empress . . .

Suddenly he felt that a human being was really watching from close by. So even here there was gall! He crouched behind a hazel-bush, as still as an animal. The man in the little clearing, fifty paces in front of him, was peering into the wood. When he had heard nothing for a while he went on with his work. He was digging. Andreas leapt towards him from tree to tree. When a twig cracked the man outside looked up from his work, but at last Andreas came quite close to him. It was one of the farm hands from Castle Finazzer. He buried the house dog, then threw the earth back into the grave, flattened it down with his spade, and went away.

Andreas threw himself on to the grave and lay for a long time in brooding thought. "Here!" he said to himself. "Here! All this wandering is futile, we cannot escape from ourselves. We are dragged hither and thither, they sent me all this long way—at last it comes to an end somewhere—here!" There was something between him and the dog, he did not know what, just as there was something between him and Gotthilff, who had brought about the dog's death. Threads ran to and fro, and out of them a world was woven, behind the real one, and not so empty and desolate. Then he wondered at himself: "Why am I here?" And he felt as if another man were lying there, and that he must enter into him, but had forgotten the word.

Evening had fallen without a gleam of red in the sky, without a sign to mark the beauty of the changing day. From the heavy clouds a dismal gloom descended, and from the misty air a quiet rain began to fall on Andreas as he lay on the grave. He felt cold, rose, and went down.

In his dream that night the sun was shining. He ran deeper and deeper into the forest and found Romana. The deeper he went into the forest the brighter it shone: in the middle, where everything was darkest and most radiant, he found her sitting on a little island meadow, round which shining water flowed. She had fallen asleep haymaking, her sickle and rake beside her. As he stepped over the water she looked up at him, but as she would look at a stranger. He called to her, "Romana, can you see me?" Her eyes were so vacant.

"Why, yes, of course," she said, with a strange look. "Do you know, I don't know where the dog is buried."

He felt strange, could not help laughing at what she said. She shrank from him in fear, stumbled on the heap of hay and sank half down on to the ground like a wounded doe. He was close to her and felt that she believed him to be the wicked Gotthilff, and yet not Gotthilff either, and he himself was not quite sure who he was. She implored him not to tie her naked to the bed in front of all the people, and not to run away on a stolen horse. He laid his hand on her, called

her tenderly by her name—she was distraught with fear. He
let her go: she struggled after him on her knees.

"Come back!" she cried, beseeching. "I will go with you,
if it were to the gallows. Father wants to lock me in, mother
has her arms round me, my dead brothers and sisters are trying to cling to me too—but I will get away, I will leave them
all to come to you." He tried to reach her, but she had vanished.

In despair he rushed into the wood—and she came to
meet him between two beautiful maples, as gay and friendly
as if nothing had happened. Her eyes shone with a strange
radiance, her bare feet were luminous on the moss, and the
hem of her dress was wet.

"What kind of woman are you?" he cried in wonder.

"This kind," she said, holding up her mouth to him. As
he stretched out his arms to embrace her, "Why, such a
man!" she cried, striking at him with her rake. She struck him
on the forehead, there was a sharp, clear sound as if a pane of
glass had broken. He awoke with a start.

He knew that he had been dreaming, but the truth in his
dream filled him with joy to his deepest fibre. Romana's
whole being had been revealed to him with a vividness that
was more than life. All his heaviness was dispelled. Within
him or without he could not lose her. He had the knowledge
—nay, the faith, that she lived for him. He returned to the
world like one blessed. He felt that she might be standing
below, had thrown a stone at the window pane and awakened
him. He ran to the window: a pane was cracked, a dead bird
lay in the window frame. He went slowly back, the bird in
his hand, and laid it on his pillow. The little body poured
delight through his veins; he felt as if he could easily have
restored the bird to life if he had only taken it to his heart. He

sat on the bed. A thousand thoughts streamed round him; he was happy. His body was a temple in which Romana's being dwelt, and time in its flow swept round him, and lapped on the steps of the temple.

In the house everything was at first still in the greying morning, and rain was falling. When he arose from his dreaming ecstasy, day had come and it was light. The whole house was at work. He went downstairs, asked for a piece of bread, and drank from the fountain. He wandered about the house; nobody heeded him. Wherever he was, whatever he did, he was calm: his soul had a centre. He had his meal with the people; the farmer had not returned, nobody mentioned the wife or Romana. In the afternoon the carrier arrived. He was willing to take Andreas with him, but to judge from the way his business was going, he would have to leave before evening: they would spend the night in the next village down the valley.

A fresh wind was blowing into the valley, beautiful, big clouds were driving across it, and beyond the land was clear and radiant. A farm hand carried the portmanteau and valise down to the cart, Andreas followed him. At the bottom of the stairs he turned back, and a voice told him that Romana was standing waiting up in his empty room. When he entered the room and found it empty, he could hardly trust his own eyes; he searched every corner, as though she might be hidden in the whitewashed wall. With bowed head he went downstairs again. There he stood for a while irresolute, listening. Outside the grooms were talking as they helped to put the horses in. Andreas's heart was wrung. Without his will his feet carried him to the stable. The bay was standing with hanging head, its ears laid back; a few of the farm horses turned in their stalls as Andreas came in. Andreas stood—he did not know how long—in the dim place, listening to a twittering;

then through the little barred window a shaft of gold shot slanting to the stable door, and hung there, a swallow glided through, flashing, and behind it was Romana's mouth, open, moist and twitching with suppressed weeping. He could hardly grasp that she was standing bodily before him, but he did grasp it, and the fulness of his heart paralysed his limbs. She was barefoot, her plaits were hanging down as if she had that moment jumped out of bed and run to him. He could and would not ask, but his arms rose towards her. She did not come to him nor did she shrink from him. She was as close as if she were part of him, and then again it was as if she did not see him. In any case, she did not look at him, and he made no move to approach her. Her mouth struggled with words, her eyes with tears. She pulled ceaselessly at her thin silver chain as if she were trying to strangle herself, so as to withdraw from him utterly. It was as if pain were having its way with her, so that she did not even feel that Andreas was near. At last the chain broke—one piece slid into the bosom of her open gown, the other remained in her hand. She pressed it from above on to the back of Andreas's hand; her mouth twitched as if a scream must come but could not. She leaned against him, her mouth moist and quivering, kissed his—and was gone.

The piece of silver chain had slipped from Andreas's hand. He picked it up out of the straw—he did not know whether to follow her—everything was happening outside him, and at the same time in the very depths of his heart, depths to which, till now, nothing had pierced. Then he heard them looking for him outside, the moment of decision had come. The thought flashed through his mind: "Cast everything aside, tell them I am going to stay, have the baggage taken up again, tell the farm hands I have changed my mind." But how could he? How could he stand up before

Finazzer, or even before his wife? What could he say? What reasons could he give? What kind of man would he have had to be to take this upon himself and then stand his ground in a situation so suddenly reversed?

HE WAS already sitting in the cart; the horses had started, how he could not remember. "Time must pass; I cannot stay here, but I can return," he thought, "and soon, the same and yet another." Between his fingers he felt the chain that assured him that it was all reality, and not a dream.

The cart rolled downhill; in front of him he saw the sun and the wide, sunny land, behind him the narrow valley with the lonely homestead already in the shadow. His eyes were fixed ahead, but with a vacant, close look; the eyes of his heart were straining backwards. He was roused by the voice of the carrier, who was pointing with his whip up into the pure evening air where an eagle was wheeling. For the first time Andreas was aware of what lay before him. The road had wound out of the mountain valley and taken a sharp turn to the left. There a huge valley had opened; a river, no longer a brook, wound far below, but beyond it there rose the mightiest peak of the range, behind which, still high in the sky, the sun was setting. Vast shadows fell upon the valley; whole blue-black forests bristled on the riven foot of the mountain; waterfalls plunged darkling down in the ravines; above, everything was free, bare, rising boldly upwards—sheer slopes, rock walls, crowned by the snowy peak, ineffably pure and radiant.

Nature came home to Andreas as never before. It was as if the whole scene had risen from his own being at one stroke —that power, that uprising and its crowning purity. The majestic bird was still wheeling above, alone in the light; with widespread wings it swept slow circles. From where it hovered, it could see everything—the Finazzer valley and the farm, the village; the graves of Romana's sisters and brothers were as near to its keen sight as the mountain gorges in whose blue shadows it was searching for a young roe or a stray goat. Andreas' soul enfolded the bird—he soared towards it in ecstasy. This time he felt no impulse to lose himself in it; he only felt its supreme power and gift flowing into him. Every shadow, every clog, fell away from him. It was borne in upon him that, seen from high enough, the parted are united, and loneliness is an illusion. He possessed Romana wherever he was—he could take her into him whenever he would. That mountain, rising before him and towering to the skies, was a brother and more than a brother. As it took the tender fawn to its breast in its mighty spaces, covering it with cool shade and hiding it from its pursuer with blue gloom, so Romana lived in him. She was a living being, a centre, with a paradise about her no more unreal than that which towered up beyond the valley. He looked into his own heart and saw Romana kneel down to pray; she bent her knees as the fawn, when it lies down to rest, folds its frail legs, and the movement was dear to him beyond words. Circles dissolved in circles. He prayed with her, and when he looked, he knew that the mountain was simply his prayer. An unutterable certainty came home to him. It was the happiest moment of his life.

WHEN he came downstairs to rejoin the people of the house he found the girl Zustina busily arguing with a small, middle-aged man whose almost crescent-shaped nose gave him a curiously dashing expression, and who had in his hand something in a cotton handkerchief which filled the room with a smell of fish.

"No, really, it cannot go on, the way you let people palm things off on you," he heard her say. "If it were another day

I would answer for it to mother. But really, today you must take it back, and don't forget the decorator. Argue it out with him, point by point, just as I told you. Decorators are crafty and don't know what conscience is, but a man who can talk like you ought to be a match for anybody. The draw will be exactly a week after the Feast of Our Lady's Birth, so that everything must be delivered the day before. If a single thing is missing, half a silver ducat will be struck off his pay. I want it exactly like a Corpus Christi altar, with drapery and wreaths in front, and the urn with the lottery tickets in the middle between banks of fresh flowers. He's to charge no extras for putting it up. He's to bring it here, and Zorzi will have to help in the arranging and decorating. Now go and tell him all that so that we may be proud of you, and leave your book here. I will cast it up."

The elderly man was going away as Andreas entered. "Oh, there you are," said Zustina. "Your luggage has just arrived. Zorzi will fetch men to carry it up. Then he will show you a good coffee-house, and take you to my sister's if you like. She will be glad to see you. He's useful for errands of that kind," she added. "For that matter, there is absolutely no need for you to make a bosom friend of him at once. But after all, that's your affair. It takes all kinds to make a world, and we all have to get through it as best we can. What I say is, you must take the world as you find it."

She ran to the stove, looked into the oven, basted the meat; a few garments, which seemed to belong to her mother and brothers, were whipped into a big cupboard. She chased the cat off the table, and attended to a bird hanging in the window. "There was something else I wanted to say to you," she went on, coming to a standstill in front of Andreas. "I don't know whether you have much money on you, or a letter to a banker. If it's money, then give it to a business friend or any one you happen to know in the town to keep for you. Not that there are dishonest people in the house, but I won't take the responsibility. I've got enough to do to keep the house tidy and teach my two brothers and look after my father, for my mother generally works away from home. Besides, you can imagine how much I have to work and plan to get ready for the lottery. How easily offended . . . I'm sorry we can't possibly offer you a ticket, even though you are in the house, but you are a foreigner, and our patrons are very particular in these things. The second prize is very nice too—it's a gold and enamel snuff-box. I'll show it to you as soon as it comes home from the jeweller's."

Meanwhile she added up, standing, the little account-book, using for the purpose a tiny pencil which she had had hidden in one of the curls of her toupet, for her hair was dressed as it might be for a ball, in a high toupet. She wore cloth slippers and a taffeta skirt with silver lace, but she had thrown over it a checked dressing-jacket which was much too big for her and left completely bare her charmingly slender but by no means childish throat. Amid the muttered exclamations with which she interspersed her talk, her eyes darted from Andreas to the stove and the cat. Suddenly something flashed through her mind; she flew to the window, leant far out, and called shrilly down: "Count Gasparo, Count Gasparo —listen! I've got something to say to you."

"Here I am," said the man with the hooked nose and the fish, unexpectedly coming through the door into the room. "Why scream at me through the window? Here I am"—and he turned to Andreas. "I have only just heard below that you are the young foreign nobleman whom I have the honour to welcome as my guest. I wish both for your and our own sakes that you may be happy under our humble roof. You occupy the rooms of my daughter Nina. You do not yet know her,

and so you cannot yet appreciate the proof of respect and confidence we have given you in placing that apartment at your
disposal. The room of such a being is like the robe of a saint
—it harbours powers. Whatever you may experience in this
town—and you have come here to gather knowledge and experience—within those walls peace will re-enter your mind,
and steadiness your soul. The very air of those rooms breathes
—how shall I put it?—virtue invincible. Rather die than
sacrifice that virtue was the iron resolve of my child. I, sir"—
he touched Andreas with his hand, which was white and extremely shapely, but too small for a man and therefore distasteful—"was in a position neither to strengthen my child in
such a resolve nor to reward her for it. Mine is a wrecked existence. Storms have hurled me from the summit of my family." He withdrew, letting his hand sink with an inimitable
gesture. With a bow he left the room.

Zustina's face was radiant with admiration at the Count's
speech. And indeed the way in which he had pronounced
these few sentences was a masterpiece of decorum and artistry.
Dignity was mingled with humanity; gravity and experience
were tempered with confidence. The elder spoke to the
younger, the host to his guest, the old man tried by life spoke
as a father to the untried youth, and the Venetian nobleman
to a nobleman—it was all there. "What do you think of my
father's way of speaking?" she asked. In her sincere and childish pleasure she seemed to have forgotten that she had called
him back for anything at all. "He can find the tone for any
occasion," she cried, her eyes shining. "He has had a great
deal of trouble and many enemies, but no one can deny his
great talents." While before she had been quicksilvery and
eager, but tart, she was now kindled from within; her eyes
flashed and her mouth moved with an indescribable childlike

zest. There was something of the squirrel about her, yet she was a resolute, honest little woman.

"So now you know my father too, and before an hour has passed you will know my sister, and some of her friends too, for certain. The most distinguished of them all is the Duke of Camposagrado, the Spanish ambassador. He is such a great gentleman that when the King of Spain speaks to him he puts his hat on. Don't be startled when you see him: he looks like a wild beast, but he's a very great gentleman. Then there's one of her friends I would like myself—but why speak about me? He's an Austrian officer, a Slavonian; that means he has an Austrian captain's commission and perquisites, the cattle customs on Hungarian and Styrian oxen coming in by way of Trieste—a fine business. He's a handsome man too, and madly in love with Nina. Just think—he never gets up from table without drinking her health and then, every time, throwing his glass through the window-panes into the canal or against the wall; but when it's a special day he simply breaks all the glass on the table, just in honour of Nina. Of course he pays for the glasses afterwards. Isn't it savage? But in his country it's the greatest of compliments. He's a great gambler —however, you will get to know him yourself, and live like the others. If he were my husband I would soon break him of it."

"But one thing," she went on, looking at him with a charming expression of gravity and importance, "if you get mixed up in disputes, misunderstandings, quarrels, and so on, get your own way. Don't let anybody, man or woman, get round you with tears. That's a silly weakness, and I can't bear it. But I'm not speaking about Nina's tears. Nina's tears are as real as gold. When she cries she's like a little child. Nobody has the heart to refuse her what she wants, for she's ten times kinder than I am, although she is twenty-one, and I'm not sixteen yet. But how can it interest you," she added, with an arch look, as she busied herself about the bird in the cage, "to hear me talking about myself? You didn't come to Venice for that. Go downstairs. Zorzi will be waiting for you down there."

Andreas was already on the stairs when she came after him. "One thing more—it just occurred to me. You look good-natured, and a good man must be warned at the first step. Don't let anybody inveigle you into accepting his bills, even though he should offer you others to cover them which are due before his. Never. Do you understand me?" For an instant her hand rested lightly on Andreas's arm. It was exactly the same gesture as her father had made before, yet how much truth there is in the saying that though two may do the same thing, the result is worlds apart. The little hand was so charming and the motherly, womanly gesture enchanting. She was already back in the house, and as Andreas went downstairs he heard her calling to Zorzi through the window on the other side.

"She's a lovely little thing, isn't she?" said Zorzi, who was standing below, as if he had guessed what was busying Andreas's thoughts.

"But what is all this about the lottery?" asked Andreas, after a few steps. "Who distributes the prizes and what has the family got to do with it? It looks as if they were organizing it themselves."

The artist did not reply at once. "And so they are," he said, slackening his pace at a street-corner to let Andreas catch up with him. "Why shouldn't I tell you? The lottery is being arranged in a circle of rich and distinguished gentlemen, and the first prize is the girl herself."

"How do you mean—the girl herself?"

"Well, her virginity, if you like to put it that way. She's a good girl, and has taken it into her head to rescue her family from their poverty. You ought to hear how nicely she speaks about it, and how much trouble she has taken with the subscription list. For whatever she does must be done properly. A great gentleman, a friend of the family, has taken over the patronage." Here he lowered his voice. "He is Signor Sacramozo, the patrician, who was lately governor of Corfu. A ticket costs no less than twenty-four sequins, and not a name has been put on the subscription list that has not been approved by Signor Sacramozo."

Andreas had suddenly blushed so furiously that a haze blurred his eyes, and he nearly slipped on a squashed tomato lying in his way. The other looked at him sidelong as he walked. "An affair of the kind," he went on, "can be arranged among men of breeding who have the decency to keep it quiet, otherwise the authorities would intervene. So the gentlemen of the town would be rather unwilling to let a foreigner into an arrangement of the kind. But if you really care about it, I'll do what I can for you, and perhaps I could get a ticket for you in some roundabout way. For instance, one of the ticket-holders, for a consideration, which won't be small, might hand over his chance to you without your name being mentioned." Andreas did not know what to answer, and quickly changed the subject by saying how surprised he was that the elder daughter should know no better way of coming to her family's help, and leave it to the little sister to sacrifice herself in this strange fashion.

"Well, it isn't really so unusual, what she's doing," returned the other, "and there's nothing much to be hoped for from Nina. The little one knows that better than anybody. Nina can't manage money, and what you give her today melts between her fingers tomorrow. She's a beauty, but she's no match for Zustina in brains. I'll give you an instance: Once I wanted to present to her a rich and noble gentleman from Vienna, Count Grassalkowicz—you'll know the name. And you'll realize what it means to make the acquaintance of a man who, as you know, has two palaces in Vienna and one in Prague, and whose estates in Croatia are as big as all the possessions of the Republic put together. 'What's the man's name?' says she, and when it was repeated to her, up goes her nose. When she does that there's no more to be got out of her than out of a shying horse. 'The name,' she says, 'sounds like a common oath, and the man will be like it. Take him where you like. I won't have anything to do with him.' That's Nina."

Andreas thought that an introduction to Signorina Nina, by such a friend, was less of an honour than he had imagined, but he kept his thoughts to himself.

They had reached an open square, with wooden tables and wicker chairs in front of a little coffee-stall. At one of them a man dressed all in black was writing letters. At another, a coarse middle-aged man with a blue chin, wearing an odd kind of long frogged coat, sat at his ease, listening unmoved to the pleadings of a young man who hardly even dared to sit down, let alone draw up his chair to the table, so that Andreas could not look at him without a feeling of pity and distress.

"Look at those two," whispered Zorzi, taking possession of the chocolate Andreas had ordered for him. "That's a rich Greek and his nephew. The old man is a millionaire, and the poor lad is his only relation. But he isn't pleased with him because the young man married against his will, and he won't even let him into his house. The young man can hardly keep his head above water. He's in the hands of money-lenders, Jews and Christians, and is always running after his uncle.

Take a quiet look at them: the old man will hardly deign to see him, let alone give him an answer. He goes on smoking and lets him talk—look how the miserable beggar is wriggling for fear of getting so much as the smell of his smoke. And after a while, you'll see, he'll pay for his coffee and go away, and in the end the young man will fall on his knees before him, and the old man will take no more notice of him than if he were a dog. He'll hang on his coat, and the old man will shake him off and go on his way as if there were nobody there. You can see the same show several times a day, in the morning in front of the Exchange, then here, and in the evening on the Riva. Isn't it amusing to see what beasts people can be to each other, and how obstinate they can be in their spite?"

Andreas was hardly listening, so preoccupied was he by the appearance of the man writing. He had an inordinately long, narrow body, which, as he wrote, stooped over the table, under which his long legs could only fit as it were by apology, inordinately long arms which could, at a pinch, find room, and inordinately long fingers which held the bad, squeaking pen. His posture was uncomfortable and even ridiculous, but nothing could have more finely revealed the essence of the man than this discomfort, and the way he bore it, overcame it, was unaware of it. He wrote hurriedly, the breeze tugged at the page, he ought to have lost his temper, and yet there was self-command in all his limbs, a—strange as the word may seem—courtesy towards all the lifeless objects which rendered him such sorry service, a superiority to the discomfort of the situation which was incomparable. A strong gust blew one of the sheets over to Andreas. Andreas started up, and hastened to return it to the stranger, who, turning quietly round, took the proffered sheet with a slight bow. Andreas met his dark eyes; he thought them beautiful, although they were set in a face that nobody could call handsome. The head was far too small for the figure, and the sallow, rather sickly face so strangely awry that the absurd image of the shrunken face of a dead toad flashed through Andreas's mind.

He would have liked to know a great deal about the man, but he did not want to learn it from Zorzi, who bent towards him and whispered, "I'll tell you who he is as soon as he's gone. I don't want to mention his name now. He's the brother—well, the brother of the great gentleman who I told you was the protector of the family you're living with. You know who I mean—the one under whose patronage the lottery is being arranged. He is a Knight of Malta," he went on, but at once paused as the writer raised his head, "but as you see, he doesn't wear on his cloak the cross which it is not only his right, but his duty to wear. He has travelled a great deal, they say; he has been far into the interior of India, and even at the Great Wall of China, and some say he is in the service of the Jesuits, but others say he's nothing more nor less than a freemason."

The rich Greek and his beggarly nephew stood up—the gross callousness of the one, the bestial servility of the other, were revolting. In both, human nature seemed to have lost its dignity. For Andreas it was past understanding that so vile a spectacle could take place in the neighbourhood of a being such as he imagined the Knight to be. Indeed, when the two raised their voices, the one spitting like a cat, the other whimpering, he even felt he must rush between them and silence them with his stick. The Knight of Malta raised his eyes for a moment, but looked away over the two, as if they were not there, and, closing his letter as he rose, nodded to a lad who now ran up, took the letter with a bow, and went off with it, while the Knight walked away in the other direction.

When he had disappeared round the corner, the square seemed desolate to Andreas. Zorzi stooped and picked up a folded sheet of notepaper from under the table. "The wind has blown some of Knight Sacramozo's correspondence under our feet," he said. "Excuse me a moment. I'll go and take it to him."

"Let me take it" came from Andreas's mouth: his tongue seemed to say it of its own accord. His hand was already on the paper; the fulfilment of his wish meant infinitely much to him; he snatched the sheet out of the other's hand and ran after the Knight down a narrow alley.

There was more than grace, there was a really inimitable distinction in the way the Knight listened to him and took the paper, and Andreas thought he had never seen so wonderful a harmony between the bearing of a human being and the sound of his voice. "You are very kind, sir," came from his lips in German, perfectly pronounced. His genial and at the same time spiritual face seemed to express a profound kindliness arising from his soul. In the space of a moment Andreas felt himself received with benevolence, caught up into an atmosphere which ennobled every fibre of his being, and then dismissed. He stood before the stranger as if inanimate, he felt his body clumsy, his attitude uncouth. But there was in every limb an awareness which imprinted deep within him the image of the tall figure stooping slightly towards him, in easy assurance, in gracious civility, as flame stoops quivering to flame.

He went back, his memory already groping for the expression of those eyes, the sound of that voice, as though he had lost them for ever, wondering, "Have I ever seen him before? How else could his image have been impressed on me in one moment? I can learn about him from myself!" But great was his astonishment when he felt, rather than heard, swift and light steps hurrying after him, which could only be the Knight's, when he saw the Knight catch up with him and heard him, in the same winning voice, with the most perfect courtesy, declare that he must have made a mistake. "The letter you were so kind as to give me, sir, is neither written by my hand nor addressed to me. It must belong to you—in any case, I must beg you to dispose of it!"

Andreas was embarrassed and confused. A few hazy thoughts crossed his mind, the fear of seeming to intrude stabbed him like a hot needle. In his predicament, it seemed to him easier to say something definite than to make some vague reply, for which he would never have found the words. He reddened at a sudden movement of his hands, which had already stretched out for the letter; but averred only the more definitely that the letter most certainly did not belong to him, that it was in no way his to dispose of. The look with which the Knight at once acquiesced was rather the look of a man who will on no account insist than of one persuaded of error, and the faint shimmer of a smile played across his face, or only his eyes, as he again bowed courteously and turned away.

"It is time," said Zorzi, "if you want to meet our lovely Nina today. She will be up, and if we are lucky will have no visitors yet. Later she drives out, or dines with her friends. Well?" he asked, as they walked, "did you make the acquaintance of the Knight, and give him back his letter? Think —the fool writes two or three such letters a day, ten pages at a time, to one and the same person, though he sees her every day, and so far as I know isn't even her lover. And besides, she's half crazy, and is either lying ill in bed, or on her knees in some church. She has no husband, nor any other relation. The Knight is her only visitor, and as she does not go out he hasn't even the fun of passing for her cavalier. But he hides the affair from everybody, as if she were a girl or a nun."

"How do you contrive to know everybody's secrets?" asked Andreas, wondering.

"Oh, you hear all kinds of things," returned the other, with the laugh Andreas had already so much disliked. "But here's the house. We'll just go up—or rather, wait here a minute. I'll run up and see how things are and whether she will receive you."

Andreas could not be sure how long a time now passed. Perhaps the artist only stayed away as long as, in the ordinary way, he needed to go upstairs, have himself announced, and announce a visitor: perhaps he had had to wait upstairs, so that a much longer time passed.

Andreas moved a few steps from the house door through which Zorzi had vanished, and went to the end of the rather narrow street. It ended in an archway, but, strangely enough, under the archway a bridge led over a canal to a little egg-shaped square with a chapel. Andreas returned, and was annoyed that he could not, after those few minutes, recognize the right house in the row of somewhat simple and uniform house fronts. The door of one, dark green, with a bronze door-knocker in the shape of a dolphin, seemed to be the one through which Zorzi had vanished, yet the door was shut, and it seemed to Andreas that he could still see Zorzi as he stepped into a passage through an open door. Still, there was no danger of their missing each other if Andreas went back to the bridge again to have a look at the little square with the church. The street and the square were completely deserted; a step would be audible, let alone a call, or repeated calls, if Zorzi were looking for him, so he crossed the bridge. Below, on the dark water, a little boat was moored to it; not a human being was to be seen or heard; the little square had a forlorn, deserted look.

The church was of brick, low and old: in front, on the side facing the square, it had an entrance which was little in keeping with it; wide steps bore a colonnade of white marble, with a classical pediment carrying an inscription. In the Latin words some of the gilded letters were larger. Andreas tried to read a date in them.

When he again lowered his eyes a woman was standing by the side of the church, some distance away, looking at him. He could not quite make out where she had come from; she could hardly have left the church by a side door, for she was standing rather as if she had been on her way to it, and had stopped irresolute, or perhaps startled by Andreas's presence. He had heard no steps approaching or crossing the square, and he found himself wondering whether, with her respectable, plain dress, she wore house-shoes which had muffled her footsteps, then wondered at himself for wondering. For she was nothing more than an apparently young woman of the lower classes, with the black shawl over her head and shoulders, from whose pale but apparently very pretty face two dark eyes were watching the stranger with a curious and, unless distance deceived him, anxious fixity—with the same fixity, he felt, whether he now pretended to be studying the capitals of the Corinthian columns or returned the look. All the same, he had no reason to stay there, and he had already set his foot on the lowest of the stone steps, thus withdrawing from the woman's field of vision.

But as, raising the heavy curtain, he entered the church, the woman entered too through a side door, and went to a prie-dieu standing near the altar. And now Andreas had the distinct impression that here was a woman oppressed by sickness, whether of body or mind, seeking relief from suffering in prayer.

He had now no other wish than to leave the church again

as quietly as possible, for it seemed to him that the woman,
now and then, looked anxiously round at him, as though he
were an unwished-for witness of her painful solitude. In the
church, compared with the square, which lay in the harsh
sunshine, the light was dim; in the cool, stuffy air a faint
smell of incense still lingered, and Andreas, who had no desire to pry, but merely to leave the place, certainly did not
keep his eyes fixed searchingly on the woman—however,
apart from that it was certain, he could have sworn, that she
had turned not to the altar but to his own self, with her hands
clasped in entreaty, that she had even struggled to move towards him, but had been hindered, as though heavy chains
lay about her body from the hips downward. At the same moment he seemed to hear a distinct moan: soft as it was, it
could not have been a hallucination. True, the next moment
he could not but regard, if not the movement, then any reference to himself as his imagination, for the stranger had shrunk
back into the prie-dieu and was motionless.

Without a sound he crossed the short space separating
him from the door, and took pains to raise the curtain so little
that no ray of the harsh light should break the holy twilight
in which he was leaving the sorrower. As he did so his eyes
involuntarily sought the prie-dieu again, and what he now
distinctly perceived astonished him so much that he stood still
in the folds of the curtain, breathless. There at exactly the
same spot sat another woman—sat no longer, but was standing up in the prie-dieu; she turned her back to the altar and
peered over at Andreas, bent forward, then furtively looked
round at him again. In her dress the woman did not greatly
differ from the other, who must have departed with an almost
incredible swiftness and stealth. The new one was dressed in
the same dark, unassuming colours—Andreas, on the way,
had seen the wives and daughters of the humbler townsfolk

dressed in the same decent costume—but this one wore no kerchief on her head. Her black hair hung in ringlets on both sides of her face, and her bearing was such that it was impossible to mistake her for the oppressed and grieving creature whose place she had taken so suddenly and noiselessly. There was something impudent and almost childish in the way in which she repeatedly turned her head as if annoyed, then peeped over her shoulder to note the effect of her angry look. She might just as well have been trying to frighten off an intruder as to arouse an indifferent onlooker's curiosity; it even seemed to Andreas, as he now finally turned to go, as though she had signalled to him behind his back with open arms.

He was standing in the square, a little dazzled, when someone came out of the church behind him, and brushed past him so quickly that he felt the air move. He saw one side of a pale young face, which turned sharply away from him, with flying curls that nearly touched his cheeks. The face was twitching, as if with suppressed laughter. The swift, almost running steps, the abruptly averted face as she brushed past him—all this was too violent not to be intentional; it looked rather like the mischief of a child than the insolence of a grown-up. Yet the figure was that of a grown woman, and the audacious freedom of the body was so strange, as she ran towards the bridge in front of Andreas, flinging her slender legs till her skirts flew, that for a moment Andreas thought it might be some youth in disguise playing a prank on the foreigner he obviously was. And yet again, something told him without possibility of doubt that the being before him was a girl or woman, as she herself came to a standstill on the little bridge as if waiting for him. In the face, which he thought pretty enough, there was a dash of impudence; her whole behaviour looked absolutely wanton, yet there was something about it which attracted rather than repelled him.

He did not wish to meet the young woman on the bridge: there was no other way back into the street. So he swung round again and mounted the steps into the church, thinking that having now given the woman a definite sign of refusal, he would be rid of her. He found it strange enough that the other woman was no longer in the church. He went right up to the altar, glanced into the little chapels right and left, looked behind the columns—nowhere a trace. It was as if the stone floor had opened and swallowed up the mourner, casting up in her place that other strange creature.

When Andreas again emerged on to the square, he saw, to his relief, that the bridge was clear. He went back into the street, wondering whether he had not, after all, missed Zorzi coming out, and whether Zorzi might have gone to look for him in the direction they had come from. A clean-looking house next door to the one with the brass knocker now seemed to him to be the right one, because the door was standing open. He went in, meaning to knock at some door on the ground floor, ask for Nina, then go up himself and discover the artist's whereabouts. He did so all the more quickly since he imagined that, from about the second house after he had crossed the bridge, a light footfall and a rustle of skirts had dogged his steps. From the entrance hall the stairs led upwards, but Andreas turned aside and went into the courtyard to look for a porter's lodge or some other human dwelling. The courtyard was small, enclosed by walls, quite overgrown with vine-leaves to a considerable height: the loveliest ripe grapes of a dark red kind hung down into it, strong wooden posts supported the living roof; there was a nail driven into one of them with a bird-cage hanging on it. At one point in the vine-leaf roof there was a gap, big enough for a child to climb through. From that point the glow of the radiant sky above fell into the courtyard, and the beautiful shapes of the

[63]

vine-leaves were sharply outlined on the tiled floor. This not very big place, half room, half garden, was filled with pleasant warmth and the scent of grapes, and silence so deep that Andreas could hear the restless movements of the bird which, untroubled by his approach, hopped from perch to perch.

Suddenly the heedless bird dashed itself in terror against the bars of its cage, the beams of the vine-roof rocked, the opening darkened abruptly, and over Andreas's head, at the height of a man, a human face looked in. Black eyes, the whites glittering in contrast, fixed his startled gaze from above, the mouth half open with strain and excitement, dark curls on one side slid down among grapes. The whole pale face was wild and tense, with a flash of satisfaction, almost childish in its candour. The body lay somehow on the light trellis of the roof, the feet probably rested on a hook in the wall, the fingertips on the top of a post. Then a mysterious change came over the expression of the face. With infinite sympathy, even love, the eyes rested on Andreas. One hand forced its way through the leaves, as if to reach his head, to stroke his hair; the four fingers were bleeding at the tips. The hand did not reach Andreas, a drop of blood fell on his forehead, the face above him turned white. "I'm falling," cried the mouth . . . one moment had been the reward of unspeakable effort. The pale face was wrenched away, the light body jerked upwards, then slid back over the wall. How it reached the ground on the other side Andreas could no longer hear; he was running to the front of the house to cut off the mysterious being's retreat. It could only be the house on the right; either she would come out of it, or she had jumped down into the courtyard and must be hiding there. He stood in front of the house door— it was the one with the dolphin. It was shut and did not yield to his pressure.

He had already raised the knocker, when he thought he heard steps approaching within. His heart was beating so that he thought those inside must hear it. Hardly ever in his life had he been in such a state; for the first time something inexplicable, departing from any conceivable order, had sought him out, and he felt that the secret would never let him rest: he saw the girl climbing up the naked walls, wrenching herself upwards by the crevices to reach him; he saw her, with bleeding hands, crouching in a corner of the courtyard, trying to escape him. His thoughts went no further: a rapid step approaching the door half robbed him of his senses. The door opened. Zorzi stood before him.

"For God's sake, tell me who it was!" cried Andreas, and before Zorzi could answer, before he could ask, had hurried past him to the end of the passage.

"Where are you going?" Zorzi asked him.

"Into the courtyard—let me go."

"The house has no courtyard: there's a blank wall here, with the canal behind it and the garden of the Redemptorist monastery beyond."

Andreas could not understand a word. He had lost all sense of direction; he told his story, and realized that he could tell nothing, that he had not the power to tell how momentous was the experience he had been through.

"Whoever the person is," said Zorzi, "rest assured that if she ever shows herself in this quarter again, I shall find out who she is: she won't escape me, whether she is a man in disguise or a street woman having some fun."

Andreas knew only too well that neither the one nor the other even approached the truth. He could understand nothing, yet, in his heart of hearts, rejected any explanation. How gladly would he have hurried back into the church, to find, if not his mysterious enemy and friend, the tameless, strange woman who climbed up walls to swoop down on her prey from above—then at the very least her companion; for now it seemed impossible that the two beings, one of whom had risen in the other's place, like the glass of red and yellow wine in the hand of the conjurer, should be ignorant of each other. He could not imagine why he had not thought of the connection before. He felt how careless his search of the church had been; he ought to have been able to find a trace—a crack in the wall—a secret door. If only he had been alone, how eagerly he would have hurried back! The imperious need to seek and find would have urged him back again, and then again, a third and fourth time. It had often happened so: a letter mislaid—a key we know we have; but Zorzi would not let him go. "Leave your climbing man-woman—you'll see more than that in Venice—and hurry up to Nina. She's expecting you. I can't tell you all that's been going on up there again. The Duke of Camposagrado, her protector, in a fit of rage and jealousy, stuck a rare bird she had had sent to her by a Jewish admirer, Signor dalle Torre, into his mouth, living, and bit its head off. Then he was suspicious about the Hungarian captain and Nina, and had him thrashed half out of his life, and, what's more, he seems to have got hold of the wrong man, and now the *sbirri* are after him, and have searched her lodgings. In fact, everything is upside-down, and that's just the moment for a newcomer to get into her good graces."

Andreas was only half listening. The staircase was narrow and dark; he believed, he hoped, at every turn to see the strange woman appear, and even at the top, in front of Nina's door, he half expected her to flit by. It now seemed beyond the possibility of doubt that a secret connection had existed between the two gestures—the imploring gesture of the mourner had been meant for him, just like the signal of the young girl. His excitement, his impatience to unravel the mystery of this being, was hardly bearable; one thought alone calmed him; she had, in some incomprehensible fashion, found the way to be alone with him for an instant: a high wall, perhaps with water flowing below it, had not deterred her from doing what seemed impossible to any creature but a cat: the blood flowing from her fingers had not daunted her. She would find the way to him again, always, everywhere.

They found Signorina Nina on a sofa in a very easy, very pretty posture. Everything about her was light, and of a most charming, delicate plumpness. Her hair was as fair as bleached gold, and she wore it unpowdered. Three things which were charmingly curved, and perfectly in keeping, her eyebrows, her mouth, and her hand, were raised to greet the entering guest with an expression of quiet curiosity and great friendliness.

An unframed picture was leaning with its face to the wall. There was a gash through the canvas, as though it had been slashed by a knife. Zorzi picked it up and looked at it, shaking his head. "What do you think of the likeness?" he said, holding out the portrait to Andreas, who had sat down on a stool at Nina's feet. The portrait was such that an untrained eye would have been struck by the likeness. Nina's features were there, but they looked cold and mean. Her brows, with their faint upward curve, were charming because they were traced on a face which was almost too soft; a severe judge would have found her neck not slender enough, but there was a something in the set of the head on the neck that was enchantingly helpless and womanly. In the portrait the curve of the eyebrows was vulgar in its emphasis; the neck, cut through by the knife, was fleshy and lascivious. The eyes were fixed on the beholder with cold, insolent fire. It was one of those painful portraits of which it may be said that they contain the inventory of a face, but reveal the soul of the artist. Andreas felt a wave of inward repulsion.

"Take it out of my sight," said Nina. "It reminds me of nothing but annoyance and brutality."

"I shall mend this one," said Zorzi, "and paint another, only this time on a Flemish, not a Venetian, ground. It will be still better, and next time I shall make both the gentlemen pay. I should be an ass if I could not manage to make them both pay me."

"Well, what do you think of it?" she asked, when the artist had vanished with his production.

"I think it is a very good likeness and very ugly."

"That's a pretty compliment."

He made no answer.

"Now you have been with me for not more than a minute and have already said something unkind. Do you think too that men are given greater strength and sharper wits and a louder voice just to make life harder for us poor women?"

"I don't mean it in that way," Andreas hastened to say. "If I were to paint you, the picture would turn out quite different, you may be sure of that."

He said so much, and would have liked to say a great deal more, for she seemed unspeakably charming. But the thought that Zorzi might come back into the room at any moment disturbed him, and he said no more. Perhaps he had said enough —he did not know—for it is not words that matter, but a tone of voice—a look.

Nina looked absently past him; on her upper lip, which was curved like her eyebrows, and seemed as if it were ready to yield to something that was to come, there hovered the shadow of a smile—it seemed to be waiting for a kiss. Unthinkingly, Andreas bent forward, a little dazed, looking at

[68]

the half-open lips. Romana rose before him, only to vanish
into air. He felt as if something delicious, yet intimidating,
was settling softly on his heart, to dissolve there.

"We are alone now," he said, "but who knows how long?"
He stretched out his hand for hers, yet did not take it, for he
seemed to feel Zorzi's hand on the door-handle. He stood up
and went to the window.

Andreas looked through the window and saw below him a
pretty little roof-garden. On a flat terrace orange trees stood in
tubs, lilies and roses grew out of wooden boxes, and ramblers
formed a walk and a little arbour. A figtree in the middle even
bore a few ripe figs.

"Does the garden belong to you?" he asked.

"It doesn't belong to me, and I should like so much to
rent it," returned Nina, "but I can't pay those greedy people
what they want. If I had it I should have a basin made with
a little fountain in it—Zorzi says it could be done—and have
a lamp put in the arbour."

Andreas saw himself going into the neighbour's house,
paying the rent down on the table—then he saw himself
coming back to Signorina Nina with the lease. In imagination he was already giving orders for the trellis round the roof-
garden to be raised: climbing roses and convolvulus were
winding up the slender lattice-work, turning the little place
into a living-room, with the stars looking in from above. The
night breeze played through it, the inquisitive looks of the
neighbours were shut out. Fruit stood in dishes on little tables,
among lights under glass shades: Nina was lying on a sofa
in a light wrap, much as she lay before him in reality. But
what a different Andreas stood before her! As in a dream he
felt that other self: he was no chance visitor, startled by
every creaking door, granted a vague, absent-minded quarter
of an hour. He was the legitimate lover, the master of the

enchanted garden, the master of his mistress. He was lost in a vague sense of happiness, as though the sound of an Aeolian harp were being wafted through him. He did not know how little need there was of all these schemes, that the very next moment might have meant happiness.

"What is it?" asked Nina, and in her voice there was the tone of faint wonder that came so naturally to her.

Her voice recalled him to himself. It occurred to him that it must be possible to look down from the roof-garden on to that roof of vine-leaves which stretched from one blank wall to the other, and on to the canal which flowed between that courtyard and the garden of the Redemptorist monastery. The thought of his unknown came to him, but it startled him. That being was in the world—that was a fact from which he could never escape. His heart was wrung, he felt as if he must seek a refuge. He turned back into the room, and, leaning on the back of the sofa, bent over Nina. Her upper lip, which was delicately arched like her eyebrows, was raised in slight wonder.

"I was thinking that I am living in the rooms where you used to live, and that I am living there alone—while you live here," he said, but his words came heavily. "If you had the little garden down there, and the arbour with the lamp in it, I should be glad to live there with somebody—really glad—but not with the one that man carried away. I should not like to live with that woman in any house, in any arbour, on any island. And you have no arbour, and no lamp in it!"

He would have liked to kneel before her, to lay his head in her lap; but he said all this, and especially the last sentence, in a cold, almost gloomy tone, for he thought that a woman must divine all that was going on in him. Though he spoke with this hard sarcasm of the Nina of the picture, he felt that she must know that another Nina was closer to him, and he to her, than could ever be said in words, and that his whole being was ready to create the surroundings whose absence he emphasized so caustically. But at the same moment a strange, sad picture rose before him—it was the memory of childish dreams, which now seemed far remote, and had been repeated to nausea: he had crept hungry to the pantry to cut himself a piece of bread; he had pressed the loaf to him, knife in hand, but again and again had cut past the loaf into the void.

His hand, without boldness, without hope even, had taken Nina's hand, which was charming without being thin, and delicate without being small. She yielded it to him, he even thought he felt the fingers close about his with a soft, steady pressure. Her look was veiled, and the depths of her blue eyes seemed to darken; the shadow of a smile still lay on her upper lip, a fading, almost anxious smile that seemed to call for a kiss. Nothing could have startled him more deeply than such signs, which might have provoked another to boldness, even insolence. He was utterly dazed. How could he grasp what was so simple and so close? He did not think of the woman over whom he was leaning, but of her life. In a lightning flash he saw her mother, her father, her sister, her brothers, he saw the choleric duke rise from the space round the sofa, the bleeding head of a parrot in his hand; the head of a Jewish admirer rose noiselessly beside him —he looked like the servant, but wore no wig; and the Hungarian captain, whose hair was in plaits, ferociously brandished a curved knife.

He wondered if all the ready money he possessed would be enough to rescue Nina from all these phantoms—and had perforce to admit: for a week perhaps, for three days. And what good was a single gift, even though it should beggar him, when, it seemed to him, decency demanded that he should provide an income, perhaps even a lodging, a house, newly furnished, and servants—at least, he reflected, a maid and a manservant? Gotthilff's face grinned up at him; the beauty of the moment dissolved. He felt he must let go of Nina's hand; he did so with a gentle pressure. She looked at him; again something like wonder was mingled with her expression, yet it was cooler than before. He had taken his leave, he did not know how, and had asked permission to return.

Downstairs he found Zorzi, who had the picture, wrapped up in paper, under his arm and seemed to be waiting for him. He dismissed him quickly. He repented bitterly of having told this man about his unknown; he was glad that Zorzi did not begin to speak of her. The last thing in the world he should have done was to put on her track just the man who seemed to be spying on him and everybody else. He told him that he would soon visit Signorina Nina again; he did not believe it himself. Hardly had Zorzi departed with his picture when he was on his way through the street; under the archway, over the bridge, to the church.

The square lay deserted as before: the empty boat hung motionless below the bridge. It looked to Andreas like a sign of encouragement. He walked as if in a dream and did not really doubt—had no other thought than that the mourner would be sitting there, and would raise her arms anxiously, imploringly, towards him as he entered. Then he would withdraw, knowing that behind his back the other would rise from the same prie-dieu to follow him. This mystery was not past for him, but a thing that revolved in a circle, and he only had to step back into the circle to restore it to the present.

He entered the church—it was empty. He returned to the square, stood on the bridge, and looked in every house, and found nobody. He went away, wandered through some streets, then after some time returned to the square and entered the church through the side door, went back through the archway, and found nobody.

Journal of Herr von N's Tour to Venice, 1779

I REMEMBER things very exactly—always had a good memory, won the Grand Cross of Excellence at school because I could recite the rulers of Austria forwards and backwards. I also remembered all my mother's maids, and all my grandfather's minerals, and the names of the stars in Orion.

Reasons for the tour to Venice: Artists, great names. Palaces, behaviour in drawing-rooms, starting a conversation. To make an appearance, to please. What I already knew about Venice: Uncle had friend whose relatives had been cast into oubliettes (with nails and razors) . . .

Arrival: Early morning. Hungry. Chilly. Starts out to look for lodgings. Troop of actors waiting on canal bank. An actress ogles him from the lap of a fellow-actor.

Walks through a street or two. The half-naked gentleman, he has a hat with a veil of coarse lace on his arm, a fine but tattered shirt. He addresses him, says he knows Vienna, mentions names. Declares he has gambled away everything he possesses. I lend him my cloak; he speaks very nobly of generosity, of bygone times. The gentleman tells how he took a lady of fashion to Grassalkovich's; she said, "Brutto nome, pare una bestemmia" (an ugly name, it sounds like a curse), and would not have him as a lover. When he is dressed, his tone is much more sociable, less elevated.

Smell of cooking. The stranger will not let him breakfast

here, promises to procure him a lodging at a nobleman's, goes
with him.

The lady of the house, the nobleman, the old man. I give
money for breakfast to be brought. Am given the room of the
daughter, who has left home. Everybody is connected with
the theatre. Groans from above: the artist has colic. We go up,
the stone is removed; meanwhile the nobleman brings the
little fish in his daughter's handkerchief. We eat real Venetian
frittura.

Up again to the artist, he shows me the portrait of a beautiful woman (for dalle Torre), promises to take me to see her.
On the way, tells the story of the Duke of Camposagrado's
two pictures; when the brothers send him theirs, he laughs
immoderately and assigns a sum of money for them to send
him the Goya, copy the Tintorettos. Artist promises to present
me to the Duke.

Arrive at the beautiful lady's. Bird in cage, fine porcelain,
hyacinths in front. Camposagrado. Present; details of the
Pyrenean village where the Duke is magistrate.

The young lady in the other room with him. Camposagrado very angry, devours the bird and goes. I am introduced,
behave with reserve. The old woman suggests I should give a
present. I withdraw, cannot take things lightly. This would
be the moment for an irresponsible blackguard or a clever
swindler. I invite her to supper.

Go out on to the Piazza. Miss a procession, see a patrician
putting on a harlequin costume. Go to the theatre. The veiled
(masked) lady. Letter received on the Piazzetta.

The Knight Sacramozo sits down beside me. His appearance. The servant with the letter. The servant seems to know
the Knight. Tell the Knight that I have invited the courtesan.
He is surprised that it all fits in.—Go to bed. Mosquitoes.

Next morning: appointment with the Knight. To the

lady's, at her morning toilet. Am first shown into an anteroom, while the lady retires with the Knight. The lady comes, makes somewhat casual apologies. The Knight goes to breakfast with me, explains his conception of love. Former passion for the courtesan. His attempted suicide.

In the afternoon the nobleman returns to bring me my cloak, takes me to the notary.

In the evening, near Madonna dell'Orto. The beautiful lady at a window.

In the church, Camposagrado with servants to light him; returns alone, is attacked by a dog. He masters the dog with his teeth.

Herr von N's Adventure in Venice

ANDREAS: two halves which gape asunder.—Andreas's character not yet formed: he must first find himself in these vicissitudes. His shyness, his pride—all untested till now. —Not clear about his own states of mind—always too much, too little. Doubts whether he really committed the crime on the dog.

Andreas: main trend, courage—the courage incorporated in the air of Venice, courage in the night of storm. Morality: courage.

Tour due to the calculating *snobisme* of his father.

How Andreas imagines the life of great gentlemen (from the tales of the lackey, his grandfather, from his own experiences too). From the deer-rutting into the castle, changes clothes, hair dressed, calls for a mistress to take her to the opera *Armida.*

Andreas (at bottom) goes to Venice chiefly because the people there are always masked. After the adventure in the country with the haughty Countess, who had treated him like a lackey, the idea, half-dreamed, had taken shape in his mind that the adventure would have been glorious if he had been masked. In a general way he is now haunted by the difference between being and seeming—for instance, when he sees haycocks which look like countrywomen in hats or like monks, and give him an eerie and solemn feeling, and are *really* senseless things.

Chapters (provisional): I. Castle Finazzer. II. Arrival. III. Three New Friends. IV. The Knight of Malta. V. Double Life. VI. A Conversation. VII. The Demonic. VIII. Departure.

Chapter I. The end. The mountains:—he has no wish to live there; at this moment he is richer than the mountaineer, richer than the mountain-dweller; he feels no need to relate things to Romana—it is entirely self-enjoyment, but possible only through her. When he had that—it was the pledge that he would possess Romana too.

Camposagrado: a thick-set man, with a pearl drop in one ear containing a fragment of the Host.

CHAPTER V. The New Friend (The Knight of Malta).

Andreas had fallen into an unsatisfactory state of mind. The thought of home poisoned the "here": the "here" made him think more sadly of home.

He delivered the letter and was told that the master was dead. The business friend gone away. He asked for his trunk, a sign that he was longing for news from home. The bread tastes stale. He misses the coaches, the elegance; the people mean so little, compared with the Graben and the Kohlmarkt. A lady descending from her equipage in Vienna.

He tries to see Nina, though without real hope. (Zorzi tells him that the Knight wants to know his name; asks whether he needs anything. Andreas declines.) He dislikes the part of him that wants to go to her. He is not received.

Evening. Talk with Zustina on the staircase. He asks her why she does not wish to marry. How could she suspect that he was speaking of himself? She rebuffs him. Her justification: "They are gentlemen: there is good in every one of them. The mother of a simpleton has taken a ticket for him." He, jealous of happy people. He tells her that he is probably leaving Venice. She is unmoved.—Her picture of the world: family tyrants or gamblers of all kinds. She grows remote.

Various visits to Nina, a second time two days later, a third—but always obstacles. Once somebody is with her, another time "out," or "ill"—once he is shown in and hears her in the next room, but "she has had to go out." Yet he is always invited to return.—The situation becomes quite inexplicable when Zustina says to him: "Nina is so sorry that you are neglecting her."—Feeling of helplessness.

Sights of the town. A trial. Processions. Jesuits. Churches. Pictures: Tintoretto: distinction, boldness, self-confidence.

Envy of all human beings, hypochondria, growing distaste for people. Too many people, would have liked to sweep them all away from him. Longing for trees (to embrace a tree). Looking towards the mountains. Recollection of that moment. Melancholy. His thoughts become more disorderly and impure.

Sea-monster for ten soldi from Crete, peculiar interior. To fill the void in him, goes not to the church but to the booth. The Spanish woman (the mask).

The merman: "What a spectacle—but alas! only a spectacle!"—gives him all that the theatre did not give him, although an animal, and hardly a real one. Pain that the merman should impress him more than the real theatre.

The mask. Her arm rests on his. The mask speaks tenderly. "Our first meeting was a great day for me. I had just arrived from a dreadful place; your face was the first—I could not but love it. I was free for anything, would have liked to swoop down from above, sure that I could fly. Have you any idea of what it means to be a prisoner?" (he thinks of the lead roofs).

He doubts. She: "I am speaking of real things—cannot you feel it?" (the pressure of her hand). He assures her that when he was with Nina that time, he thought of nothing but her. "And on your later visits?"

The mask speaks tenderly; she speaks of Nina—he puts things together: "It is she." The blood surges to his heart.

The mask: "I *forced* a certain person to ask your name. There is a lifetime between that day and this."

Andreas resolves to put various questions to Zustina in order to find out the truth about his unknown. Again does nothing. It means too much effort.

In the house: "Your friend was asking for you"—a vine-leaf with a drop of blood on it.

Lonelier here among people than there on the dog's grave.

A mask wishes to take him to gaming-rooms. He refuses, turns back in the anteroom, asks her to tell him at any rate who she is and where she is going to take him. The mask has told him that there are various people interested in him besides the Knight. (Two persons at least. How does she know?) On the staircase, he thinks he recognizes the young Spanish woman, or another young person from Nina's house. (She knows too about his visits to Nina.)

Enters a church, hopes to see the Spanish woman. Is rapt into a dreamlike height, but only for a moment. There is somebody kneeling behind him, sighing, like a being at his mercy. This person leans against the edge of the step—looks into the distance.

THE NEXT day to the Customs House again. Letter about the condition of the Empress. Discomfort. The whole world so dreadfully puppet-like.

Somebody follows him in a gondola, catches up with him: the Knight, who says he has been looking for him in the little coffee-house. A letter, similar to the first, has been thrown into the Knight's house. "Do you really know nothing about it? Might I ask you to go over in your mind the people you have met in society? Nothing stands alone: everything is fulfilled in circles. Much escapes us, and yet it is in us, and all we need to know is how to bring it to the surface. Somebody I am deeply devoted to is greatly distressed by this affair. I will tell you what was in the letter. Have you any relatives in Italy?" (*fluidum* of kinship).

Andreas: "I should like to tell you so much about myself that your suspicions would be disarmed."—Strange lack of self-confidence that his word does not seem to suffice even to himself! At the same time, mortal fear that, once the suspicion is removed, the Knight will lose all interest in him. How happy he felt when the man was sitting by him! Wonder that even this man should suffer some secret torment.

Pleasant stroll afterwards. Knight: "Do not miss going to Murano—you hear the best music there. Your ambassador often goes there too."

Meanwhile a one-armed messenger brings a letter for Andreas. "Who is it from?"—"Your Honour knows." Knight wonders at the coincidence. He asks the Knight to go with him. The Knight refuses. Is piqued—assumes that Andreas was laughing at him. "You receive the messenger I was telling you about."

FIRST sight of the Knight. Intimation of harmonious contrast between appearance and spirit. Something witty about him that is simply that contrast.

At first, Andreas's chief objection to the Knight: the casualness of the acquaintance. "He cannot be worth much, since he had time to spend with me."

The hours with Sacramozo were the radiance in his day. How astonished he was when Sacramozo spoke to him! Then he was annoyed, because it made the Knight lose in stature.

How the Knight, in his eyes, always grows in beauty out of his ugliness, and he gradually comes to feel that the essence of the man is all love, or all form. His double nature: when he speaks on mystic subjects (for him, given the right connections, everything in the world, even the most commonplace circumstances and doings, can be included in them) he is candid, accessible to union, merely human, communicative of himself, accessible by enthusiasm.

When he is in ordinary surroundings, he is completely set apart by courtesy; inconceivable that he could be touched, influenced, reached. It is impossible, when he is in this state, to attempt to remind of the other. Here he exercises a power which is as coercive as the other is persuasive. Sometimes, in his man-of-the-world aloofness, he seems still stranger to Andreas: the idea "the power of despair" to be applied to him in this situation.

Meetings with the Knight. The only being able to concentrate him: at the same time bewilders him: by being at home in the world: by his discretion, his acceptance of everything as a matter of course—Andreas's fear in imperfect moments: that everything in Sacramozo may be merely show.

The Knight does not invite him home; seems to take for granted that he has friends, that he knows where the pictures are to be seen, etc.

The essence of his being: the secrets; alludes to them by *minus dicere*, not by *plus dicere*. The essence of his being a knowledge of the mystery of how man is organized.

CONVERSATIONS with Sacramozo:
Andreas full of prejudices; the worst against himself; his money prejudices, his prejudices as regards the world—as regards himself: thinks he has thrown away his happiness, everything is deteriorating, everything is stale. Sacramozo:

"You are rich in hidden powers.—You exclude the extraordinary—you are wrong. You speak of happiness. How could you enjoy it? Ask rather—*who* is it that enjoys it?"

Sacramozo teaches him to realize the function of poetry through Ariosto: poetry is not concerned with nature. The poet is a poet in virtue of his penetration of nature (of life).

As to Ariosto: the true domain of poetry is the impossible (the youth whose body moved through his armour).

Poetry as the present. The mystic element in poetry: the conquest of time.—

It is in the transitions that we recognize the sublime. All life is a transition.

In all our doings we must follow examples: there lies the grandeur of Christianity.—Unspiritual Christians cheat God: dirt behind the altar.—

To know our element: we really live only under the eyes of one who loves us. Sacramozo: "Attention means as much as love. I beg you to treat my soul with attention. Who is attentive? The diplomat, the official, the doctor, the priest . . . not one attentive enough. The statement 'I have neglected nothing'—who can pronounce it of himself with a clear conscience?"

What we truly participate in, to that we are already half united. Sacramozo on the participation of Negroes in their masters' pleasure: he has found what he sought—he has received a letter.

Sacramozo explains the repulsion of the soul for what it has recently experienced.

How far a man like Sacramozo has outgrown all fears, yet all terrors are near him, to be called up at the slightest touch: what fear, terror, timidity mean.

How far, for Sacramozo, all material is material for the divine.—Andreas broods: "Why with me, of all people?"—

[83]

(Andreas must overcome that.) Sacramozo: "Everything is everywhere, but only for the moment."

To be able to ask somebody's pardon—how far this means a high stage reached.

All that a man like Sacramozo is henceforth incapable of —there lies his grandeur.

Sacramozo objects to the expression "to go deeper into things"—it should be replaced by "to become aware"—"to remember."

Spirit is of *one essence*. In the spiritual world, there are no stages, only degrees of penetration. Spirit is action, perfect or less perfect. At some point you are preventing the world from thinking. Human beings are the sufferings and acts of the spirit.

Through Sacramozo, Andreas realizes that he loves Romana Finazzer.

Sacramozo believes in the twofold. Thus he tells the two determining experiences of his life. "It takes a man of natural genius (like Francis of Assisi) to be determined for ever by a single experience. The ordinary human being, when his way is cut off in one direction by some dreadful experience, will move in the other."—As a rule, too, we create an individual out of a type by crossing it with another species: Narcisse is a rogue, but a respectable musician (cf. Goethe's *Note*).

Knight: "You often mention your uncle in a peculiar way—he must mean a great deal to you" (more encouragement from Sacramozo inconceivable). Andreas blushed. The story of Uncle Leopold and the two momentous days. Beside the death-bed: the widow, the second family—peasant lads.—The della Spina: "We have both lost so much, dear lady."—While Andreas is speaking, Castle Finazzer, that day of gloom, comes back to him. The Knight (with a warm-hearted look): "You told that beautifully."

The human is nobly contained in him, and is beautifully detached.—He proposes a visit.

CHAPTER VI. A Visit.

"Who knows his own element?"

By the company of the Knight of Malta, by but a single allusion to him, Andreas's existence is refined and concentrated. If he meets him, he can be sure that something remarkable or at least unexpected will happen to him afterwards. His senses grow keener, he feels more capable of enjoying the individual in others. Feels himself in a greater and higher sense an individual. Love and hate are closer to him. He feels the constituent elements of his own being grow more interesting to himself, has the presentiment of beauty behind them. He feels the Knight's mastery in the playing of his own part. There is no situation in which he could not imagine him. In the Knight, he encounters supreme receptiveness for identity.

He tells himself all this, though in morbid self-reproaches. "What kind of man am I for the first man of any distinction I meet to make such an impression on me?"

Beginning. The Knight catches him up on the Riva dei Schiavoni. "What a good thing I have met you." (A vague impulse has sent Andreas there.) "I nearly sent for you. You are wanted . . ."

Secret about Maria. At Andreas's first visit she makes a tiny, helpless gesture towards a dark corner behind her sofa with a certain stiffness about her waist—and at that moment, Andreas has a presentiment that here there is a secret for him insoluble, that he will never know this woman, and feels that the infinite has touched him with a sharper pang than any pain he has ever known: he has three or four memories which all bear within them this *pointe acérée de l'infini* (spearhead of the infinite) (the meeting with the old woman and the child on that first morning)—feels this unfelt pain without realizing that, at that very moment, he *loves*.

At his first visit, Maria says, "*Somebody* will write to you again." Once he receives from Maria a letter that is passionate, almost cynical. He hurries to her; she is not at home. Later, he finds her. She is in great distress: "I have been told about the letter"—she has to bring herself to something like a confession—"my hand is bewitched: it acts against my will. I would like to cut it off, but the fifth commandment forbids that . . ." (Problem: how far am I responsible for my hand?)

Elegance and distinction, the phantoms Andreas has pursued, are embodied in Maria in their most perfect form, as nobility of the soul. He now sees the Viennese countesses as mere marionettes, worked by their breeding.

Sacramozo's relationship to Maria is this: that he wants to amuse her in order to keep her alive, because she alone makes life worth living to him (however little, for that matter, he demands or expects from her).

Sacramozo has for Maria "religion, not love" (Novalis). —The Knight: "I found her in Genoa. Wicked people declared they had a right to her. I protected her—and managed to bring her here. But I mean no more to her on that account than you do. I look upon every day as the last. Day by day, I think, 'She will escape you!' "—Andreas: "Do you think she will enter a convent?"—Knight: "She nearly did. But she seems to have abandoned the idea. She told me she had received letters which dissuaded her."

Maria married to a wicked man at thirteen. She is a widow: her husband was cruel. The religious crisis which caused the split in her. A prayer (Sacramozo tells Andreas this)—Maria regards it as a punishment for having implored Christ to be her accomplice in her love-affair, and thus having been guilty of blasphemy. Since then, Maria filled with disgust for the act itself (she feels the vague fatigue, has a physical knowledge of the thing which appals her).

Her astral body, consisting of her thoughts, fears, aspirations, which is often touched, with immense sensibility, by a remark, a mere piece of news, by a "silent fall of distant stars"—she feels this whole as her "I": this whole must become blessed, this whole would never have been capable of surrendering in love, this whole Andreas can never embrace, this whole is her burden and her suffering.

A midway aspect of Maria—in which the *lady* is uppermost: that all is not yet united in her, that she is neither resigned nor exhausted, that the possibilities of dying a martyr's death or petrifying in aristocratic *morgue* still lie open to her.

Sacramozo knows from confidences that Maria at time loses her identity. His surmises as to her condition.

THE LADY (Maria) and the cocotte (Mariquita) are both Spanish: they are dissociated aspects of one and the same personality, which play tricks on each other. The cocotte writes Andreas the letters. The cocotte hates Sacramozo and all his sentimental fuss. Once, Andreas encounters the cocotte as he is taking leave of the lady: once, the kind lady is transformed before the mirror into the malicious cocotte. The cocotte is afraid of Sacramozo, believes he has the evil eye (she fears, too, that he might kill her, and he actually pursues her with a knife).—The cocotte sleeps with him, this makes Andreas fall more deeply in love with the lady; he can no longer understand Sacramozo's Platonism. In the early morning the bed is empty, he hears moans, and, with gestures of appalling distress, the *other* takes flight. During this troubled time, he once finds in his valise the fichu of the Finazzer girl.—The cocotte declares that she has to go to a rich old man from time to time.

(Portrait of Maria and Mariquita in the journal) To be with Maria is to pursue the most subtle and profound conception of the individual: Maria's religious aestheticism tends in this direction. Her chief concern is the unity, the uniqueness of the soul (but she is thwarted by the body). It would be impossible to pay her a compliment on her beauty or a detail of her figure. She declares that no tree, no cloud, has its like. She has a horror of love, whose instrument is the quid pro quo. (She brings to mind the Princess in *Tasso*.)

In Mariquita, it is each physical detail that seems unique and immortal—knee, hip, smile. Beyond that, she does not trouble her head much about uniqueness, she does not believe in the immortality of the soul. Her conversation, arguments, even her thoughts are all pantomime, all latent eroticism, not a word is meant for more than the moment—she perpetually courts caresses from everything around her.

The link between Maria and Mariquita is a small, asthmatic King Charles's spaniel, Fidèle by name, a suspicious and disdainful animal which, save on *one* occasion, is always hidden in Maria's house (again the problem of *Yesterday*: faith, constancy, and change)—Maria dimly suspects the chaos within her; that is what she has in common with Mariquita. Thus they have the spaniel in common.

ad Maria-Mariquita: the Franciscan father's views on the case: the views of the physician, materialistic (La Mettrie, Condillac). The anecdote of the man who was driven mad by one accident and restored by another.—"What conclusion do you draw from that?" asked the Knight.

Maria always in mittens, hands always cold: Mariquita's hands always as if suffused with liquid, gentle fire.

Unrestraint the essence of Mariquita: constraint the essence of the Countess. The Countess speaks of the hundredweight-heavy chains with which heaven tries its own. We are responsible for more than ourselves. The constraint in the Countess's love-letters.

With Maria, Andreas learns the value of inward freedom; with Mariquita, he feels a horror of absolute freedom. With Mariquita, he cannot but crave for the universal bond of union; with Maria, for the universal solvent: thus his nature must be revealed to him.

Maria is marvellously well dressed, Mariquita likes dirt and disorder.

Maria can hardly endure the scent of flowers; one day, Andreas finds her half fainting, surrounded by strongly scented flowers: Mariquita has bought the flowers at market that morning and sent them to Maria by a Friuli man.

Maria is a Christian, with mystic, Molinistic leanings; Sacramozo is indifferent (Galiani); Mariquita is a pagan, she believes in the moment and in nothing else.

What Mariquita thinks of Maria (in letters or monologues, from time to time): she hates her, sees all her imperfections, thinks her a *coward* (just as Michelangelo thinks himself a coward in contrast to Savonarola), yet she is her most personal theme, the only one that interests her. She envies her her distinction, without being quite aware of what that distinction is, what it is that lends to Maria's every action a royal, immaterial worth (like the horn on the brow of the unicorn, like a tower in the moon); she even tries to make Maria herself suspicious of this privilege, to submerge her in the common (though she would be the one to suffer most by it)—she writes to her: "your revery of yesterday, that there is no such thing as the common, that it can all be overcome, that life could be lived in a perpetual *élan*, with none of your crouching in a corner—is an illusion of your fathomless vanity, of your stupid incapacity to face reality."

Mariquita's stories (about Maria): sometimes as if she were an old hag, then: "that must be taken metaphorically. People must always be taken metaphorically. She is quite a pretty woman, but a fiend all the same. That is why she wants people to think her an angel. But I can tell you one thing, no woman in the world is seen through as I see through her. My eyes go beneath the skin."

MARIQUITA: the different aspects of the demonic: mischief-making, shrewd, cynical, restless, godless. Shameless, libertine, dread of churches. Boundlessly inquisitive. Brilliant, *ingénue.* Utterly forgetful.

The element connecting all her phases—a kind of puppet-like activity. She must have something going on: she hates repose, meditation—for then she is afraid of dissolving in the other.

Once Mariquita breaks out to the duenna (Andreas pretends to be asleep): "Curse her! She would like to shut me up in a convent because I am growing a bit too much for her! I'll have to set him at her a bit."—Duenna: "Couldn't you give her something to make her disappear for good?"—Mariquita: "She has a hideous strength, not only when she is praying, but at other times—a kind of inward elevation which makes me feel as if I were going to be sick; I am quite weak compared to her."—Duenna: "Couldn't you contrive to make one of your best poses occur to her while she is praying?"—Mariquita: "Then she feels me coming and holds me down, those are my nastiest moments. Then I hate as the man in hell must hate God."

(The mask only learns of her relationship to Maria bit by bit; at first, she hopes to liberate herself entirely quite soon.)

Scene where the cocotte, in great distress because Maria wants to enter a convent, tells Andreas to seduce Maria;—

her strange, cringing look in this scene. Andreas' suspicion that the sorceress has something to do with experiments of the kind which led to the "Moreau horrors," that she may be providing material for an experimenter of the kind.

In trying to awaken the soul in Mariquita, Andreas endangers Mariquita's life (her separate existence): she hints anxiously at this. Thus she once takes him into her arms and with tears in her eyes declares she is ready to sacrifice herself to the happiness he might find with another. He feels that she is really in earnest.

Mariquita demonic to the verge of sorcery. Succubus. Once she sleeps with two men at the same time; she says: "Suppose I had slept with the one a day, six hours, two hours, half an hour, ten minutes after the other—what then?"

Mariquita hates the idea of "truth." "If only I never had to hear the silly word—if only you would leave me in peace with your philosophy—since the world is, after all, 'edible, so to speak.'"

Her gloomy image of the Knight. The Key of his life fills her with horror. When she speaks of him, she turns pale.

Mariquita never writes, only sends messages by word of mouth; writing only exists to complicate and compromise everything.

Mariquita's lodging: two rooms in a ramshackle palace, in the utmost disorder. The duenna, the old crone, lives in a big den behind. The bright room, as open as an aviary, where Mariquita bathes, takes her meals, and receives her guests. A little garden outside. The rich Jewish admirer, dalle Torre. Mariquita at first treats Andreas badly, but invites him back in a letter full of veiled allusions to Maria as soon as she notices that Maria likes to see him. She hopes ultimately to seduce Maria by means of Andreas.

On the very day on which Andreas receives the letter of

invitation, Sacramozo receives a letter full of insults: she is tired of him and is going to look about for another friend.

Mariquita, on the first visit, though she treats him badly, fondles his hand, saying: "Pretty hand—a pity you belong to a cold and miserly master."

She tells him why people love him: his gravity, his reserve, nobody can tell what he will be like, nobody can be sure of having him entirely.

Mariquita—a kind of vertigo of existence. One night she goes for a drive with Andreas in the mail-coach. *Embrouilleuse*: everything goes wrong, the baffling, desperate confusion of all things—a whole concatenation of ill-planned arrangements, nothing comes right. Café in Mestre, in the carriage she is another being. Treats him as if he were a Casanova, imputes to him meetings with the Countess (complete with all psychological and realistic details), then, in the end: "Forgive me!"—then, with violence: "And why not? Why don't you take her?" He tries to tear himself away from her, then she hints at a secret, promises she will soon reveal her soul.

An adventure with Mariquita in the night of storm. She tries to throw the unconscious gondolier—the gondolier stunned by a blow from Andreas—into the water.

The courtesan wants to seduce the wild man; an outing into the country is undertaken for the purpose.

ANDREAS'S conflicting feelings in the presence of the two women: to be with Maria makes him happy, the world seems more beautiful; Mariquita makes him gloomy, tense, fierce—afterwards ill-tempered, fatigued.

It seems incomprehensible that Maria's hand should ever be seen, felt in a sensual movement. Mariquita's foot returns pressure like a hand, clings, presses, like a softer, blinder, still more sensual hand.

Andreas: his feeling for Maria growing, so that his head swims at the thought of an intimacy (—merely to lay his hand on her knee), even when he thinks intensely of her womanhood. He grows jealous of Sacramozo. By becoming very insistent, he enables Mariquita to appear.

Andreas and the idea of "fashion": people of fashion are to him what Savonarola or a very aloof young nobleman was to Michelangelo. The love of the fine lady: that is his first goal; he imagines that he will be changed by it, as his grandfather was changed by the favours of the archduchess. He says to himself: "If I were her lover . . ."—but he cannot really imagine himself in that situation; it seems to him that he would then be a different man (for a moment, he thinks that the Knight believes him to be her lover) . . . gradually it dawns upon him that for him, Maria dwells in the sphere of the unattainable; he has a premonition that his fate lies here, that he is confronted here with a challenge which, as it were, he will have to cope with again and again. He suspects that Maria's love must be directed to something in him which is unattainable to himself, utterly remote from his vanity, his restlessness, his consciousness.

With Maria, Andreas is excessively shy, so perfectly does she guide the conversation. The mere thought of asking her an intimate question (for instance, whether she knows anything about the existence of her illegitimate sister) gives him the same feeling as the thought that he might touch the mystery of her body—his head swims. Maria's soul lies like a veil over her body.

Ultimately, his relationship to Maria is such that he is tormented by jealousy of Sacramozo's "objectless" friendship.

His astonishment that human beings of such a kind exist: with them everything is softer and harder, uglier and more conscientious, more self-possessed as a whole, more sensitive in detail—he feels as though new senses must come to birth in him to comprehend this. He begins to suspect that there is something haphazard about our senses.—He realizes that he is merely drifting, like a pig in a rising flood.

He feels how the Knight sustains and elevates him, every one of his sayings enlightens, he feels that he is entirely Sacramozo's creation, but the feeling does not oppress him. He does not know whether to wonder more at the woman or the man.

LAST Book.

What Sacramozo needs to win this woman is a lofty love of self, a religion of the self.

Sacramozo holds himself guilty of the death of someone he has loved: Mariquita says outright that he has poisoned a woman.

Sacramozo believes himself responsible for the insanity of a charming young woman who now vegetates like a greedy animal.

To see the "other" in her eyes—that has made him a philosopher. In exactly the same way, a strange change came over his father just before his death. Thus he comes to believe that *masks* are the distinguishing factor. In this sense, he says that neither Molière nor Goldoni has created a character in the individual.

In particular, he reproaches himself with having slept with this person when she was already a "lunatic." Would she like to have a shell which contains the voice of her dead lover? In that sense, they also discuss the duality in Maria's handwriting.

At Sacramozo's: portrait of the lady with the Star Cross Order: Countess Welsberg (his mother). Sacramozo on the sayings of his German mother: he forbids himself to remember her: later, he will be allowed to remember her all the more completely.—Sacramozo has understood that his cousin's return is a dispensation, has learned to be an exile: at Welsberg, his lower nature would have prevailed, the higher development of his nature would have been checked.—Sacramozo wished to buy Welsberg Castle. The night he spent in the room with the Pyramid of Life painted on the wall (his thoughts often turn on the stages of life. His uncle of ninety-three).—Sacramozo takes for granted that of two dreams, the later always throws light on the earlier—thus everything that comes later always relates to everything that has gone before—in all directions.—The Welsberg dream: in the second he is governor, not recognized as such, who is guilty of everything, who had to pronounce sentence of death, etc.

Sacramozo: faith and superstition in time: in hours of exaltation, he is convinced that he alone possesses the real key to the world, everybody else glides past the secret lock unheeding—everything serves him, even a landscape seen once, a pool of dark water in the West Indies. He would be absurd if he were not right. He is right in everything, even in taking Andreas to the Countess. His knowledge: he knows that the body forgets nothing (just like the macrocosm, the great body).—He knows Maria's life far better than the confessors.—Sacramozo's fate: the Key of Solomon in Hebbel's epigram.

The symbolism of the Rosicrucians appeals to him: the use of words in an absolutely symbolic sense, so that the words spurn the world. For, he says, everything is in the soul, everything that has power to raise spirits, and the spirits that are to be raised. "Every word evokes spirits; whatever spirit calls, its like responds" (Novalis).

In this way he can grasp the essence of poetry—the magic of configurations. To him, Goldoni (Zustina's world, the utterly unmetaphysical) is abhorrent, Molière means little, mime is indifferent; the vital thing is the incantation. True poetry is the arcanum that unites us with life, separates us from life. To differentiate—we live only by differentiation; —if we differentiate, death itself can be borne, only the impure is horrible (a fine, pure hour of death like Jung-Stilling's) —but to unite is as indispensable as to differentiate—the *aurea catena* of Homer—"Separabis terram ab igne, subtile a spisso, suaviter magna cum ingenio" (Thou shalt separate earth from fire, the subtle from the dense, smoothly and with great skill) (*Tabula smaragdina Hermetis*).

Sacramozo knows the power of the creative function. "We know only in so far as we create. We only know creation in so far as we are ourselves God. We do not know it in so far as we are world" (Novalis). Sacramozo knows: Things are simply what the power of a human soul unceasingly makes them. Incessant creation. The relation between two human beings as a sylph born of them (Rosicrucians).

He seeks life where it is to be found: in all that is most delicate, in the folds of things.

The abyss in such a being as Sacramozo: the despair of the onlooker, who must ask: "Do I exist at all if I must go?— Shall I *have existed?*—Have I known hate-love??—or was it all nothing?"

What does a man like Sacramozo *want*—a fury of impotence—"His Impotenceship."

He suffers the sylph born of Andreas and the Countess, which is the stronger, to kill the weaker, whose father he is.

Sacramozo on the mystic limbs of men: it is rapture merely to think of them, to move them in silence (Maria's dream).

On the Powers: the man who is capable of prayer: "If the Countess could pray, she would be healed."

Sacramozo's mystic love of children, human beings as such, neither man nor woman, but both in one.

Andreas has to learn from the Knight: to discern what

has real existence, to overcome the mean and common (—everything Austrian is mean and common, the hordes of chamberlains, everything in masses. In Vienna, the chief concern of everybody is to be taken for somebody).

Sacramozo's pessimistic outlook: whether I am a Christian or an atheist, a fatalist or a sceptic—I shall decide that as soon as I know who I am, where I am, and where I cease to be.

Sacramozo: "The hope and desire of man to return to his former condition is like the desire of the moth for the light" (Leonardo).

The look he fixes on the friends of his youth. Women amuse him more than men, men move him more deeply.

Sacramozo—that is his offence—believes it is possible to lead a second life, in which everything left undone can be done, every failure made good.—"Forty years—I have nothing more to gain, but I must lose nothing more."

Sacramozo knows the moment that is auspicious for Andreas's union with Maria. He chooses that moment for voluntary death—he is sure he will return, to be united to a transformed Maria. (He knows that elements are also transformed.) That Andreas will then be forced to yield before him—how, he purposely avoids considering—fills him with sorrowful sympathy for Andreas.

He has always known that this would happen to him in his fortieth year. He divides his life thus: three periods of twelve years: the first, fulfilment, revelation; the second, confusion; the third, damnation or ordeal. Then three years of action, then the fortieth—*annus mirabilis.*

"The truly philosophic act is suicide" (Novalis).—Suicide on the one hand as the most sublime act of self-enjoyment, the indisputable dominion of the spirit over the body, on the other as the most sublime communion with the world; harmony in contrast, at last, with the final word of Oriental philosophy (Neoplatonists on suicide).

How, in the smallest, subtlest detail, the body is to be persuaded—there lies the mystery and the difficulty. Subsequently, attention to and reverence for that which does not return.

"The destruction of the law of contradiction is perhaps the supreme task of higher logic" (Novalis). "Gradual increase of *inward* stimulus is thus the chief concern of the artist of immortality" (Novalis).

Conversation with Maria on suicide: ". . . above all, you ought to be sure of destroying yourself entirely."—Here Sacramozo smiles.

Sacramozo: "Every morning the sun rises on millions of men, but where among those millions is the one heart that responds to it in pure music like the pillar of Memnon?—I stood with ten thousand on a hill, a pilgrimage, etc.,—but my heart was separated from theirs. When has the morning sun *ever* really illuminated me? Once, perhaps, in that brief dream. But I shall go where a virgin light will meet me on virgin shores."—"Every beginning is serene. Hail to him who can always begin again!"

DAY of Sacramozo's Death.

The preparation. Fasting. Aspect of the world. Qualms of doubt. Anxiety, resolve wavers, grows firm again.

Last conversation with Maria: farewell and meeting again: the powerful effect of this conversation on her.

The last afternoon, evening. His thoughts *during*. The drops: the realization that he can stop between one drop and the next. Ecstasy of dissolution, how it fades at the thought that he can stop. The aspect of the world between life and death: the finality sanctifies the ecstasy: an enormous *hon-*

ouring of God in His creatures: a moving into the temple of God. Access of fear of death: paroxysm. Transfiguration.

Before death: hears water flowing, desire to conjure up all water he has ever heard flow.

Stages of dissolution: a wonderful drawing near to every being that is borne towards him by a quiet, shining river; the beings rise like swimmers out of a holy stream: he knows that nothing he has done in his life has been in vain. The approaching beings single, like a kiss melting the soul—the blueness of a garment, the breath of a lip, the voice of a bird (the objects in the room: sky-blue stuff, a mask, silver candelabra, flowers, fruit, bowls of water) (Ramakrishna, the herons in the blue sky)—he takes it as the promise of an ineffable union, and now knows that he cannot turn back.

The death-room of the Knight with alabaster lamps and flowers. His ecstatic letter of farewell: universal love. For him, this is no vague dissolution, but the most sublime preservation of personality.

AT THE same time, Andreas wins Zustina in the lottery. She wants to give herself to him, hoping by that to win him so that he will remain her husband. Confesses the trick by which she made him win, which was very cleverly contrived. Her tears and her recovery: evidence that Nina too is in love with him.—News of Romana.—Zustina speaks of the way in which Nina loves him as contrasted with her own, deduces both, very shrewdly and delicately, from their physical constitution. At this moment, Zustina is extraordinarily beautiful. Zustina: "when Nina is in love, everything stops for her soul: the world has changed—she cannot understand how she could have lived yesterday. Till now I was never in love —and if there is no way of being in love but Nina's, I do not know love even now. For the world is always the world for me, even though it contains a being whom it is delicious to meet."

LAST Chapter.

As Andreas takes flight and travels up the mountain, he feels as if the two halves of his being, which had been torn asunder, were coming together again.

At San Vito, he finds a farmhand driving home by night. When he reaches Castle Finazzer the next day, Romana is not there. Gradually it comes out that she has fled to the alp on his account; then that she has had a terrible fever, has constantly spoken of him, then taken a vow never to see him again unless he comes from *Vienna* to make her his wife (prudery now as infinitely exaggerated as previous candour).

He leaves a decisive letter for Romana.

Last Chapter. He leaves at daybreak. They arrive at sunrise. Up to the mountain pasture with the mother. Romana creeps into the farthest cleft and finally threatens to throw herself down from there.

Andreas or The United

The Lady with the Spaniel

GENERAL PLAN (rough), 12. IX. 1912.
I. Arrival. Lodging. Lottery. Visit to the cocotte. First
meeting. II. The Knight of Malta. Conversation. Visit to the
Countess after another visit to Nina. III. Developments in
the affair with the widow. Amorous friendship with the
Countess. Jealous of the Knight. IV. The Countess is moved:
her story. The widow: the present in its most fiery form,
impish, knowledge of the "other." V. The Countess begins
to withdraw (change of confessor), evening visit. The note
with the threat. VI. . . . VII. Evening visit; Andreas feels,
as he goes up, how completely he has changed. The weight
of experience: there is nothing in it all that did not have to
happen.

ANDREAS.—Reason for sending him on the tour: difficult,
protracted convalescence after a mental crisis, some listless-
ness, loss of sense of values, confusion of ideas.

Influence of a Father Aderkast who has suspended life
for Andreas, made it illusory (performances of Calderon).—
The meeting with Father Aderkast (who bears down on him
fulsomely—he feels as if his whole past were breaking in
upon him, inescapably) interwoven with an adventure with
Mariquita: the more distraught Andreas grows, owing to the

repeated meetings with Father Aderkast, whose insistence he can hardly understand, the more charming he seems to Mariquita.

Andreas does not really believe in his experiences; what happens to him, of all people, cannot be worth much: he is always at extremes, on the one hand sensual, on the other idealist.—He always assumes that people must know what is going on in him.—His demands were gentle and without insistence, he was content with little.

Andreas's apprenticeship: to recognize the existence of higher things, to recognize the substance of life.

In his childhood memories there remains a painful confusion which his whole life will hardly suffice to unravel. To die reconciled to one's childhood. (Journal: "I should like to die reconciled to my childhood.")

His grandfather, a ferryman at Spitz on the Danube, came down from the forest district. Takes Princess Brunswick across the ferry. She notices him and hires him as a groom in place of one who has fallen ill. The Emperor rides to meet her with a hundred cavaliers, has himself presented to her last under the incognito of Count Falkenstein, but as he kisses her hand, presses it, so that she starts up and falls into his arms, and he now kisses both of her hands in turn. (This in 1716, the grandfather born 1699; Andreas's father, born in 1731, is now fortyeight.) Spanish customs in these stories.

CLOSE of the tour chapters: encounter with the "woman on the Aar"—the adventure with the inconsolable widow.

Leaving the Finazzer farm: he does not believe himself; he develops in himself the figure of another, who will return. Now startled in the house on the river, where the mourning widow comes towards him with her "Really you! It is really you! You cannot escape yourself!"—The mood of supreme exaltation, which has lasted for several days since the moment of the mountain, suddenly reversed in this adventure (the widow's hand on his breast in the night).

A German-speaking widow from the lowest-lying of the Sette Communi. The picture of the accident painted on paper, the wedding-ring attached. Sends her sixteen-year-old daughter to kneel and weep by the river. Her cough (hysterically exaggerated by herself)—at times she tells the story in fuller detail. The picture is her prayer-book, her all.—Impression on Andreas: "A single moment!"—From that moment he can pray, it goes home to him. (In between, the merchant's servant, watching his luggage, sudden breaking off of prayer. Idle, empty chatter with a fellow traveller about the gentry of the *terra ferma*)—The widow's complaints and soliloquies, have not stopped for seventeen years: the daughter's callous way of detailing it all, saying in a weary drawl, "Nothing gives her pleasure, for her, the world is her coffin"—when the mother says the same thing, but in a raving way, so that even in her anguish there is still a hint of the breath of God, of the inexhaustibility of nature and life. On the other hand, even the daughter's bearing is dreadful as she listlessly drags herself along by her mother's side, listlessly answers, "Yes, yes"—with wandering eyes, listlessly says, "Father has been dead for eighteen years now, and she will not stop, she will never get over it till she lies in her grave."—Here Andreas becomes aware of the mysteriousness of the connection ruling between the moment and the year, even between the moment and life as a whole: how in a way a moment can devour a whole life (—something similar in the Countess's fate).

He hears her talking, interrupted by weeping; she means to drown herself. The daughter hard beyond her years. He begins to feel that the whole of existence is grounded on a wholesome feeling of self-confidence, like Mount Kaf on an emerald. After all these imaginings, he feels inseparably united to Romana—in very truth her spouse.

The scene where the daughter tries to drag her mother away so as to stop her making herself a nuisance to the stranger, by telling her mother, who is clinging to the stranger's breast, the bitterest, iciest truths. "That is a strange man. Chance, which he will curse, made him stop here for the night. He cares nothing about what has happened to you, he curses the place and your screams; they pierce his ears. Hardly will his carriage have turned the corner when he will have forgotten you and me like the vermin in a dirty inn."— Andreas's feelings terribly torn, profoundest inadequacy in face of this absolute infinity of wretchedness. He despises himself for every comfort he possesses . . . —here the recollections of the tour break off abruptly.

He did not reflect on all these experiences in detail, yet they were all present in him; each one was in some way always there, his soul was like a quivering magnetic needle: all these things perpetually diverted it from its pole; he was empty and overburdened. His nature needed and longed for passion which, by carrying us away, relieves us of the burden of self.

The house on the river, with the inconsolable widow, encompassing him utterly, in all its rooms, outhouses, etc.—In her haggard face a sudden brightness, the eyes kind, the mouth pretty, the natural in its truest, purest form in her.— Question: whether the existence of his parents is not hell in disguise.

Andreas roaming sadly about: these quite small details: picking up a twig, throwing it away with love, but gently, not far from him, still feels it as it lies there, licks blades of grass for joy.

He has listened to the widow as no one has for a long time past: that is why she comes to him in the night, touches his breast—where, after a long lapse of time, she becomes aware of a human feeling, something of him she has lost wakes and comes to life again.

The evening, at supper: she walks up and down, raving of the dead man. The daughter says: "The wind is in the south."—She takes the stranger's hand: "O take that—only that—away from me,—that I did it of set purpose, knowing what I was doing. Do I not stand like a stone in the wall? It is toppling, that is just why it must stand fast!—can you understand me? The lust of murder (imp of the perverse) is nothing compared to it. I did it out of frozen horror of the world"—(at once contradicts herself, accusing herself of devilish selfishness). Frightful paralysis, in which life, even movement, stands still, transfixed. The daughter pushes her away: "The gentleman's supper is ready, leave him alone!"—how young the mother looks in her moments of greatest anguish. —The daughter: the priest dismisses her from the confessional for obdurate despair.

Andreas: in a dull and dispirited frame of mind, certain subtleties, certain improbable, favourite associations, which his mind constantly pursues, which he feels to be reality itself, while he is never aware of the rest of life as unalloyed. He is thus visited by a sense of the actual that evening by the river where the mourning widow's house stands. Then the adventure in the night when the half-mad woman kneels on his breast. Previously, he has identified himself with the dead man, imagines that that look came from his eyes. In bed, thinks intensely of Romana.

Later, reversing the roles, he puts himself in the place of the wretched murderess, Romana in the place of the man. He is morbid enough to imagine the murder. All his mania of self-abasement converges on this point: he pictures to himself all that he has destroyed in Romana: he does not let her die completely, but live on, a joyless spirit—only by this is the richness of her life revealed to him—he feels one with her as never before, he begins to perceive the sense in life—he is happy.—"By what are we moved—by what power—from what point?" he asks, and is appalled by our ignorance of the power which is above all things.

The substance Romana continually elevated by everything that happens: he can only possess Romana when she is his *faith*.

In the widow's house. At the window, at sunrise, clouds over the river. What comes home to him most profoundly: the presentiment of all love and no love in himself: the presentiment: Nothing can happen to me. I shall not be the loser in the end. Previously, in stages, deepest temptations; his chief fear, to be cheated of the essential, of the substance of life.— To himself: "Whoever you are, religious or irreligious, child or father, you cannot be cast away, something sustains you." He imagines that he can grasp this something. What he believed himself unworthy of, what he believed to be impossible, what, in his melancholy, he believed beyond his powers—in the past it seemed possible, in dreams it was unassailably his.—One thing above all he found toilsome—to attain to himself, and in that toil his nature found fulfilment.

ANDREAS'S path: first to become capable of love, then to learn that body and spirit are one. He has suffered continually from this dualism: now the one, now the other in him seemed worthless. Now he learns to feel the one behind the other, to feel the one always sustaining the other.

How Romana comes to life in him: single features, a smile as of understanding with him. The moments when she comes to life in him bring anxiety, which alternates with gaiety. Once he thinks he sees Romana sitting on the Riva on a trunk: she is beginning to unpack. He does not dare to approach her.

Chapter I, end: Andreas sitting on the bed. It is easier for a camel to pass through the eye of a needle than for him to become the lover, in the real sense of the word, of the Spanish woman, of Zustina, or of Nina—anyone else could. Now, thinking of Romana, in a beautiful radiance: the walk. Four castles in the air in which he lives with each of them.

Episode of the townsman's wife—at the same time, estrangement from the Knight. The wife of a mending-tailor, who would like to be married to him. The tailor humours her. Humble surroundings, much given to gossip about the gentry, about foreigners in the town too. Proposes to belong to him and to procure others for him: at the same time, immense respect for virtue. Quite primitive lower-class life, like the life of the people in ancient times. The tailor's wife has sixteen brothers and sisters. Friendly eyes and a pretty mouth, accommodating, at the first meeting she treats him like a great gentleman, afterwards more as one of her own class. Her husband dies. The woman's children: the grave boy, as he gazes at him, seeming to forget himself, the girl nestling up to him with a rather deceitful look.

Here Andreas feels, in a way, at home: with the Countess he feels as if he were not alive, but only dreaming; he wonders if he has ever lived. This life in the tailor's house, which he mentions to nobody, makes him feel a liar and traitor.—During this time Andreas sits to Zorzi for his portrait, maliciously breaks off the sittings. To frighten him, Zorzi threatens him with intervention by the authorities. The catastrophe comes about through the death of the husband, the children change towards him, their bitterness. Andreas reproaches himself: "Can I say that I stand by anyone?"—He cannot bear the sight of the pictures in the churches, they humiliate him, the figures in them are so manifold. He is disgusted by his own power of entering into everybody with his mind and his heart —even the spy Zorzi, an old hunchbacked messenger, and so on. He wants to confess this self-contempt to the Knight, but does not do so. The Knight realizes his condition, sees in his changed, contemptuous way of speaking that he is at odds with himself.

THE KNIGHT gives him Ariosto to read on account of the wonderful world-sense that is his. He does not read Ariosto with an eighteenth-century mind. He understands what the Knight means when he says that there is no such thing as the past: everything that exists is present, is even born at the present moment (feeling when listening to Bach).

Fate is fulfilled in minute particulars, power resides in minute particulars. Nothing that is to work as magic is in any way vague or general, but most particular, most momentary. Love —kindled by a sudden comical fancy, a contretemps, a hesitation, as well as by a gesture of courage, of freedom. The ordinary "I" an insignificant construction, a scarecrow.

Andreas and the two women: "The nature of things is completely exhausted in polarity and intensification" (Goethe at eighty)—on the one hand, demands more of each at every meeting—to what end? (tact incorporate in the bearing of the Knight)—on the other hand, premonition of what polarity may be; in each he loves the other with the most delicate, chaste love, and in this way learns to abandon the search for the absolute in the world.

Andreas fears to become aware, in Maria or Mariquita, of the other nature, and hence to lose what is unique in the beloved. He is on the point of wishing to murder Mariquita in order to save Maria for himself. (The temptations to which his weakness is exposed at this point—"learn to live!")

Andreas

Andreas's humble wish to be Mariquita's husband. Gradual realization of the impossibility of the step: imagines letter to his parents announcing the plan.

MARIA and Mariquita.—Novalis: "all evil is isolated and isolating, it is the principle of separation"—by union, separation is abolished and not abolished, but wickedness (evil) as an apparent separation and union is actually abolished by true separation and union, which only exist in reciprocity.

Maria	*Mariquita*
wishes to be an old woman	is afraid of growing old
often imagines herself dead (here she coincides with Sacramozo's conquest of time)	dreads death
loves old people	dislikes seeing old people
is afraid of children	attracts children to her

MARIA'S emotion over an old woman whose skin nobody cares to touch.

Mariquita is greedy and an artist in cookery. Maria enjoys good food too, but suppresses her liking for it and knows nothing about cookery. Mariquita's greed of living, boundless curiosity to set her foot everywhere, to enter every possible situation, to visit every place of ill repute. Everything that Andreas points out (the beauty of flowing water, etc.) she absorbs in intenser form. She hears all the talk of the town, knows where there is anything going on or to be seen (the vegetable market towards morning, the fish market, fantastic episodes in cellars, stage-coach drives on the mainland, episode of the rope-walkers).

Mariquita an utterly baffling person, allows herself to be kissed, but no more, hints that she is a respectable woman, but has a lover, of course.—He takes her to casinos, to other places of amusement; sometimes she suddenly vanishes from his arm, or again stiffens convulsively, then looks at him with the face of Maria.—As to the Countess, it seems an unimaginable prodigy that she might give herself; with Mariquita, an absurdity that she does not. In both feelings he goes too far, both are funnels through which he falls into the void. He longs to speak to the Knight about it; instead, he meets the Duke, who is having a biting-match with the dogs.

Mariquita to Andreas: "I am infatuated with you because you were the first man I saw after my release. I know there is nothing particular about you, but I still see you with rapture in my eyes—it's all chance, after all."—"On that day I had really got out for the first time—I had already contrived to write letters."—The power to pick up adventures because she is absolutely free.

Mariquita receives him in a strange lodging which she alleges to belong to her mistress, and has had lent to her under false pretences: she pretends to be a lady's companion or something of the kind. The conflict in Andreas's mind about marrying her, since he is aware of all her failings, however charming they may be. Her random chatter at times—her dreaminess. "Shall I possess you entirely?" asks Andreas. —"Entirely, and another besides."

How Mariquita makes acquaintances: presents herself as a governess, collecting for religious purposes. Perpetual outings, she has always spied something out. Excursion with Mariquita to see the wild man. On their outings, she takes Andreas into all kinds of society, where he has to suffer mockery and scorn, where he is bewildered, imposed on and put to shame: "You would like to become an official?"—Mariquita likes to hear the story of Uncle Leopold.—Among those she takes Andreas to see there is a lunatic, she pretends to be his niece or house-keeper; he comes in, talks to himself without seeing those present.—Once she hits on the idea of enticing the other into a certain kind of house for Andreas, then sending him home with the "other" in her confusion and shame. The other does not say a word, seems mortally ashamed and frightened, so that Andreas leaves her.

Her most beautiful moments: her power of perceiving elements of purity even in the midst of apparent ugliness, at the fish market, at the vegetable market, buying provisions for a meal. *Gourmandise*. Curiosity.—He wants to travel to the widow's house with Mariquita; after protracted difficulties the plan falls through. She will never revisit any place they visited together the time before. Thus each time she unravels the web. —Andreas: "If only I knew something about your solitude. What are you like then?"

Mariquita likes to question Andreas about the Knight, it is almost as if she sometimes wavered between the two. "What would he say or do then? Ah, is he like that? Do you admire him very much? Would he like me?"

Mariquita sees the Knight speaking to Maria with loving urgency. She (the part that is hostile in her) prevents Maria from really loving the Knight.

Mariquita declares that she knows everything about the Countess, back into the first year of her life: she recounts part of her life-story—never her own. Andreas asks, "And what about you when you were a child?"

Mariquita, having once fainted from fright, turns into Maria—during the adventure in the storm, on the quay, in a strange house to which he has carried her. On that day she was tired, had not had enough sleep: a beautiful sunset, then a thunderstorm.

MARIA's story: abandoned after passionate love, marries a man she does not love, who only possesses her once: he falls very ill: she nurses him in a wayside inn—then the faithless lover comes to her window.—Maria's fundamental idea: the infinite—how can we possibly exchange one man for another.

Her psychic malady dates from the day on which, nursing her unloved husband after the death of her child, she is suddenly confronted with her lover, the faithless one. "Life has rent me asunder, God in Heaven alone can put me together again."

What happened: gradually she brings herself to answer some of the lover's letters, agrees to meet him once. In doing so, she does not think beyond the delight of the meeting, but into that delight she plunges without reserve: it is an entirely different thing from seeing him pass by so often: for her the meeting is like three dimensions compared with two—there is something added. In comparison, the image of her husband steadily loses relief. Just before the meeting, she pauses, turns round and goes home. She feels as though her husband were sitting at her embroidery frame, waiting for her, as though his eyes were on her. As she is going home, she feels her lover behind her back, but does not turn round, has the strength to reach the threshold. She goes upstairs, opens the door; her husband is actually sitting at the embroidery frame, his eyes upon her, but he is dead.

In her marriage, temporary loss of sense of value. Sitting alone at her mirror, the Countess once sees how she changes after everything in her mind has taken on a different aspect. The torture in her face struggles with triumph—then Mariquita stands up and steals downstairs.

Once, when Maria is talking to Andreas and the Knight (about Spanish titles and successions, tediously of set pur-

pose, because she does not *wish* to excite herself), she loses
the thread: the other face appears, her tone changes completely, her eyes swim, a burning look meets Andreas—then
it is over, she turns deathly pale, has difficulty in picking up
the thread. During this glowing moment, Andreas says to
himself, "I am possessed, my imagination has called up the
other"—he turns red with shame and tears come into his
eyes.—Andreas cannot bring himself to assent to the identity
of the hands, he insists on finding a difference.

In Maria, subliminal horror of everything happening in
the street, increasing reluctance to drive out, which the
Knight tries to overcome. Purification, the heart reduced to
ashes, glorifies self-mortification, interest in Platonism, tendency to Molinism.

The sermon she has heard in the afternoon about the
work of the worms in the human corpse, and how we are
forgotten even by our nearest: how there is no salvation here
save with God.

Confessor: Spaniard. Mariquita has a curious relationship
to him; she writes to him too, she threatens to lead Maria
into another way of life. She resists his look.—Strong desires
felt by Mariquita are felt as impulses by Maria.

Mariquita on Maria: she refused to be a real woman—
would not forget Christ.

Andreas—Maria: they get as far as taking a room: his
dread of possessing her—unconscious even to himself.—Maria
feels a voice warning her, repeats tonelessly what she imagines the voice said to her: "Do not do it, do not do it."

Her confessions when she is ill (apparently delirious, but
she is not delirious)—how Mariquita has cut her feet from
her body and hidden them. As she tells this, Andreas rushes
from the room. He now receives incessant letters from both.
Finally, the lady enters a convent.

Hugo von Hofmannsthal

THE KNIGHT of Malta.—He moves in a time which is not quite the present, and in a place which is not completely here.—For him, Venice is the fusion of the classical world and the Orient, impossibility, in Venice, of relapsing into the trivial, the unmeaning. Morosin Peloponnesiaco his great-grandfather. Possesses some antiques, among them an early torso.

Several beings in him: when he is gardening, out on the Brenta, in shirt-sleeves, he anticipates the bourgeois of 1840: for Andreas the premonition of how his own grandchildren will live.

Relatedness. Alone with the child, the child looks up: "Out of the substance, which I may not seek—for I have that substance—all the heavens and hells of all religions have arisen —to cast them away would be gross darkness.—The child's look: links me, the words in my mouth, to these walls, to their protection, to what is simply there."—"Impavidum ferient ruinae"—an interpretation, a summoning of inner powers, a mustering of resources: only the cataclysm reveals supreme ecstasy.

Sacramozo's two dreams at the desk in the magistrate's court at Bruneck: i) he is living alone at the castle—a cock crows, then a second time; a bell rings. He stands up, barefoot: through the soles of his feet he feels everything, down into the mountain. The miller's daughter at the gate; lights the fire, waters the cattle in the great hall—all symbolic ceremonies. Then, in the arbour, he marries her to his son. From the mountain wall opposite there issue silver ancestors, so beautiful that he cries in his dream, "I am dreaming."—ii) Everything has two meanings: he is governor, but nobody must know it. In the entrance hall, a fire, maids, the prisoner chained to the wall. Denial. The prisoner: "Do you know me, then?" Every time in between, he flies through the country:

[114]

brooks, graveyards—hither, thither. Already weary of his flight, he believes that he must discover who the other is—it is like a mislaid key.—The cock crows. He knows that it is for the third time, and knows that he has betrayed his Saviour.—The real governor comes up to him: "I have the strangest news for you: the Count of Welsberg has returned from the Turkish war"—he was believed to have been captured and beheaded at the cave by the Janissaries.

His hypochondria (indescribable dependence on the quality of the air): his haughtiness towards these things, reticence.—Antipathy to raucous shouts, barking of dogs.

A man must become devout in the struggle for perfection. His explanation of what has taught him to despise the sensuously perfect—although he responds to it (the sensuous perfection expressed in Veronese in the relation of a perfect white to a bare throat, the same in Correggio)—the dilapidated condition of Venice has taught him the vanity of all things.

Perfectomania: to plan sumptuous festivals ends in the belief that no festival is perfect but the funeral of a Carthusian monk.

His key, that he can see through the motives of others, their nature: just as, for a devout man, everything comes to an end when he realizes that his fellow man is godless, incapable of seeking God; so, for him, everything comes to an end when he feels no disinterested and steady striving upwards: he clings to what he calls the human, he is quick to divine the merely partial.—"What is the use of a confused striving, an isolated good quality? I will have nothing to do with the sieve of the Danaides, the rock of Sisyphus."

Sacramozo's interpretation of the Gospel saying: "Seek ye first the Kingdom of God and all these things shall be added unto you" (here, in created beings, he seeks the Kingdom of God). "The *ergon*," says Fama, "is the sanctification of the inner man, alchemy is the *parergon*."—*Solve et coagula*. The universal binding agent—gluten; the universal solvent—alkahest; in love, both are present. In love, always sublimate, volatilize, sacrifice life, the moment, to the higher, purer thing which is to be distilled from them—seek to fix this higher, purer thing.

The Knight: a motto: "Le plus grand plaisir de tous les plaisirs est de sortir de soi-même," in "Amours d'Eumène et de Flora" (in von Waldberg, *Geschichte des Romans*). The very evil mood that precedes his crises: he is then actually unpleasant, or rather insufferable, even discourteous. The look of contempt for everybody, even for Andreas. His crushing mockery of Andreas: he literally annihilates him (and himself too). The consuming irony and tormenting restlessness that drive him. In this condition, one of his crises coincides with a momentous crisis in Maria: Mariquita suddenly speaks to him, mocks him. He runs away, passes through a crisis of deepest self-abasement, from which he rises to supreme purity and joyful victory. Before this, he hurries to various places (to Nina too) where he suffers rebuffs and humiliations.— "How," he wonders, "can the worthy substance arise from the worthless, the eagle from the chameleon, the jewel from dirt?"

Knight: the complete collapse of the man of forty. He can no longer expect further illumination, redeeming revelations, and cannot imagine that those older than he should have resources that are withheld from him: he can approach nobody with entreaty, in confiding discipleship: what can be redeemed in him is his *creation* (the young man there before him)—He himself is his own supreme authority: he no longer stands in life with curiosity, very many relationships are no

longer possible. He has realized all this, his morbidity inten-
sifies it: he cannot really reconcile himself to his actual age.
His attitude to the Countess is gauche: that is a task beyond
his powers: everything he does to her is a pretence. Appalling
doubts at this point: every time they arise, he has the decency
to put a stop to them and go on *doing.*—That is the most heroic
of all human conditions (see Frederick the Great).

Who could imagine him infinitely weeping, infinitely
wooing?—he lacks that touch of the actor which is indispensable to the priest, the prophet, without which they cannot
exist. How every faculty requires for its existence its own
opposite latent in it: the unspeakable delight, for the modest,
to think that they might overcome their modesty, for the
proud, the cold, to imagine themselves glowing.—Thus, in
every impulse to take, the profound impulse not to take (the
secret in Grillparzer's relationship to Kathi)—duality incarnate in Maria and Mariquita. Sometimes Sacramozo bewilders Andreas with disclosures of this kind, for instance,
once after an evening together (supper, casino) when Sacramozo greeted a large number of people.

Sacramozo's way of telling a story.—Instead of "I was
once in Japan with pilgrims," he says, "Go to Japan! You
will walk three, five days with a band of pilgrims . . . the
question is whether you will see the sun rise in purity . . ."

Knight: "Note that each of us only becomes aware in the
other of what conforms to himself; we create statues round
about us in our own dimensions. Problem: in what does
union with a human being consist? in understanding, in possessing, in first approaching that human being? . . ." (Touch
of Hindu speculation).

Knight to Andreas: "Does a young man really know what
he demands, what he wants?"—"all these connections, and

[117]

whether they lead to anything—that requires guidance from above."—The Knight possesses the conception of power, which Andreas has yet to acquire.

Knight and Andreas compared: Andreas: Belief in authority ramifying to the uttermost periphery of existence, so that he feels that everything he experiences is analogous to, but not identical with, something *real,* just like his actions. The real doers are elsewhere; his inhibitions, his naïveté in face of life, are his own. Knight: doubts not himself but his fate. In suffering, in enjoyment, he had the whole, two-sided, in one, but with him everything remained partial (while Andreas has the presentiment of how everything is united, but not "the grasp to get it"). Knight knows: my command is a command, my smile has a general power to win—but, *en somme,* what is the good of it?—Knight has not Andreas's wavering, his doubts, his fitfulness—he is sure of results, but it can often happen that he finds himself in a vacuum with them: *"Eh bien!* what now?" says his double. "Aha!—well, well, what of it!"

Andreas's dawning realization that there is for the Knight, who can talk to everybody, before whom all barriers fall, *one* barrier all the same. There is in the thought something which moves him almost to tears.

The affair with the letter. Chapter V.—Zorzi: "The Knight has left a letter behind." Andreas: "Let me take it back to him"—almost as if his tongue had pronounced the words of its own accord: the fulfilment of his wish means infinitely much to him. Runs after him. Knight puts it in his pocket, unforgettable hasty gait. Knight returns a few minutes later. "You are mistaken. The letter did not belong to me." Andreas: "And certainly not to me." Chapter VI, a few days later. Knight catches him up. "I must ask you to tell me what could have persuaded you to give me that letter.

There are coincidences that leave one no peace. The inside and the outside of the folded letter were in a different hand; I think it belonged to me." He blushes as he speaks; Andreas vows to use the words "beautiful" and "ugly" with caution.

Knight hails a gondola in order to read the letter, begins while the gondolier is getting the gondola ready—forgets to get in. The gondolier does not like to draw his attention. Starting up, he pushes the letter into his pocket. Enters the gondola, tries to recover from the letter. Mistakes several houses for his own, then feels his own house utterly alien to him, wants to burn the letter.—Foreboding of death through the letter.

He believes that one or the other of his two servants has done away with the letter—for what possible reason? the elder to protect him? the younger to injure the elder? Cross-examines first the elder then the younger. At last he finds the letter, reads it through; he finds it among notes of travel, where his hand has put it in a kind of trance, at a particular place, next to a particularly significant note on Japan. Deeply and singularly shaken by this slight experience.—His degree of sympathy, and hence his comprehension of his two servants. He cannot possibly disturb the elder, who has relatives visiting him: it occurs to him that that is the reason why he went up the front staircase. He reflects on this himself; his servants in Japan, where he had fourteen of them, men and women, come into his mind. He casually becomes aware that he is forming within himself a whole chain of thought, always turning on this servant—his old servant: he and the servant always at cross purposes: the young one, who is always quarrelling with the elder. The Knight locks up the letter, and at once looks for it again.

After the letter: the Knight tries to see clear in his inward tumult, to reduce to order (by Locke's method) the storm of associations: he discovers in himself courtesy, grace, modesty. His inexhaustible inward powers—full of confidence—hosts of angels which he summons. A man's whole nature must come to light in such a struggle with inward disorganization: his wonted trains of thought, his favourite associations.—Subtle association with a memory of travel: pilgrimage with Japanese, perception of light. He had resolved to hail the coming of the sun every day—why can he not always hail it?—he now tries to marshal the associations towards a higher, purer order; he knows that the only obstacle to the cosmos is inadequacy. He kneels, prays to the supreme being. Chaos and death breathe upon him: on the point of succumbing, he is like the delicate boy he was, with a fleeting colour on his cheeks.

A MEETING between Andreas and the Knight on a ship at anchor. Invitations from the captain, somewhat mysterious. Courtesans—one completely veiled (Mariquita). Sacramozo obviously embarrassed by the veiled woman: although he guides the conversation with assurance, he is deeply interested by an Indian, who takes part, but does not eat with them. —Everything has happened at Mariquita's instigation: "I wanted to see you together for once." This is the only time that Sacramozo and Mariquita meet. On the way home, they say nothing about the whole affair, nothing about the invitation. Andreas feels that the Knight believes it may have been the Countess. Their conversation turns on fate and death. That night, Sacramozo invites Andreas home for the first time.

The masque: a solemn symbolic festival. Andreas's initiation. What costume Sacramozo wore at the masque remains a secret. Echo of Hafiz's relationship to the boy cupbearer, to whom he gives happiness out of the flames of his love for Suleika.—Culminating point of the masque, a kind of meeting between Maria and Mariquita, or transmutation of Maria, who is brought in in a state of hypnosis: it comes to a bad end.

The idea the Knight has in mind: the greatest magician is he who can work magic on himself too. This his goal, since he is threatened by: confusion, the failure to understand his fellow man, the loss of the world and himself—all this in his relationship to Maria.—At the same time, Maria unwittingly feeds his knowledge of that other aspect of the world—Mariquita having set out to entice the Knight away from Maria by allowing him to suspect the side of Maria that is turned towards Andreas. (She keeps this game quite hidden from Andreas.) For Mariquita fears the Knight as Maria's strongest support in life.

Knight: "In reality, we know only when we know little; doubt grows with knowledge" (Goethe)—"There are men who love and seek their like, and there are others who love and seek their opposite" (Goethe)—But are men like the Knight capable of having a like and an opposite?—That he no longer understands anyone—the less he understands, the more he feels how Andreas is growing in feeling, intuition and knowledge—is balanced by the arcanum: he has found one who will understand, loving. Thus his withdrawal becomes lovely, as one who passes into the mirror to be united with his brother. The circle comes to have profound meaning for him. The predominance of the circle in the works and notes of Leonardo.—When the sun is low, we live more in our shadow than in ourselves.

The allomatic: the meagreness of earthly experience. He is drawn to the Countess because the other element in her means so much to her—he suspects that she is a soul far advanced on the way of transformation. What attracts him in Andreas: that he is so open to influences from others; the life of others is present in him in the same purity and strength as when a drop of blood, or the breath exhaled by another, is exposed to powerful heat in a glass ball—even so the destinies of others in Andreas. Andreas is, like the merchant's son (in the *Tale of the Six-Hundred-and-Seventy-Second Night*), the geometrical locus of the destinies of others. (The *lucerna*, or lamp of life: an alabaster ball, in which the blood of one far distant shows, as it moves and shines, how things stand with him: in misfortune, it bubbles up or glows darkly, at death it fades, or the vessel bursts.)

Sacramozo and Andreas: how the Knight gradually comes to set the other in his own place: this connected with Andreas's loathing of the continual recollection of his adventure with Gotthilff. Only he holds the past in horror who, remaining at an inferior stage, imagines that it might all have turned out otherwise. "If, when that being first kissed me, I was just anybody, everything turns stale; if I was singled out (with the anticipation of every hour till death) then all is sublime." Love is the anticipation of the end in the beginning, and therefore the victory over decay, over time, over death—Novalis's note on the mystic powers of self-creation with which we credit women, so that we expect them to love anyone (theme of *Sobeide*, also of *Death and the Fool*). Love is the attraction exercised on us by those animate objects with which we are called to operate. To operate means to lead an animate organism to perfection by transformation—in connection with Maria: to find the strength, the power to feel, of oneself, the chain of experiences as necessary—the egocentric at a higher stage.

The Knight no longer hopes to have children by Maria. Andreas might become his "son without a mother."

Speaking of Maria, Sacramozo says, "The earthly possibility of her union with me existed, but not the higher one."

For him, Maria is his collaborator in virtue of the purity of her being. His power to unite—he wishes to unite Andreas with Maria. They are to be a couple *now*—later, Maria reborn with Sacramozo reborn (in whom Andreas will also exist).— He must know the truth, thus he knows Maria's life-story— but the only thing of value to him is the life-secret of every being. And since life is both on the surface and in the depths, the life-secret can only be grasped by the union of the two.

He may have been mistaken in all he did, his bearing justifies him.—Self-enjoyment, the highest, purest—Sacramozo seeks it: the union with himself, complete identity, harmony of self-realizing with self-knowledge. He tries to impart this condition to Andreas, who is helped by love. The Countess participates in that condition, though for pathological reasons: every impulse which issues from Mariquita is saturated for Maria with the atmosphere of selfhood elevated to the state of mystery—in the same way, Maria is for Mariquita the only thing worth experiencing (she loves and hates her). Maria's confession of the rapture she feels in merging into the "other," in the mere hint of that state (the first is, for her, a rapture mingled with horror)—that that is for her the life of life; every sweetness, even every anticipation of the union with God, threatens to plunge her into it. (Conversation with the Spanish confessor about this, her self-reproaches. She feels responsible for more than herself. The Jesuit sets her mind at rest.)

ad Sacramozo: "Quod petis in te est, ne quaesiveris extra" (That which thou seekest is within thee; seek it not outside) —To be master of our own self would be to have all things, even the subliminal, present to the mind.

A being of supreme consciousness can never feel fear, except in actual danger, because fear in all other cases presupposes something obtruded, not present to the mind.

Magician who thinks he moves an invisible limb. What else is this but to feel one's will, to look on and feel oneself as one exercising his will, not in the material world (like Napoleon), but in the spirit.

Sacramozo: "The most sacred relationship is that between the appearance and the essence—and how constantly it is outraged! One would think that God had hidden it among thorns and thistles.—We possess a whole arsenal of truth which would have power to change the world back into a stellar nebula, but every arcanum is locked fast in an iron crucible—by our inflexibility and our stupidity, our prejudices, our powerlessness to understand the *unique*."

The Knight and the world: to think that everything, everything, is veiled. The veiled image of Saïs stands everywhere. His ardent craving for the purity of all things.

His other aspect, which he alone sees: so childish, even weak, inadequate. Would like to wipe himself out of existence. Feels that Maria puts him to the test, sees through him. Her inhibition—in that he sees his own inadequacy. Loneliness and mingling with men are the same thing.

The antinomy of being and having: for him, in the spiritual world, where all that matters is leadership, election, as for Andreas in the human world. His great love for one of the most beautiful women he possessed.

In Sacramozo, the growing belief that his fictitious existence (as Sacramozo) prevents the ultimate growth of Andreas into the bold lover, of Maria (round whom he sees another element hovering like an aura) into the happy beloved.

Knight: "Kneel?—as one kneels to receive teaching from a teacher revered like gods—that gesture—I shall have died without finding it on my way. Will this youth be he who is capable of kneeling?" (he leads the figure through all the potentialities which the world holds for him). "And shall I find the way to be he?—Not by circumventing his inadequacy, but by absorbing it into myself?"

On death: "To have to leave the theatre before the curtain has risen."

Dissolution, striven for, means peace as to one's own being, the great or the small, the limited or the mighty, the accepted or rejected, about one's own lifetime and the epochs of time and the symbolic vision of things, and about the poor and needy.

The Knight great in his total defeat—a being struggling for his fate: In Andreas's union with the transformed Maria, he finds all in one, faith, love, fulfilment.

Andreas, beside the bed on which Sacramozo's body lies, must feel that, in a supreme sense, he may have been right.

Andreas: Outcome of tour to Venice: he feels with horror that he can never return to the narrow life of Vienna, he has grown out of it. But the state of mind he has attained brings him more distress than joy, it seems to him a state in which nothing is conditioned, nothing made difficult, and therefore nothing exists. All only brings to mind relationships without being so. Everything is stale, there is nothing to seek, but for that very reason, nothing can be found.—Question: whether these fragments in the kaleidoscope could rearrange themselves. Envious recollection of his grandfather's journey down the Danube, his first situations, success through vigour and courage, piety and loyalty, and, with it all, a certain robust selfishness and cunning.

Andreas's return.—He was what he might be, yet never, hardly ever, was.—He sees the sky, cloudlets over a forest, sees the beauty, is moved—but without that self-confidence on which the whole world must rest as on an emerald;—with Romana, he says to himself, it might be my heaven.

2

The Letter of Lord Chandos

THIS is the letter Philip, Lord Chandos, younger son of the Earl of Bath, wrote to Francis Bacon, later Baron Verulam, Viscount St. Albans, apologizing for his complete abandonment of literary activity.

I T IS kind of you, my esteemed friend, to condone my two years of silence and to write to me thus. It is more than kind of you to give to your solicitude about me, to your perplexity at what appears to you as mental stagnation, the expression of lightness and jest which only great men, convinced of the perilousness of life yet not discouraged by it, can master.

You conclude with the aphorism of Hippocrates, "Qui gravi morbo correpti dolores non sentiunt, iis mens aegrotat" (Those who do not perceive that they are wasted by serious illness are sick in mind), and suggest that I am in need of medicine not only to conquer my malady, but even more, to sharpen my senses for the condition of my inner self. I would fain give you an answer such as you deserve, fain reveal myself to you entirely, but I do not know how to set about it. Hardly do I know whether I am still the same person to whom your precious letter is addressed. Was it I who, now six-and-twenty, at nineteen wrote *The New Paris, The Dream of Daphne, Epithalamium,* those pastorals reeling under the splendour of their words—plays which a divine Queen and several over-indulgent lords and gentlemen are gracious enough still to remember? And again, was it I who, at three-and-twenty, beneath the stone arcades of the great Venetian *piazza*, found in myself that structure of Latin prose whose plan and order delighted me more than did the monuments of Palladio and Sansovino rising out of the sea? And could I, if otherwise I am still the same person, have lost from my inner inscrutable self all traces and scars of this creation of my most intensive thinking—lost them so completely that in your letter now lying before me the title of my short treatise stares at me strange and cold? I could not even comprehend, at first, what the familiar picture meant, but had to study it word by word, as though these Latin terms thus strung together were meeting my eye for the first time. But I am, after all, that person, and there is rhetoric in these questions—rhetoric which is good for women or for the House of Commons, whose power, however, so overrated by our time, is not sufficient to penetrate into the core of things. But it is my inner self that I feel bound to reveal to you—a peculiarity, a vice, a disease of my mind, if you like—if you are to understand that an abyss equally unbridgeable separates me from the literary works lying seemingly ahead of me as from those behind me: the latter having become so strange to me that I hesitate to call them my property.

I know not whether to admire more the urgency of your benevolence or the unbelievable sharpness of your memory, when you recall to me the various little projects I entertained during those days of rare enthusiasm which we shared together. True, I did plan to describe the first years of the reign of our glorious sovereign, the late Henry VIII. The papers bequeathed to me by my grandfather, the Duke of Exeter, concerning his negotiations with France and Portu-

gal, offered me some foundation. And out of Sallust, in those
happy, stimulating days, there flowed into me as though
through never-congested conduits the realization of form—
that deep, true, inner form which can be sensed only beyond
the domain of rhetorical tricks: that form of which one can
no longer say that it organizes subject-matter, for it pene-
trates it, dissolves it, creating at once both dream and reality,
an interplay of eternal forces, something as marvellous as
music or algebra. This was my most treasured plan.

But what is man that he should make plans!

I also toyed with other schemes. These, too, your kind
letter conjures up. Each one, bloated with a drop of my blood,
dances before me like a weary gnat against a sombre wall
whereon the bright sun of halcyon days no longer lies.

I wanted to decipher the fables, the mythical tales bequeathed to us by the Ancients, in which painters and sculp-
tors found an endless and thoughtless pleasure—decipher
them as the hieroglyphs of a secret, inexhaustible wisdom
whose breath I sometimes seemed to feel as though from behind a veil.

I well remember this plan. It was founded on I know not
what sensual and spiritual desire: as the hunted hart craves
water, so I craved to enter these naked, glistening bodies,
these sirens and dryads, this Narcissus and Proteus, Perseus
and Actaeon. I longed to disappear in them and talk out of
them with tongues. And I longed for more. I planned to
start an *Apophthegmata*, like that composed by Julius Caesar:
you will remember that Cicero mentions it in a letter. In it
I thought of setting side by side the most memorable sayings which—while associating with the learned men and witty
women of our time, with unusual people from among the simple folk or with erudite and distinguished personages—I had
managed to collect during my travels. With these I meant to

[131]

combine the brilliant maxims and reflections from classical and Italian works, and anything else of intellectual adornment that appealed to me in books, in manuscripts or conversations; the arrangement, moreover, of particularly beautiful festivals and pageants, strange crimes and cases of madness, descriptions of the greatest and most characteristic architectural monuments in the Netherlands, in France and Italy; and many other things. The whole work was to have been entitled *Nosce te ipsum.*

To sum up: In those days I, in a state of continuous intoxication, conceived the whole of existence as one great unit: the spiritual and physical worlds seemed to form no contrast, as little as did courtly and bestial conduct, art and barbarism, solitude and society; in everything I felt the presence of Nature, in the aberrations of insanity as much as in the utmost refinement of the Spanish ceremonial; in the boorishness of young peasants no less than in the most delicate of allegories; and in all expressions of Nature I felt myself. When in my hunting lodge I drank the warm foaming milk which an unkempt wench had drained into a wooden pail from the udder of a beautiful gentle-eyed cow, the sensation was no different from that which I experienced when, seated on a bench built into the window of my study, my mind absorbed the sweet and foaming nourishment from a book. The one was like the other: neither was superior to the other, whether in dreamlike celestial quality or in physical intensity—and thus it prevailed through the whole expanse of life in all directions; everywhere I was in the centre of it, never suspecting mere appearance: at other times I divined that all was allegory and that each creature was a key to all the others; and I felt myself the one capable of seizing each by the handle and unlocking as many of the others as were

ready to yield. This explains the title which I had intended
to give to this encyclopedic book.

To a person susceptible to such ideas, it might appear a
well-designed plan of divine Providence that my mind should
fall from such a state of inflated arrogance into this extreme
of despondency and feebleness which is now the permanent
condition of my inner self. Such religious ideas, however,
have no power over me: they belong to the cobwebs through
which my thoughts dart out into the void, while the thoughts
of so many others are caught there and come to rest. To me
the mysteries of faith have been condensed into a lofty allegory which arches itself over the fields of my life like a radiant
rainbow, ever remote, ever prepared to recede should it occur
to me to rush toward it and wrap myself into the folds of its
mantle.

But, my dear friend, worldly ideas also evade me in a like
manner. How shall I try to describe to you these strange
spiritual torments, this rebounding of the fruit-branches above
my outstretched hands, this recession of the murmuring
stream from my thirsting lips?

My case, in short, is this: I have lost completely the ability to think or to speak of anything coherently.

At first I grew by degrees incapable of discussing a loftier
or more general subject in terms of which everyone, fluently
and without hesitation, is wont to avail himself. I experienced
an inexplicable distaste for so much as uttering the words
spirit, soul, or *body.* I found it impossible to express an
opinion on the affairs at Court, the events in Parliament, or
whatever you wish. This was not motivated by any form of
personal deference (for you know that my candour borders on
imprudence), but because the abstract terms of which the
tongue must avail itself as a matter of course in order to voice

a judgment—these terms crumbled in my mouth like mouldy fungi. Thus, one day, while reprimanding my four-year-old daughter, Katherina Pompilia, for a childish lie of which she had been guilty and demonstrating to her the necessity of always being truthful, the ideas streaming into my mind suddenly took on such iridescent colouring, so flowed over into one another, that I reeled off the sentence as best I could, as if suddenly overcome by illness. Actually, I did feel myself growing pale, and with a violent pressure on my forehead I left the child to herself, slammed the door behind me, and began to recover to some extent only after a brief gallop over the lonely pasture.

Gradually, however, these attacks of anguish spread like a corroding rust. Even in familiar and humdrum conversation all the opinions which are generally expressed with ease and sleep-walking assurance became so doubtful that I had to cease altogether taking part in such talk. It filled me with an inexplicable anger, which I could conceal only with effort, to hear such things as: This affair has turned out well or ill for this or that person; Sheriff N. is a bad, Parson T. a good man; Farmer M. is to be pitied, his sons are wasters; another is to be envied because his daughters are thrifty; one family is rising in the world, another is on the downward path. All this seemed as indemonstrable, as mendacious and hollow as could be. My mind compelled me to view all things occurring in such conversations from an uncanny closeness. As once, through a magnifying glass, I had seen a piece of skin on my little finger look like a field full of holes and furrows, so I now perceived human beings and their actions. I no longer succeeded in comprehending them with the simplifying eye of habit. For me everything disintegrated into parts, those parts again into parts; no longer would anything let itself be encompassed by one idea. Single words floated round me; they congealed into eyes which stared at me and into which I was forced to stare back—whirlpools which gave me vertigo and, reeling incessantly, led into the void.

I tried to rescue myself from this plight by seeking refuge in the spiritual world of the Ancients. Plato I avoided, for I dreaded the perilousness of his imagination. Of them all, I intended to concentrate on Seneca and Cicero. Through the harmony of their clearly defined and orderly ideas I hoped to regain my health. But I was unable to find my way to them. These ideas, I understood them well: I saw their wonderful interplay rise before me like magnificent fountains upon which played golden balls. I could hover around them and watch how they played, one with the other; but they were concerned only with each other, and the most profound, most personal quality of my thinking remained excluded from this magic circle. In their company I was overcome by a terrible sense of loneliness; I felt like someone locked in a garden surrounded by eyeless statues. So once more I escaped into the open.

Since that time I have been leading an existence which I fear you can hardly imagine, so lacking in spirit and thought is its flow: an existence which, it is true, differs little from that of my neighbours, my relations, and most of the land-owning nobility of this kingdom, and which is not utterly bereft of gay and stimulating moments. It is not easy for me to indicate wherein these good moments subsist; once again words desert me. For it is, indeed, something entirely un-named, even barely nameable which, at such moments, reveals itself to me, filling like a vessel any casual object of my daily surroundings with an overflowing flood of higher life. I cannot expect you to understand me without examples, and I must plead your indulgence for their absurdity. A pitcher, a harrow abandoned in a field, a dog in the sun, a neglected cemetery, a cripple, a peasant's hut—all these can become the vessel of my revelation. Each of these objects and a thousand others similar, over which the eye usually glides with a natural indifference, can suddenly, at any moment (which I am utterly powerless to evoke), assume for me a character so exalted and moving that words seem too poor to describe it. Even the distinct image of an absent object, in fact, can acquire the mysterious function of being filled to the brim with this silent but suddenly rising flood of divine sensation. Recently, for instance, I had given the order for a copious supply of rat-poison to be scattered in the milk-cellars of one of my dairy-farms. Towards evening I had gone off for a ride and, as you can imagine, thought no more about it. As I was trotting along over the freshly-ploughed land, nothing more alarming in sight than a scared covey of quail and, in the distance, the great sun sinking over the undulating fields, there suddenly loomed up before me the vision of that cellar, resounding with the death-struggle of a mob of rats. I felt everything within me: the cool, musty air of the cellar filled with the sweet and pungent reek of poison, and the yelling of the death-cries breaking against the mouldering walls; the vain convulsions of those convoluted bodies as they tear about in confusion and despair; their frenzied search for escape, and the grimace of icy rage when a couple collide with one another at a blocked-up crevice. But why seek again for words which I have foresworn! You remember, my friend, the wonderful description in Livy of the hours preceding the destruction of Alba Longa: when the crowds stray aimlessly through the streets which they are to see no more . . . when they bid farewell to the stones beneath their feet. I assure you, my friend, I carried this vision within me, and the vision of burning Carthage, too; but there was more, something more divine, more bestial; and it was the Present, the fullest, most exalted Present. There was a mother, surrounded by her young in their agony of death; but her gaze was cast neither toward the dying nor upon the merciless walls of stone, but into the void, or through the void into Infinity, accompanying this gaze with a gnashing of teeth!—A slave struck with helpless terror standing near the petrifying Niobe must have experienced what I experienced when, within me, the soul of this animal bared its teeth to its monstrous fate.

Forgive this description, but do not think that it was pity I felt. For if you did, my example would have been poorly chosen. It was far more and far less than pity: an immense sympathy, a flowing over into these creatures, or a feeling that an aura of life and death, of dream and wakefulness, had flowed for a moment into them—but whence? For what had it to do with pity, or with any comprehensible concatenation of human thought when, on another evening, on finding beneath a nut-tree a half-filled pitcher which a gardener boy had left there, and the pitcher and the water in it, darkened by the shadow of the tree, and a beetle swimming on the surface from shore to shore—when this combination of trifles sent through me such a shudder at the presence of the Infinite, a shudder running from the roots of my hair to the marrow of my heels? What was it that made me want to break into words which, I know, were I to find them, would force to their knees those cherubim in whom I do not believe? What made me turn silently away from this place? Even now, after weeks, catching sight of that nut-tree, I pass it by with a shy sidelong glance, for I am loath to dispel the memory of the miracle hovering there round the trunk, loath to scare away the celestial shudders that still linger about the shrubbery in this neighbourhood! In these moments an insignificant creature— a dog, a rat, a beetle, a crippled appletree, a lane winding over the hill, a moss-covered stone, mean more to me than the most beautiful, abandoned mistress of the happiest night. These mute and, on occasion, inanimate creatures rise toward me with such an abundance, such a presence of love, that my enchanted eye can find nothing in sight void of life. Everything that exists, everything I can remember, everything touched upon by my confused thoughts, has a meaning. Even my own heaviness, the general torpor of my brain, seems to acquire a meaning; I experience in and around me a blissful, never-ending interplay, and among the objects playing against one another there is not one into which I cannot flow. To me, then, it is as though my body consists of nought but ciphers which give me the key to everything; or as if we could enter into a new and hopeful relationship with the whole of existence if only we begin to think with the heart. As soon, however, as this strange enchantment falls from me, I find myself confused; wherein this harmony transcending me and the entire world consisted, and how it made itself known to me, I could present in sensible words as little as I could say anything precise about the inner movements of my intestines or a congestion of my blood.

Apart from these strange occurrences, which, incidentally, I hardly know whether to ascribe to the mind or the body, I live a life of barely believable vacuity, and have difficulties in concealing from my wife this inner stagnation, and from my servants the indifference wherewith I contemplate the affairs of my estates. The good and strict education which I owe to my late father and the early habit of leaving no hour of the day unused are the only things, it seems to me, which help me maintain towards the outer world the stability and the dignified appearance appropriate to my class and my person.

I am rebuilding a wing of my house and am capable of conversing occasionally with the architect concerning the progress of his work; I administer my estates, and my tenants and employees may find me, perhaps, somewhat more taciturn but no less benevolent than of yore. None of them, standing with doffed cap before the door of his house while I ride by of an evening, will have any idea that my glance, which he is wont respectfully to catch, glides with longing over the rickety boards under which he searches for earthworms for fishing-bait; that it plunges through the latticed window into the stuffy chamber where, in a corner, the low bed with its chequered linen seems forever to be waiting for someone to die or another to be born; that my eye lingers long upon the ugly puppies or upon a cat stealing stealthily among the flower-pots; and that it seeks among all the poor and clumsy objects of a peasant's life for the one whose insignificant form, whose unnoticed being, whose mute existence, can become the source of that mysterious, wordless, and boundless ecstasy. For my unnamed blissful feeling is sooner brought about by a distant lonely shepherd's fire than by the vision of a starry sky, sooner by the chirping of the last dying cricket when the autumn wind chases wintry clouds across the deserted fields than by the majestic booming of an organ. And in my mind I compare myself from time to time with the orator Crassus, of whom it is reported that he grew so excessively enamoured of a tame lamprey—a dumb, apathetic, red-eyed fish in his ornamental pond—that it became the talk of the town; and when one day in the Senate Domitius reproached him for having shed tears over the death of this fish, attempting thereby to make him appear a fool, Crassus answered, "Thus have I done over the death of my fish as you have over the death of neither your first nor your second wife."

I know not how oft this Crassus with his lamprey enters my mind as a mirrored image of my Self, reflected across the abyss of centuries. But not on account of the answer he gave Domitius. The answer brought the laughs on his side, and the whole affair turned into a jest. I, however, am deeply affected by the affair, which would have remained the same even had Domitius shed bitter tears of sorrow over his wives. For there would still have been Crassus, shedding tears over his lamprey. And about this figure, utterly ridiculous and contemptible in the midst of a world-governing senate discussing the most serious subjects, I feel compelled by a mysterious power to reflect in a manner which, the moment I attempt to express it in words, strikes me as supremely foolish.

Now and then at night the image of this Crassus is in my brain, like a splinter round which everything festers, throbs, and boils. It is then that I feel as though I myself were about to ferment, to effervesce, to foam and to sparkle. And the whole thing is a kind of feverish thinking, but thinking in a medium more immediate, more liquid, more glowing than words. It, too, forms whirlpools, but of a sort that do not seem to lead, as the whirlpools of language, into the abyss, but into myself and into the deepest womb of peace.

I have troubled you excessively, my dear friend, with this extended description of an inexplicable condition which is wont, as a rule, to remain locked up in me.

You were kind enough to express your dissatisfaction that no book written by me reaches you any more, "to compensate for the loss of our relationship." Reading that, I felt, with a certainty not entirely bereft of a feeling of sorrow, that neither in the coming year nor in the following nor in all the years of this my life shall I write a book, whether in English or in Latin: and this for an odd and embarrassing reason which I must leave to the boundless superiority of your mind to place in the realm of physical and spiritual values spread out harmoniously before your unprejudiced eye: to wit, because the language in which I might be able not only to write but to think is neither Latin nor English, neither Italian nor Spanish, but a language none of whose words is known to me, a language in which inanimate things speak to me and wherein I may one day have to justify myself before an unknown judge.

Fain had I the power to compress in this, presumably my last, letter to Francis Bacon all the love and gratitude, all the unmeasured admiration, which I harbour in my heart for the greatest benefactor of my mind, for the foremost Englishman of my day, and which I shall harbour therein until death break it asunder.

This 22 August, A.D. *1603*

PHI. CHANDOS

Colours

From the Letters of a Man Who Returned

I HAVE not been feeling in particularly good form of late and know it, perhaps, only since a certain little experience which befell me three days ago—but I will try to describe it chronologically, although you may not be able to make much of the story. Briefly, I had to go to a conference, the final, decisive one in a series of negotiations which aimed at the merging of the Dutch company for which I have been working for four years with an Anglo-German firm; and I knew that the day was decisive—to some extent also for my future life—and—I didn't have myself in hand! Oh, how little did I have myself in hand! I felt myself growing ill from within, but it wasn't my body; I know my body too well. It was the crisis of an inner indisposition; earlier attacks of it could hardly have been more insignificant; that they had amounted to anything at all, that they were connected with this present whirl, I now understood in a flash, as in such crises one understands more than in the normal moments of life. These earlier attacks had been quite trivial, absurd stirrings of displeasure, quite unimportant, almost ephemeral perversions and uncertainties of thinking or feeling, yet undoubtedly something quite new to me; but I do believe, fleeting as these things are, that I have never felt anything similar until a few months ago when I stepped once more upon European soil. But how enumerate these occasional attacks of a Next-to-Nothing? Nevertheless, I must— or tear up this letter and leave the rest forever unsaid. Now and again in the mornings it happened, in these German hotel rooms, that the jug and wash-basin—or a corner of the room with the table and clothes-rack—appeared to me so non-real, despite their indescribable banality so utterly not real, ghostly as it were, and at the same time ephemeral, waiting, so to speak temporarily, to take the place of the real jug, the real wash-basin filled with water. Did I not know you to be a person to whom nothing actually seems big, nothing small, above all nothing absolutely absurd, I could not continue. I can, after all, leave this letter unsent. But it was so. In the other countries abroad, even during my most miserable times, the morning jug or pail with the more or less fresh water was something self-understood and at the same time living: a friend. Here it was, one might say: a ghost. From it there emanated a slight unpleasant vertigo, but not a physical one. I could then step to the window and experience precisely the same with three or four cabs which stood waiting on the other side of the street. They were ghosts of cabs. To look at them caused me an almost imperceptible nausea: it was like a momentary floating above the abyss, the eternal void. Something similar (you can imagine that I didn't pay much attention to these sensations rippling through me) could be brought about by the sight of a house or a whole street: but you must not perchance think of sad, tumbledown houses, rather of the most commonplace of today's or yesterday's façades. Or even a few trees, these few meagre but carefully tended trees which they grow here on their squares, out of the asphalt, enclosed by railings. I could gaze at them and know that they reminded me of trees—were not trees—and at the same time something quivered through me, something that divided my breast like a breeze, such an indescribable wafting of the eternal Nothing, the eternal Nowhere, a breath not of death but of Not-Life, indescribable. Then it happened on the train, more and more frequently. During these four months I travelled a great deal by train, from Berlin to the Rhine, from Bremen to Silesia, in all directions. There it could happen, in the most banal light, at three o'clock in the afternoon, at any time: a small town to the right or left of the line, a village or factory, or the whole landscape, hills, fields, appletrees, scattered houses, all in all; they took on an aspect, a peculiar ambiguous air so filled with inner uncertainty, malicious unreality: so transitory it lay there—with such ghostlike transitoriness— My dear friend, I have spent three and a half months of my life in a cage, whose only view was over an empty pen filled with a store of half-dried buffalo dung, high as a man, through which an ailing buffalo cow dragged itself about until finally it could move no further and lay there between life and dying: but yet, in the pen, in the yellow-grey heap of dung and the yellow-grey dying beast there still dwelt some life; when I looked out at them and when I think back to them—there still dwelt some life there, the same as that which dwells also in my breast,— and in the world, into which I can glance for a moment from my train window, there dwells Something—I have never shuddered at death, but at that, which dwells there, at such Non-Living I shudder. Yet it is probably nothing more than that I sometimes have something of the evil eye, a kind of slight poisoning, a hidden and creeping infection which seems to be lying ready in the European air for him returning from far away after he has been long, perhaps too long, absent. That my ill was of a European nature, of this I became aware (in

these things everything is sudden, most inexplicable intuition) at the same moment as I realized that it had now reached
my inner self, that now I, I myself, my inner life, lay under
this evil eye as had, during former attacks, those outer things.
Through a thousand simultaneous feelings and half-feelings
my consciousness dragged itself along, dizzy and disgusted: I
believe that in these moments I had once more to think everything that I had thought since I first set foot in Europe, and
in addition everything that I had suppressed.

Today I cannot put into clear words what passed turbu-
lently through my whole self; but that my business and my
self-earned money had come to disgust me—this realization
came dancing along at that time on the immense and yet
soundless agitation of my uprooted soul, like driftwood on
the back of a South Sea wave as high as a house. I had swallowed into myself twenty thousand examples—how they forget life itself in favor of that which should be nothing but a
means toward life and should be considered nothing but a
tool. For months I have been surrounded by a deluge of faces
ravaged by money which they owned or by money which
others owned. Their houses, their monuments, their streets,
they were for me in this somewhat visionary moment nought
but the thousandfold mirrored grimace of their spookish Non-
Existence; and suddenly, as is my nature, I reacted with a wild
disgust against my own little bit of money and everything
connected with it. I longed, like the seasick for *terra firma*,
to leave Europe and return to the good faraway lands that
I had left. As you can imagine, this was not a good condition
in which to represent interests at a conference table. I know
not what I wouldn't have given to cancel that meeting. But
this was unthinkable, and I just had to go there and make the
best of it. I still had almost an hour. To walk around in the
busy streets was impossible; to drop in somewhere and read

the newspapers was equally impossible, for they talked only too much the same language as the faces and the houses. I turned into a silent sidestreet. There in one house I see a very decent-looking shop, without a show-window, and near the entrance a sign: "Comprehensive Exhibition, Paintings and Drawings." I read the name, but lose it promptly from my memory. Although it's twenty years since I entered a museum or art exhibition, I think it may distract me from my ridiculous mood, which at the moment matters most, and I walk in.

My dear friend, there's no such thing as chance; I was meant to see these pictures, was meant to see them at this hour, in this agitated condition, in this sequence. There were in all about sixty paintings, middle-sized and small, a few portraits, otherwise mostly landscapes; in only very few was the human figure important; on most of them it was the trees, meadows, ravines, rocks, ploughed fields, roofs, garden plots. As to how they were painted I cannot offer any information; you probably know almost everything that's done in this line, while I, as I've said, haven't seen a painting for twenty years. Nevertheless, I remember very well, during the last period of my relationship with W., when we lived in Paris (she had great understanding for pictures), frequently having seen in studios and exhibitions things which bore a certain resemblance to these—very bright, almost like posters, in any case quite different from paintings in the galleries. At first sight these here seemed to me loud and restless, quite crude, quite strange; in order to see the first of them as pictures at all, as a unity, I had to prepare myself—but then, then I saw, then I saw them all thus, each single one, and all together, and Nature in them, and the strength of the human soul which here had transformed Nature, and tree and bush and field and slope which were painted here, and also that other strength, that which was behind the paint, that essence, that indescribable sense of fate—all this I saw, so that I lost the sensation of myself to these pictures, and got it back powerfully, and lost it again! My dear friend, on account of this, what I'm trying to say and never will be able to say, I have written you this whole letter! But how could I put into words something so incomprehensible, something so sudden, so powerful, so indivisible! I could obtain photographs of the pictures and send them to you, but what could they give you —what could the pictures themselves give you of the impression they made upon me, which is probably something completely personal, a secret between my destiny, the paintings, and me. A freshly ploughed field, a great avenue against the evening sky, a gorge with crooked fir-trees, a garden plot with the rear wall of a house, a farm cart with scraggy horses on a pasture, a copper bowl and an earthenware jug, a few peasants round a table eating potatoes—but what good can this do you? Shall I tell you about the colours? There is an incredible blue, most powerful of blues, which constantly reappears, a green like that of molten emeralds, a yellow that deepens into orange. But what are colours if the innermost life of objects doesn't break through them! And this innermost life was there, tree and stone and wall and gorge gave of themselves their innermost, almost casting it at me—not, however, the voluptuousness and harmony of their lovely inanimate lives, as sometimes, in days gone by, like a magic atmosphere it had flowed towards me from old paintings: no, only the impact of its existence, the ferocious wonder of its existence surrounded by incredibility, made a dead set at my soul. How can I make it clear to you that here each Being— the Being of each tree, each strip of yellow or greenish field, each fence, each gorge cut into the stony hill, the Being of the pewter jug, the earthenware bowl, the table, the clumsy armchair—lifted itself toward me as though newly born from the frightful chaos of Non-Living, from the abyss of Non-Being, so that I felt—nay, so that I knew—how each of these objects, these creatures, was born from a terrible doubting of the world and how with its existence it now covered over forever the dreadful chasm of yawning nothingness! How can I make it even half clear to you the way this language talked into my soul, the way it threw toward me the gigantic justification of the strangest indissoluble condition of my inner self, the way it made me understand at once what, in my intolerable stupor, I could hardly bear to feel, and which nevertheless (so much did I feel it!) I could no longer tear out of myself! And here an unknown soul of incomprehensible power was giving me the answer, by revealing to me a whole world! I felt like one who, after endless stumbling, finds safe ground under his feet, like one round whom a storm rages, into whose raging he longs exultantly to shout. It was in a storm that these trees were born under my eyes, were born for my sake, their roots stretching into the earth, their branches stretching against the clouds; in a storm these earth rifts, these valleys between hills surrendered themselves; even in the bulk of the rock blocks was frozen storm. And now I could, from picture to picture, feel a Something, could feel the mingling, the merging of formation, how the innermost life broke forth into colour and how the colours lived one for the sake of the others, and how one, mysteriously powerful, carried all the others; and in all this could sense a heart, the soul of the man who had created it, who with this vision did himself answer the spasms of his own most dreadful doubt. I could feel, could know, could fathom, could enjoy abyss and summit, without and within, one and all in a ten-thousandth part of the time I take to write these words—and was as though two men, was master over my life, master over my strength, my intellect, felt the time pass, knew there were now only twenty minutes left, now ten, now five, and stood outside, hailed a carriage, and drove away.

Conferences of the kind in which the magnitude of figures appeals to the imagination and in which the variety, the dispersal of energies involved require a gift of comprehensive vision, are determined not by intelligence but by a mysterious power for which I know no name. It is sometimes—not always —found among the more intelligent. During this hour it was with me as never before and possibly as never again. I succeeded in procuring for my Company more than the board of directors, in their most optimistic hopes, had expected from me, and I procured it as in a dream one picks flowers from a bare wall. The faces of those gentlemen with whom I was dealing approached me astonishingly close. I could tell you a few things about them which haven't the remotest connection with the subject of our business. I realize now that a great burden has been lifted from me.

P.S. The man is called Vincent van Gogh. According to the dates in the catalogue, he should be alive. Something in me compels me to believe that he is of my generation, little older than myself. I know not whether I shall step a second time in front of these pictures, but I shall very likely buy one of them; I shall not, however, take it with me, rather hand it over to the art dealer for safe keeping.

End of May, 1901

WHAT I have written to you, you will hardly be able to understand, least of all how these paintings could move me so. It will appear to you as a whim, like something isolated, an eccentricity, and yet—if *only* one could put it down, if *only*

one could tear it out of oneself and bring it into the light!
There is something of this in me: the colours of things, at
strange hours, have a power over me. But what actually is
colour? Could I not equally well have said: the shape of
things, or the language of light and darkness, or I know not
what unnamed thing? As for hours, which are these hours?
Years pass, and they do not occur.—And is it not childish to
tell you that something mighty, which I do not know, has at
times mastery over me? If I could seize it, not seize—since it
seizes me—but hold it, before it vanishes again. But does it
vanish? Has it not a mysteriously forming power in me, somewhere, whither an inner constant sleep bars my way? And
now that I have once spoken, I am driven to speak even more
of it. There floats around these things something inexplicable
to myself, something like love—can there be love toward the
amorphous, toward the insubstantial? But still, and yes, and
still: so that you should not have a poor opinion of what I
have written, I will continue to write, because I am trying to
understand what is driving me, and because I would like to
prevent your thinking with contempt about something—
which I hold dear.

Have you ever heard the name Ramakrishna? It doesn't
matter. He was a brahmin, a penitent, one of the great Indian
saints, one of the last, for he died only in the eighties, and
when I arrived in Asia his name was everywhere still alive. I
know a certain amount about his life, but nothing which
moves me more than the short account of how his illumination, or his awakening, came about; in short, that experience
which singled him out among men and made him into a saint.
It was no more than this: a boy of sixteen, he was making his
way across country, between fields, and he raised his eyes
skywards and saw a flock of wild heron fly across the sky at a
great height; and nothing but this, nothing but the whiteness

of the live beating of wings under the blue sky, nothing but these two colours against one another, this everlasting Inexpressible, penetrated at that moment into his soul and loosened what was united, and united what was loose, so that he collapsed as one dead, and on rising to his feet again he was no longer the same person who had fallen down. It was an English clergyman of the average type who told me about it. "A violent optical impression void of all higher meaning," he told me. "It's a case, you see, of an anomalous nervous system." Void of all higher meaning! Would that I were one of your educated people, would that your sciences (which cannot be anything but wonderful, all-revealing languages) were not a closed world to me, that I were not an intellectual cripple, that I possessed a language into which the inner wordless certainties could flow! But alas!

I will try, however, to tell you of an occasion when it happened, not for the first time, but possibly with greater force than before or since. A Vision it is, nothing else; and now for the first time it strikes me how equivocally we use that word: that it has to designate to me something so commonplace as breathing and at the same time . . . That's what happens to me with language: I cannot chain myself to any of its waves, so as to let it carry me; it flows by beneath me and leaves me on the same spot.

Did I not say that the colours of things, at strange hours, have power over me? But is it not rather I who gain power over them—the whole, full power to snatch from them for whatever span of time their wordless, abysmal secret? Is not the strength in me, do I not feel it, like a swelling in my breast, an abundance, a strange, exalted, enchanting presence, with me, in me, in the place where the blood comes and goes? Thus it was in the early morning on that grey, stormy, rainy day, in the harbour of Buenos Aires—so it was then and ever since. But if everything were in me, why could I not close my eyes and dumbly, blindly, enjoy an inexpressible feeling of my Self? Why did I have to stay on deck and gaze, gaze before me? And why did the colour of the foaming waves, this abyss which opened and closed again; why did this thing which approached in heavy rain, spattered by froth; why did this small discoloured ship (the customs tender it was) working its way towards us, this ship and the cave of water, the heaving wave rolling along with it—why did the colour of these things seem to me (seem! seem! I knew very well that it was so!) to contain not only the whole world, but my whole life as well? This colour, which was a grey and a livid brown and a darkness and a foam, which held an abyss and a plunge, a death and a life, a dread and a lust—why here, before my gazing eye, my enchanted breast, was my whole life, past, future, rolling towards me, foaming up in inexhaustible presence? And why was this immense moment, this sacred enjoying of the Self and at the same time of the world, which widened out towards me as though its breast had opened, why was this twofoldness, this interwoven, this outer and inner, this intermingling You bound up with my gazing? Why—unless colour is a language in which the wordless, the everlasting, the immense, abandon themselves, a language more exalted than sounds because, like a flame of eternity, it flares up from mute existence and renews our soul? Alongside this, music is for me as the feeble life of the moon is alongside the appalling life of the sun.

Be that as it may. Perhaps I am half-way, between the obtuse, crude person who senses nothing of all this and the one with an educated soul who deciphers and reads here where I merely gaze at the signs. It has remained with me from my youth that someone called the firmament an unrevealed thought. This may apply here. The southern sky, it is true, with its glowing fires, had sometimes on rare nights, when my whole being rose toward it like an unruffled mirror of water, appeared to me like a gigantic promise under which death shuddered away like an organ sound. But perhaps all this which appeared to me like a promise was but the crude foreboding of a very great thought, which my soul could not master.

Colour. Colour. To me now that sounds a wretched word. I fear I have not explained myself to you as I would like. And I do not want to strengthen anything in myself which would isolate me from mankind. But truly in no moment am I more a human being than when I feel myself living with hundred-fold strength, and this happens to me when that which has always lain mute and closed before me and is nothing but massiveness and strangeness, when this opens and, as in a wave of love, entwines me with itself. And am I not then at the inner core of things as much a human being, as much myself, as ever I could be—nameless, alone; not, however, petrified in aloneness, but as if there flowed from me in waves the strength that makes me the chosen mate of those strong, silent powers which sit around me mutely as on thrones? And is not this the spot you always reach on dark paths, when you live active and suffering among the living? Is not this the mysterious heart-kernel of personal experience, of dark deeds, dark sorrows, when you have done what you should not and yet had to do, when you had experienced what you had always divined but never believed, when everything had collapsed around you and the Frightful could nowhere be undone? Did not the embracing wave then wind itself out of the innermost centre of experience and draw you into itself, till you found yourself alone, never again to be lost to yourself, great, and as though relaxed in all your senses, nameless, and smilingly happy? Why should not silently wooing Nature, who is nothing but life lived and life that wants to be lived again, impatient of the cold glance with which you greet her, draw you into herself at rare hours and show you that she, in her depths, also has secret grottoes wherein you can be one with yourself, you who were estranged from yourself in the outer world?

And why should not colours be the brothers of sorrows, if the former, as the latter, draw us into eternity?

As long as no loftier ideas (and they would have to grip me with equal strength) make such suppositions contemptible to me, I shall hold on to these.

Fear

A Dialogue

The Dancing Girls: Laidion, the taller; Hymnis, the smaller.
The second mate from a merchant ship.

HYMNIS: May I come in?

LAIDION: Yes, do.

HYMNIS: Is it Pamphilos who is with you?

LAIDION: Yes, but come in all the same.

HYMNIS *entering:* But that's not Pamphilos.

LAIDION: Never mind. He's a sailor. Go on telling about the people on the island.

THE MAN: Well, what am I to tell?
He gets up.

LAIDION: About the king, how they carry him and how everyone dances round him and touches him.

THE MAN: Why do you want me to tell about such things? I must go now.

LAIDION: You must tell. I want you to stay and tell.

THE MAN: What shall I tell in front of that girl there? I don't know anything.

LAIDION: What you told me about the island and the people on the island, more of it.

THE MAN: You know that by now. I'm off. Your sister will stay with you.

[155]

LAIDION: That's not my sister.

THE MAN: I'll leave you with your friend. I must get back
to my ship.

LAIDION: Stay here and tell me more. Then I'll send for
something to eat, then you sleep and rest and spend the
night with me and tomorrow morning you go to your ship.

THE MAN: No, I must get back to my ship now.

LAIDION: I thank you for your courtesy. Does everyone on
your ship have such good manners?

THE MAN: Goodbye.

LAIDION: Go wherever you like.

He goes off.

HYMNIS: What did he give you?

LAIDION: . . . .

HYMNIS: That belt hanging there, is that from him?

LAIDION: . . . .

HYMNIS: Is this string of dark green stones from him, too?
But they are not real.

LAIDION: Of course they're real. Why shouldn't they be
real?

HYMNIS: Real ones have to be transparent.

LAIDION: Those there have little veins of gold.

HYMNIS: Who knows if it's real gold?

LAIDION: . . . .

HYMNIS: Are you asleep? If you want to sleep, I'll leave
again. Do you know what he put there? Four drachma.
For a sailor that isn't bad, what with the presents as well.
I always like men off ships much better than soldiers.
Now I see you want to sleep. So I'm off. . . . Well, I'd
like you to know, this evening I saw Demonassa dance, together with her sister, Bacchis. They're supposed not to be
sisters at all, by the way. Ha! There's nothing so unheard
of about their dancing. But what a fuss the men make over

them! Demonassa has pretty shoulders and a good back and moves well from the hips, that's all. And Bacchis, she has nicely jointed arms and legs, and pointed fingers. Hussies both of them, but the one shows it and the other hides it: that's what puts them over. We two could do everything they do, if you only wanted to. There's not a thing about it which hasn't been seen before. But all their pantomimes are invented by poets, each by a different one, and they have verses recited at the same time, and in this way they throw dust in the peoples' eyes, as if one hadn't seen all that before and done it oneself. Bacchis is best when she has a lot to do with her hands: when a nymph is transformed into a young tree, or Ampelis into a vine: that's what she's really good at. I wouldn't mind having her wrists. And animals she's good at, too: the young deer which fears the wind and plays with the wind, or the bird in the net. Demonassa is good when she can do a lot with her head and neck: she dances something while Bacchis stands stiff and rigid in the middle, holding the Medusa mask in front of her face, and Demonassa comes dancing along, unsuspecting, and suddenly she has to turn into stone; then she makes a movement of throwing back her head, and a convulsive stiffening, first of all down to her hips, then down to her feet, till you feel the ice-cold shiver run down your back.

LAIDION: My God, how flat and futile all that is! There we dance for twelve or twenty men, among them a few rich old dodderers and the rest parasites. We dance and then we are tired and then everything turns ugly: everything crowds in on me, the faces of the men, the lights, the noise, like the beaks of greedy birds everything pecks me in the face. I would rather die than lie with them and drink and listen to their shouting. Then I wish myself as

far away as a bird can fly. I have always known that somewhere there is an island like the one he told me about.

HYMNIS: What kind of island is that?

LAIDION: Oh, I don't know. Leave me alone.

HYMNIS: Sailors are great liars, you know.

LAIDION: I know perfectly well those were no lies he told
me. I would like to keep him here twenty nights, and I
wouldn't allow him to stop telling me.

HYMNIS: What do you care about these strange places?
Surely you wouldn't like to be there! What would you do
among those coloured barbarians?

LAIDION: Fool! What do you get out of dancing? Are you
ever happy for one moment?

HYMNIS: Oh, shut up! You've got your melancholia again!
I have fun when I dance, when they tear their wreaths
from their heads and throw them to me. Then I hold
them, then I am really myself.

LAIDION: But inside yourself? Are you happy inside? Can
you forget yourself, can you get rid of all fear, get rid of
the shadow that darkens the blood in your veins?

HYMNIS: What fear? I have no fear when I dance.

LAIDION: But you have wishes, and wishes are fear. All your
dancing is nothing but wishing and striving. You spring to
and fro: are you fleeing from yourself? When you are
hiding, are you hiding from the eternal restless yearning
within you? You are aping the gestures of animals and
trees: do you ever become one with them? You step out of
your garment: do you step out of your fear? Can you ever,
even for two hours, lose all fear? They can. They have no
fear of dancing like that in the open under the sacred trees.

HYMNIS: Who on earth are these people you're talking
about? Do they skip on one foot and cover themselves with

the lobes of their ears? Are they spotted like leopards or
striped like the animal called zebra?

LAIDION: They are of a golden colour, and their mouths
are strong like the mouths of wild animals. Their hips are
strong and slender.

HYMNIS: Would you like to be like that? Pah! I'm sure their
skin stinks enough to make one sick.

LAIDION: The trees there are much bigger than our trees;
their blue-black shadow is like something alive; you can
touch it like the body of a fruit. Their gods are in the trees
and between the trees, he says, and even so they are not
ashamed to do it.

HYMNIS: They dance?

LAIDION: Once they dance like this, once a year. The young
men crouch on the ground, the girls of the island stand in
front of them all together, so motionless that their bodies
are like one body. Then they dance and in the end they
give themselves to the youths, without choosing—whoever
seizes one, his she is. For the sake of the gods they do it
and the gods bless it.

HYMNIS: Such shamelessness!

LAIDION: The happy ones! They are without fear.

HYMNIS: What do you mean by that, Laidion?

LAIDION: Oh, can't you understand me? You see, I grew up
in the house of my mother, and was a naughty child, and
always wanted something and didn't have it. So it went on
from morning to night. Then I turned fourteen and began
to yearn—and then they brought me to the rich Kallias;
there I lay and walked around and stared in amazement
and shuddered and bit myself in the wrists with impatience, and then I gave myself to the one I was in love
with and he was filled with hatred and bitterness because

I had first been the other one's, and so that passed, and then came another one and still another . . . I believe there wasn't a moment when I didn't long to get away from myself.

HYMNIS: You always had it too easy. Have you ever been beaten? Have you in your whole life, I wonder, known real hunger?

LAIDION: I can imagine a girl who is beaten and is blissfully happy. And you can lie in darkness and be hungry and feel happier than an Indian prince. But to lie there in the world like Argus and be covered with eyes, one eye always open: to be in the arms of a man who loves you, whom you think you love, and at the same time with your whole soul to listen for the indifferent murmuring of water nearby, to have to listen because something forces you, something holds you like a vise, is it yearning, is it fear . . . as if with this murmuring your whole life were running out of your veins. Or they have invited you to a country house, and you are riding along on a mule and should be gay and not think of anything but that you are young and that more than one would be glad to stand all night long by your door, but there, all of a sudden, under your eyes, stand the trees on the highway like menacing messengers, the mountain in the distance like a judge, as if your lost life were at stake and you sit in guilt and pain tied down to the animal, like one led to a place of execution, and your hundred eyes miss nothing, neither the beetle which crawls past in the dust, leaving you to your fate, nor the bird in the air, singing high above you, leaving you to your fate.

HYMNIS: What are you talking about, Laidion? You have never been dragged on a mule to a place of execution.

LAIDION: It doesn't need a mule, nor a tribunal. My foot

touches a dry branch, Hymnis, and its miserable existence enters into me, like the beauty of violets and roses it enters into me through the eyes and makes me its slave, and at night I must lie with open eyes and think of this accursed piece of wood and be at its mercy and have to imitate its twisted body with crooked rigid limbs, so that a night-bird watching me would take me for a Thessalian witch or one possessed—does one not then have cause for fear? Has one not cause for fear when in the morning the sun is so small, when sometimes in the morning it hangs like something childish strung up by children in the branches of the figtree, and then climbs up? But what, after all, is not fearful? And what could it be that makes us dance if not fear? It holds the strings up there, fastened to the centres of our bodies, and pulls us to and fro and makes our limbs fly. And when I, as Bacchante, fling my feet, and my arms and hair fly towards the stars, do you think it is pleasure? Don't you see that it is fear that makes me leap?

HYMNIS: Are you so much shaken by fear?

LAIDION: It does not always show its skinny leopard's arms. Sometimes it holds a mask before its face and disguises its voice: then it is called Hope. Sometimes I believe that to hope is more dreadful than to fear. Utterly emptied out you lie there after a night of hope. There's nothing like it to suck the soul out of your body. A happy man knows no hope. They are unspeakably happy when they dance before their men and before their gods, and know nothing more about one another and all are together and each one alone.

HYMNIS: Are you talking about the barbarian women on the island again?

LAIDION: Yes, I'm talking of those on the island. They are

unspeakably happy during this hour, more than all their life long. Before that, they sat on clean mats for seven days and seven nights filled with fear and anguish. Can you imagine how one sits on a clean mat?

HYMNIS: It doesn't take much to imagine that! Do you think I don't know how to keep myself clean?

LAIDION: I tell you, if I would pour all the water from my well, all the water of the world, over this mat here, and if I would rinse the floor around it, that would still not make it clean. Is the air, by any chance, clean? Does clean air blow anywhere beneath the stars? Isn't there every-where yearning and fear, desire and depravity? Doesn't everything, everything, lie between a death and a lust, troubled and soiled? I tell you, if something really clean, really pure, would come along, the sea would foam up and form a lane and our hearts would leap out of us and roll along and come to rest for ever on this purity. Just to think of a clean mat makes me tremble. Perhaps they are really lying on clean mats. Then they would be animals or gods or both at once, and we ought to worship them. I don't believe I have ever seen anything pure. I have never seen anything on which I would like to lay my heart.

HYMNIS: So you have never been in love, Laidion?

LAIDION: If I were drunk and made my bed in the gutter, I wouldn't want to have it talked about afterwards when I've sobered up.

They are silent.

LAIDION: I can feel how they feel when I close my eyes in such a way that the upper lid just trembles over the lower.

Like you there the men sit, very small, very far away. And in the trees hang the gods, fearful, with wide-open eyes, but into those who have risen from the clean mats nothing can instil fear. They are charmed. Everything—fear, desire, all choice, all unquenchable restlessness—everything has been transformed at the limits of their bodies. They are virgins and have forgotten it, they are to become women and mothers and have forgotten it: to them everything is ineffable. And then they dance.

She begins to sway from the hips. Somehow one feels that she is not alone, that many of her kind are around her and that all are dancing at once under the eyes of their gods. They dance and circle as dusk falls: shadows loosen themselves from the trees and sink down into the crowd of dancers, and out of the tree-tops rise great birds housing the departed spirits, and join the circle, and beneath them all the island vibrates like a boat filled with drunken people. And nothing on the island defies the power of the dancers; at this moment they are as strong as the gods; the arms and hips and shoulders of the gods are intermingled with their movement; from nowhere can the blue net of death or the coral-red sword of the gods fall upon them. They are givers of birth and the newly born of the island, they are the bearers of death and life.

At this moment Laidion hardly resembles herself any longer. Under her tense features appears something terrifying, threatening, eternal: the face of a barbarian deity. Her arms rise up and down in a frightening rhythm, death-threatening, like clubs. And her eyes seem filled with a hardly bearable tension of bliss. And there she lies already on the bed, breathing hard and short, surrounded by the small empty room, reality, and Hymnis, who covers her with a small red rug. She opens her eyes after a while, and sits up. She is very pale.

LAIDION: Hymnis! Hymnis! Here I lie and know it—*and I have none of it!* I want to scream and bite into my pillows, bite into my arm, and see my blood flow—that such a thing exists in the world and I have none of it! Like a glowing coal it will burn in me, that that man had to come and tell me that somewhere there is such an island where they dance and are happy without the thorn of hope! For that's it, Hymnis, that's everything, Hymnis, to be happy without hope.

Moments in Greece

THE MONASTERY OF ST. LUKE

W E HAD BEEN riding that day from nine to ten hours. As the sun stood high overhead, we had lain down to rest in front of a small rest-place near a well of pure water and a huge, beautiful plane tree. Later, lying prone on the ground, we had again quenched our thirst, with the mules, from a thread of running water. At first our road was cut into a slope of Parnassus, then into a primeval petrified river-bed, then into a depression between two cone-shaped mountains; finally it passed through the green corn-fields of a fertile plateau. Some stretches were silent with the silence of millenniums—nothing but a lizard rustling across the road and a sparrow-hawk circling high in the air; others were alive with the life of flocks of sheep. Then came the barking of the wolflike dogs, which bared their teeth so near to the mules that we had to drive them off with stones. Sheep, heavy with wool, stood massed together in the shadow of a rock, trembling from their heated breathing. Two black rams butted one another with their horns. A handsome young shepherd carried a small lamb over his shoulders. On a flat stony landscape rested the motionless shadow of a cloud. In a strangely formed hollow, wherein lay thousands of single great boulders among which grew thousands of small, pungently aromatic shrubs, a large tortoise dragged itself across the road. Then, towards evening, a village showed itself in the distance, but we passed it by. At the side of our road was a cistern, the spring caught in its depths. Near the fountain stood two cypresses. Women hauled up the clear water and brought it to our animals to drink. Across the evening sky sailed tiny clouds, in twos and threes. Sheep-bells sounded from near and far. The mules moved on faster, drawing in the air drifting towards us from the valley. A perfume of acacias, of strawberries and thyme, was wafted over the road. We felt that the bluish mountains were closing in on us and that this valley was the end of the road. We rode on be-tween two hedges of wild roses. A small bird, no larger than the little patch of shade beneath one of the roses, flew ahead of us; the hedge on the left, on the valley side, ended, and we looked down and across, as though from a balcony. Down to the bottom of the small, bow-shaped valley and on the opposite slope, half-way up the mountain, stood groups of fruit-trees among dark cypresses. Between the trees grew flowering hedges. Sheep moved in and out of them, and birds sang in the branches. Beneath our road ran other roads. These, one could see, had been laid out for pleasure, not for wanderers or shepherds. They wound along in gentle curves, always at the same height above the valley. In the centre of the slope stood a single stone-pine, a lone, regal tree—the only really large tree in the whole valley. It could have been as old as the hills, but the grace with which it rose and held its three crowns in delicate curves towards the sky suggested something of eternal youth. Low walls now bordered the road to right and left, with orchards behind them. A black goat stood with its forelegs propped against an ancient olive tree, as though wanting to climb it. An old man, pruning knife in hand, waded up to his waist in blossoming briar-roses. One had the feeling that the monastery was quite near, not more than a hundred yards or even less, and we were surprised not to see it. In the wall on the left was a small open door; in the doorway leaned a monk. The long black gown, the high black headgear, the casual way he stood there, gazing towards us in this paradisial solitude—all this gave him the air of a magician. He was young, with a long, light red beard, its cut reminiscent of Byzantine portraits, an eagle-nose, restless, almost intrusive blue eyes. He greeted us with a bow and a spreading of both arms, in which there was something forced. We dismounted, and he led the way. Crossing a small garden enclosed by walls, we entered a room, where he left us alone. The room had the minimum of furniture. Under a Byzantine image of the Holy Virgin burned a perpetual flame; opposite the entrance an open door led on to a balcony. We stepped out to find that we were in the centre of the monastery, which was built into the mountain. Our room, which, from the garden side, was on the ground floor, lay here two storeys high above the cloisters. The church, with the reflection of the evening sun on its thousand-year-old reddish walls and cupolas, closed off one side; the other three sides were formed by houses similar to that in which we were standing, with the same kind of small wooden balconies as that on which we were leaning. The houses were irregular, of different colours, and the little balconies were light blue, yellowish, or pale green. From the house which formed the corner a loggia, like a drawbridge, led to the church. Parts of the building looked immeasurably ancient, others no older than a generation. Everything breathed peace and a scent-sweetened serenity. From below, a fountain murmured. On a bench sat two older monks with ebony-black beards. Opposite them, on a second-floor balcony, leaned another of uncertain age, his head on his hand. Small clouds sailed across the sky. The two monks rose and went into the church. Two others came down a staircase. They also wore the long black gowns, but the black caps on their heads were not so high, and their faces were beardless. Their gait had the same indefinable rhythm: as far removed from haste as from slowness. They disappeared simultaneously through the church door, not so much like men entering a house as sails vanishing beyond a rock, or as great unobserved animals stalking through the forest and disappearing behind trees. Inside the church faint voices began chanting psalms, following an age-old melody. The voices rose and fell; there was in them something endless, as remote from lamentation as from desire, something solemn which might have been sounding from eternity and continue to sound far into eternity. Above the yard from an open window a voice followed the melody, from cadence to cadence; a woman's voice. This sounded so strange it seemed like an hallucination. But it started again, and a female voice it was. And yet it wasn't. The echo-like quality, the utterly faithful following of this solemn, hardly any longer human sound, this will-less, almost unconscious voice, did not seem to issue from the breast of woman. It sounded as if mystery itself were singing, something insubstantial. Now it was silent. From the church, with the soft, dark, tremulous men's voices, there came forth an aroma of wax, mingled with honey and incense, like the fragrance of the chant itself. Now the feminine voice began again, following the phrases of the singing. But other similar voices from the same open window, not far from my balcony, joined in, *mezza voce* and not seriously, as though in mockery; the beautiful voice broke off; and now I realized that they were the voices of boys. Immediately their heads appeared at the window. There was one among them, gentle and beautiful, like a girl, whose fair hair fell over his shoulders to his waist. Other choir-boys, standing down in the courtyard, called up. "The brother!" they shouted. "His brother! The shepherd! The shepherd!"

Later I happened to be there when the brothers took leave of one another. The young shepherd stood in the light of the sinking sun, dark, slender, and warrior-like, against a background of sheep and dogs. In his strong bronzed hand he held the small hand of the boy with long hair. A monk in black robe, a handsome, beardless, twenty-year-old novice, with a smile which, round his young mouth and smooth cheeks, was thoughtless and vain, but in the neighbourhood of his dark eyes submissive and knowing, stepped into the half-open door. He did not call to the boy, just waved. The gesture of his raised hand was without impatience. Rather than the commander, he was the transmitter of a command, the messenger. On to a small balcony above the doorway stepped an older monk; he placed his elbows on the banister, his head in his hand, and calmly watched how the command was transmitted and carried out. The novice gave him a barely perceptible nod, a smile a trifle more bright and submissive. The beautiful boy let go the brother's hand and ran back to the novice. The shepherd turned and promptly, with long calm strides, walked downhill, into the country. The sheep, as though part of him, were already moving, surging down the road, hemmed in by the dogs. In the church the singing grew louder. During the service at this evening hour everyone was on his knees in the twilit chapel, or lying stretched out on the stone floor, or standing deep in meditation in the high pews, his face on crossed arms over the Holy Book. In the sublime composure of their chanting trembled an ardour subdued by ancient laws. The perpetual lamps swung gently in the incense- and honey-laden air. The ceremony performed here was the same as had been performed for a thousand years, evening after evening in the same spot at the same hour. What torrent of water is so venerable as to roar over the same course for ten times one hundred years? What ancient olive tree has been whispering in the wind with the same crest for ten times one hundred years? There is nothing like it save the eternal sea down in the bays and the everlasting summit of the snow-shimmering Parnassus under the everlasting stars.

The stars were taking fire over the darkening walls of the valley. The evening star was of a rare brilliance; if there were water somewhere—no more than a spring or a pool, perhaps, between two fig-trees—a shaft of its light would perforce lie there as from the moon. Under it now, here and there in the human sphere, on the near, heavy, earthly horizon, more bright stars were blazing: these were the shepherds' fires, high and low on the slopes of the dark mountains which enclosed the bow-shaped valley. Near each fire lay a lonely man with his animals. In a wide circle round the monastery, in which perpetual lamps were burning, the wealth of the monastery was spread out. The dogs began to bark, to be answered by dogs. There were more than thirty fires; the mountain slopes were alive with sleeping men. Here and there a lamb bleated from its interrupted slumber. Owlets called; the chatter of the cicadas grew loud; yet the calm, eternal night prevailed.

There, where the evening star stands, Parnassus radiates invisibly behind dark mountains. There, in the mountain's flank, lies Delphi. Under the Temple of the Gods, where once the holy city lay, there stands today a thousand-year-old olive grove, ruins of columns between the tree-trunks. And these thousand-year-old trees are too young, these Ancients are too young, they do not hark back, never have they seen Delphi and the House of the Gods. You gaze down into their centuries as into a cistern, and down there in dream-depths lies the Unreachable. But here it is near. Under these stars, in this valley, where sheep and shepherds sleep, here it is near, as nowhere else. The same soil, the same breezes, the same life, the same repose. An Unnamable is present, neither denuded nor veiled, neither tangible nor evasive: enough, it is near. Here is Delphi and the Delphic Plain, sanctuary and shepherds; here is the Arcadia of many dreams, yet it is no dream. Slowly our feet carry us back into the monastery. Huge dogs growl quite close to us. On the balcony over the doorway leans a figure. Another, a servant, steps forth sideways from the hedge—there, where the dogs are growling.

"Athanasios!" calls the monk from the balcony. "Athanasios!" He speaks rather than calls the word, calm and gently commanding. "Athanasios, what's going on there?"

"It's the guests, the two strangers, walking around."

"Good. Keep an eye on the dogs."

These words are few. The dialogue between the priest and the serving-man is short. But its tone is from the time of the patriarchs. It is composed of few links. Unchallenged self-confidence of priestly rule, a gentle tone of uncontradicted authority, hospitality practised quietly and as a matter of course, the house, the sanctuary guarded by many dogs. Nevertheless, this insignificant incident, these few words exchanged in the night, have in them a rhythm hailing from eternity. It reaches back whither the age-old olive trees do not reach. Homer is still unborn, and words such as these, spoken in these tones, pass from priest to servant, from lip to lip. Should there fall from a distant star a trivial but living object—the petal of a flower, a chip from the bark of a tree—it would nevertheless be a message that would shudder through us. That was how this dialogue sounded. The hour, the air, and the place are all-important.

II

THE WANDERER

THE SLEEP of monks is short. Soon after midnight they rang the bells, prayed, sang; before sunrise they began again. With hardly two hours of half-slumber behind us, we were all the more awake. We strode very fast along the narrow path in single file, the mules, with the guides in the saddle, in our rear. In the cool of the morning the road led back along the slope above the lovely valley, across the same plain between two barren mountains; then, in the dried-out bed of a mountain torrent, it turned down sideways, split in one direction towards Daulis, in the other toward Chaeronea in Boeotia; to this point the journey was supposed to take seven hours, with a vein of good water half-way which never gave out and which was known to shepherds near and far.

Our conversation continued until our meeting with the lonely wanderer; thus it lasted without interruption from two and a half to three hours, with not the slightest effort or conscious intention of keeping it up, and was one of the strangest and most beautiful conversations that I can remember.

There were two of us, and while talking it seemed as if each were following only his own memories, many of which we shared. Sometimes one of us recalled the figure of a friend whom the other had never seen, but of whom he had heard a great deal. Yet the deep and timeless solitude which enveloped us, the incorporeal sublimity of our surroundings—that we were descending from the foot of Parnassus to Chaeronea, from the Delphic Plain toward Thebes, the road of Oedipus— the radiant clarity of the morning hour after a night without deep heavy sleep, all this so strengthened our imagination that every word pronounced by the one carried away the mind of the other so that he believed himself capable of touching with his hands what hovered in the other's thoughts.

Our friends rose before us and, by bringing themselves, brought with them the purest essence of our existence. Their expressions were serious and of almost frightening clarity. While they were standing before us and looking at us, the smallest circumstances and things, through which our union with them had come to pass, were present. A twitching, a softening glance, a moistening of the inner hand in an agitated hour, a perplexed faltering, a gliding away, an estrangement, again a drawing near—all these very small delicate things were in us, and with the strangest vividness; yet we hardly knew whether what we remembered were the stirrings of our own inner selves or those of the others whose faces were looking at us; only that it was lived life and life that somewhere continued to live on, because everything appeared to be the present, and the mountains in this soundless, bluish life of the air were not more real than the visions that accompanied us.

With a single name carelessly dropped by one of us, we could conjure up new ones. Figure after figure rises up, satisfying us with its appearance, accompanies us, and vanishes again; others, evocative, have already been waiting to occupy the empty place. They illuminate a circle of lived life, then fall behind, as it were, on the road, while we walk on and on—as though it were upon our walking that the continuance of this enchantment depended—and the little group of men and mules remained many hundreds of yards in our rear. Those who are still alive and breathe in this light come to us as well as those who no longer exist. During these minutes our vision is pure; the mysterious power, Life, flares up in us—the revealer of the unrevealable. We see their faces, we believe we hear the sound of their voices uttering seemingly trifling short sentences, yet it is as if they contained the whole individual; and their faces are more than faces: the same quality as from the sound of their broken sentences surges up in them, comes nearer and nearer towards us, seems to be caught and confirmed in their features, in the inexpressible of their expressions, yet not quite at rest. It is a never-ending desire, possibility, readiness, something suffered and still to be suffered. Each of these faces is a destiny, is unique, the most singular that can be, and at the same time infinite, a wandering on to an immeasurably distant destination. It seems to exist only while it is looking at us, as though it were living merely for the sake of our responsive glance. We see the faces, but the faces are not everything; in the faces we see the destinies, but even the destinies are not everything. In each one that greets us is something still more distant, a being beyond both, which touches us. We are like two spirits that fondly remember having taken part in the banquets of mortal men.

Many visions of boys and men had come and gone, when there appeared still another. We saw him, who had suffered so unspeakably, emerge before he vanished from us for good. I say "our friend," though the meetings were few; he crossed our path, once, in a passionate discussion, tearing himself open without restraint, laying bare heaven and hell, a parting like brothers, then again strangeness, icelike strangeness. But his letters—one word cold and majestic, another word as though bleeding—his diary, the few incomparable poems (all from a single year of his life, the nineteenth) which he hates, despises, and tears to pieces wherever he finds them, spitting on them, stamping his feet on the scraps; the story of his last cruel weeks and his dying, noted down by his sister—thus is his picture engraved on our souls. He is poor and suffers, but who could dare to offer him help, this boy lonely beyond words? What man would even dare to approach him who, with superhuman strength, bends himself like a bow, to let off from the string the most merciless arrow, who thrusts from himself every helping hand, hides in the underworld of great cities, answers all advances with sneers, recoils from any mention of his talents, his genius, like the convict from the red-hot iron, turns up unexpectedly, now here, now there, flings a letter to his family from Macedonia, from the Caucasus, from Abyssinia, whose hopes bear the sound of threats, whose dry accounts bristle with boundless revolt and self-inflicted sentence of death; who believes he is struggling for money, money, and more money, but who is really struggling with his own demon for something gigantic, which cannot be named? And now we see him being carried down from the Abyssinian mountains, down a lonely, rocky path, in the silent air: an eternal Present, as here; it's as if they are carrying him towards us. He lies on a litter, his face covered by a black shawl, the diseased knee huge as a pumpkin, rising up under the blanket; the beautiful emaciated hand, the hand loved by his sisters, now and again tears the shawl from his face, to give the dark-coloured people who bear him orders about the road; they had intended to descend diagonally across the slope, while he insists on a steep, fast descent, across country. Indescribable rebellion, defiance of death up to the whites of his eyes, the mouth distorted with suffering, yet refusing to complain.

None of our day-visions had been so powerful as this last. What more could come? We slackened our pace, neither of us speaking. The morning sun shone almost threateningly on this solemn, foreign landscape. Gone was the natural sensation of the Present, wherein men and animals feel at ease. Strange destinies, normally invisible currents, struck some strong chord in us and revealed themselves. We would have been pleased at the sight of a flock of sheep, would have welcomed a bird in the air. Then in the distance a human being came towards us. The man walked fast. He was alone, and in these parts it is rare for someone to walk alone. The shepherd walks with his flock; he who is no shepherd rides; this man walked. He seemed to be bare-headed. In these regions, because of the sun's power, no one goes around without covering his head; so it must be an optical delusion. He came nearer, and was bare-headed. His hair was black, the whole face surrounded by a black, dishevelled beard; he swayed while walking. In his hand he carried a rough stick on which he leaned. The sun sparkled on the rocky boulders and we were under the impression that he had naked feet. This was impossible; the paths uphill and down are stony rubble, sharp as knives; even the poorest beggar here protects his feet at least with wooden shoes. The man came nearer, and he had bare feet. Rags, remnants of the kind of trousers worn by people in towns, hung round his emaciated legs. Here no one, meeting another wanderer in the solitude of the mountains, passes him by without a word. With head turned askew he tried to sidle by us ten steps off our path, without greeting. We called out to him the Greek phrase commonly used for salutation. He answered without stopping and his words were German. At this, my friend barred his way with a brief speech, a question as to whence he had come and whither he was going. Meanwhile I stood three paces away, saw congealed blood on his feet, a deep bloody wound on his strong hand. Broad shoulders, a powerful neck; the face between thirty and forty, nearer forty perhaps, suffering, made even yellower by the blackness of the beard. The eyes unsteady, flickering, savage as the look of a shy, tortured animal. He mentioned his name: Franz Hofer, from Lauffen on the Salzach, bookbinder's apprentice. Age: twenty-one. Desti-

nation: Patras. From here Patras was a five-day journey for a
robust man with a knowledge of the country, mountains between, a deserted plain, a sea-bay. When not leaning on his
stick, his body shook, his lips trembled. He'd had the fever
for three months. This was why he was making for home.
From Alexandria in Egypt as far as the port of Piraeus, a
ship's stoker let him lie in the coal-bunker; but the ship had
moved on to Constantinople, which was why he now had to
go on foot to Trieste. How was he going to find the way?
This he had on him. From under his belt he produced a scrap
of paper on which were written, in pencil by now almost
obliterated, the names of places. He pointed at one: thither
he had to go today. The place lay in the neighbourhood of
Delphi, an eight-hour walk from where we were standing,
provided one knew the way and how to decipher the few
signs on the deserted landscape. Did he know the language of
the country? Not a word: the people didn't understand you
if you spoke German or Italian, damn it! When had he last
eaten? Yesterday noon a piece of bread, and today a drink of
water from a well back there. This was the spring to which
we were walking, halfway to Chaeronea in Boeotia.

Meanwhile our men, with the mules, had caught us up,
and stood about and stared in astonishment at the wanderer.
We handed him some wine in a little cup; his hand shook
wildly and spilled more than half; then we gave him bread
and cheese, and his mouth trembled so that he could hardly
get the morsels into it. We bade him sit down; he said he
had no time, that he still had a long way to go today. At this,
something mad came into his eyes. We told him we'd give
him some money and inquired whether one of us had better
write to his home town, so that his kin should know that he
was ill and how matters stood with him. This, he said, we
should do under no condition; he would not tolerate it; it

would be a damned nuisance; it was no one's business at home how matters stood with him. Whereupon he turned and began to walk off, leaning on his stick. We followed him and insisted that he mount one of the mules and return with us; that we would bring him to Athens, to the port of Piraeus, and there put money in his hand for the journey to Trieste and beyond. Our guides, who understood our intentions, had already brought up a harnessed mule and started to lift him into the saddle. He, however, stepped back, his stick raised: travel back all the way he had just taken so many days to come! He'd be damned if he would! This no one should dare force him to do. One could see now, as he stood there with his stick raised against us (though with a noticeably trembling arm), what a big strong man he was, what unruliness was in him, and how he could be the bully of the whole village and the feared one, and how all this in him had been debased into a beastlike frightened being, who would this day and the next still drag himself along, but before nightfall die a miserable lonely death. Were we to abandon him now, he would not leave these mountains alive. We told the guides to move away, while just the two of us approached him. We made it clear we didn't want to leave him in the lurch, that he himself should tell us what he wanted from us; whatever it was, we would do it. "That's where I want to go," he said, and pointed in the direction whence we had come. In this case, we told him, he should mount a mule and have himself strapped into the saddle; we would send along with him two of the guides with their mules, who would bring him this very day to a village on the slope of Parnassus, whence he could see the bay on the far end of which lay Patras; and they would find quarters for him and buy him the customary native footwear. There he should take care of himself, allow the wounds on his feet to heal and remain quiet for six or even ten days.

Then we would join him again and take him with us to Patras.

He grasped the front and rear ends, where the saddle is raised; with an effort hoisted himself up and with the help of the guides (who called him "the foreign Mr. Beggar") he was bound fast, with decorum and reverence, side-saddle, the position in which women at home sit a horse. Then the mule set off uphill, the bound man swaying along, while we also mounted and let ourselves be carried, riding silently, down-hill towards Chaeronea.

The eager, advancing footfalls of the mules seemed strange, and it was in a strange atmosphere that we reached that brook, running swift and clear between the rocks, that the mules were unharnessed, that the men were lying on the ground beside the mules, drinking, and that we, higher up among the shrubs, let ourselves down, like them, to drink. A few hours ago he, the shipwrecked, the wandering naked human life, had also lain here, while all round the whole world lay in wait like one single enemy. I felt, while drinking here now, as if the water were flowing from his heart into mine. His face looked at me, as hitherto those other faces had looked at me; I almost lost myself to his face, and as if to save myself from his embrace, I said to myself, "Who is this? A strange man!" Then alongside this face were the others, looking at me and exerting their power over me, and there were many more. Nothing in me at this moment knew whether they were strangers among strangers, whose faces were turned towards me, or whether at some time somewhere I had said to each of them, "My friend!" and had heard, "My friend!" Without any transition something rose up, a vision, distant, something submerged, aquiver with exquisite anxiety, a boy watching the faces of soldiers pass, company after company, countless numbers, tired dusty faces, always in fours, each a single individual and none whose face the boy had not absorbed into himself, forever groping mutely from one to the other, touching each one, counting to himself, "This one, this one, this one!" while tears were rising in his throat.

A something remained circling somewhere above this, nothing but a wondering, a belonging-nowhere, a penetrating aloneness, a searching question: "Who am I?" Then, in the moment of most anxious wondering, I once more came to, the boy sank into me, the water flowed by under my face, bathing one cheek, the propped-up arms supported my body, and I raised myself and it was nothing more than the rising of one who, with his lips lying upon the flowing water, had taken a long draught.

But this hour, and then the next, as far as Chaeronea, and the following hours during which we boarded the train and were carried through Boeotia and Attica until the train ran into the station at Athens, I beheld a landscape which had no name. The mountains called to one another; the clefts were more alive than a face; each little fold on the distant flank of a hill lived; all this was as near to me as the palm of my hand. It was something that I shall never see again. It was the guest-gift of all the lonely wanderers who had crossed our path.

Everything alive, every landscape, reveals itself once, and in its entirety: but only to a heart deeply moved.

III

THE STATUES

THE FOLLOWING evening, as I climbed up to the Acropolis, the Wanderer was far away from me. Strange had it been to meet, in the Phocaean mountains, that fever-stricken man from Lauffen on the Salzach. Strangely unreal the way he had walked in silence towards his death and how nothing could persuade him to take again the road by which he had come.

But I was not tempted to think any more about it. "Passed," said I involuntarily, and lifted my foot over the fragments of ruin that lay around here by the hundreds. Only now did I notice that the sun was setting behind the Parthenon and that I was the only person still up here. There was something solemn about the streaming forth of the shadows, as though the last of life still in them were pouring itself in an evening libation onto this hill, where even the stones were decaying with age. Unintentionally, my eye chose one of those columns. There was an unspeakable severity and tenderness in the way it stood there; I felt that as I breathed, its contour rose and fell. But in the evening light, clearer than dissolved gold, the consuming whiff of mortality also played around it.

Magnificently self-composed, nevertheless, it stood there. I wanted to walk over to it; I felt the urge to walk around it; the side turned away from me, facing the setting sun, this held the promise of real life.

But before I took the first step I already stopped short. A touch of despondency blew over me, a sense of disappointment overcame me beforehand. That morning returned, the endless wandering from one thing to another. The fatigue of the road, step by step, over stones and fragments of stones; there were the excavations in the Agora, there was the Pnyx, there was the Orator's Hill, there the Tribune; there the traces of their houses, their winepresses, there were their tombs on the Eleusinian road. This was Athens. Athens? So this was Greece, this antiquity. A sense of disappointment overwhelmed me. I sat down on one of the stones that lay on the ground and seemed to be waiting for eternal night.

These Greeks, I asked within myself, where are they? I

tried to remember, but I remembered only memories. Names came floating near, figures; they merged into one another as though I had dissolved them into a greenish smoke wherein they appeared distorted.

Because they had passed long ago I hated them, and also because they had passed so fast. Their few centuries, the wretched span of time, on the other side of the enormous abyss; their history, that tangle of fabrication, untruth, empty talk, deceit; and the eternal boasting in it all, the eternal anxiety, the lightning disappearance. All was gone, even while it still believed it existed! And over it, floating, the eternal *fata morgana* of their poetry; and their deities themselves, what uncertain phantoms flitting by: there stood Chronos and the Titans, ghastly and grand, already they were gone, overthrown by their own children and forgotten; then those others come near, the Olympians: who believed in them? They, too, were gone, dissolved in a coloured mist. Gods, eternal gods? Milesian fables, a decoration painted on the wall of a wanton's house.

Where is this world, I called out, and what do I know of it? Where do I seize it? Where do I believe it? Where do I surrender myself to it entirely? Here! Or nowhere. Here is the air and here is the place. Does nothing penetrate me? As I lie here, is it here that it will be denied me forever? Will nothing be mine but this sense of the ghastly, this fearful shadowy premonition?

The sun must have sunk lower, the shadows lengthened, when a glance met mine—deep and equivocal as that of a passer-by. He walked on and was already half turned away from me, also contemptuous of this town, his home town. His glance revealed me to myself, and revealed him: it was Plato. Around the lips of the inventor of myths, the despiser of gods, hovered arrogance and spook-like dreams. In a magnificent, spotless garment carelessly brushing the ground, he walked along, the non-citizen, the regal man; he floated past, like ghosts who walk with locked feet. Contemptuously he touched time and place, he seemed to hail from the East and to disappear towards the West.

After the phantom had vanished, everything seemed sober and sad. Doubly desecrated, both the hill with its ruins and my guilt lay clear as the day. It is your own weakness, I called to myself, you are unable to revive all this. It is you yourself who tremble with transience, you who steep all about you in the terrible bath of time. When you wanted to walk around the column, you wanted merely to chase the just departed moment! — Aimlessly I stood up. I am going to read, said I to myself. I took the book from my pocket, the *Philoctetes* of Sophocles, and began to read. Clear and transparent, verse after verse stood before me, melodious and dreadful the wailings of the lonely man rose into the air. I felt the whole burden of this sorrow and at the same time the incomparable tenderness and purity of the Sophoclean line. But between me and everything that greenish veil moved again, and I was seized by that consuming suspicion. These gods, their sayings, these men, their deeds, everything appeared to me strange beyond measure— treacherous, vain. These figures, they seemed, while talking before me, to change their faces. They act, cheat—do they cheat themselves? This son of Achilles, does he believe what he says? Sometimes it appears as though Odysseus had ensnarled his unsuspecting mind with intrigue, at other times as though he were his willing, knowing accomplice. What does it mean when he suddenly revolts against him and promises Philoctetes a safe return home? He has no ship in which to take him home. What is going on in him? They threaten to take the bow away from the sick man; yet they know, they must know that without Philoctetes himself the town cannot fall. Do they realize that what they do is in vain, in vain this sly talk, and do they not admit it to themselves? All this was strange beyond measure and inaccessible. I could not read any further. I laid the book down. A wind rose, sped over the hill, and turned the pages of the book lying near me on the ground. All of a sudden the air smelled simultaneously of strawberries and acacias, of ripening wheat, of the dust on the roads, and of the open sea. I felt the enchantment of this aroma in which the whole landscape seemed to be caught; this landscape round which hung the air of millenniums. But I wanted no part of it. I bent down, put the book in my pocket, and turned to walk away.

Impossible antiquity, said I to myself, aimless searchings. — The harshness of these words pleased me. — Nothing of all this exists. Here, where I had hoped to touch it with my hands, here it is gone, here more than anywhere else. A demonic irony hovers round these ruins which in their decay still retain their secret.

I raised my foot to leave the ghostly place of the Non-existent and proceed to the little museum which is built of insignificant masonry against the slope. There, I thought to myself, laid out in show-cases, are treasures found in the rubble of the graves: they have resisted, at least for the moment, the power of time; they express only themselves and are of incomparable beauty. A goblet resembles the roundness of a breast or the shoulder of a goddess. A golden snake that once encircled an arm evokes that arm. So I shall go there. It is vain to try and struggle for the unattainable.

I quickly crossed over into the dark hall of the museum. The next room was even darker for possessing but one small window. I entered a third room.

There were statues, of women, in long garments. They stood around me in a semi-circle; I drew the curtain across the door and was alone with them.

[184]

At that moment something happened to me: an indescribable shock. It came not from outside but from some immeasurable distance of an inner abyss: it was like lightning: the room, as it was, rectangular with white-washed walls and the statues that stood there, became for an instant filled with a light utterly different from that which was really there: the eyes of the statues were all at once turned toward me and an unspeakable smile occurred in their faces. At the same time I knew: I am not seeing this for the first time—in some other world I have stood before these, have had some kind of communion with them, and ever since then everything in me has been waiting for just this shock, and so dreadfully I had to be shaken thus within my innermost self in order to become again what I had been. — I say "since then" and "at that time," but nothing of the limitation of time could penetrate the entrancement wherein I had lost myself. It was unbounded, and what it contained occurred outside of time. Somewhere a ceremony was taking place, a battle, a glorious sacrificial offering: that was the meaning of this tumult in the air, of the expanding and shrinking of the room, the meaning of this unspeakable exaltation in me, of this effervescing sociability, alternating with this mysterious anxiety and despondency: for I am the priest who will perform the ceremony—I, too, perhaps the victim that will be offered: all this presses towards decision, it ends with the crossing of a threshold, with a landing—with this standing here, I amidst these statues. And now already all this dies down into their faces turning back into stone, it expires and is gone; nothing remains but the death-sigh of despondency. Statues stand about me, five of them, only now am I aware of their number, strange they stand before me, heavy and stonelike, with slanting eyes. Their figures are enormous; built—animal-like, divine—out of overpowering forms; their faces are strange; pouting lips, raised eyebrows, mighty cheeks, a chin round which life flows; are these still human features? Nothing about them alludes to the world in which I breathe and move. Am I not standing before the strangest of the strange? Does not the eternal dread of chaos stare at me here from five virginal faces?

Yet, my God, how real they are! They have a breathtaking sensual presence. Erected like a temple, each body rises from feet of majestic strength. Their solemnity has nothing of masks: the face receives its meaning from the body. They are nubile women, brides, priestesses. In their faces is the severity of expectation, the elect strength and sublimity of their race, an awareness of their own rank. They participate in things that are above any common conception.

How beautiful they are! Their bodies are more convincing to me than my own. In this material there is a tension, so powerful that it creates in me a tautness, too. Never before have I seen anything like these proportions and this surface. Did not the universe, for a fleeting moment, open up to me?

From where else rose in me this foreboding of a departure, this rhythmical expansion of atmosphere, whence this whole portentous restiveness, this soundless tumult, which threatens me or which I can command? — It is, I answer myself, unerringly like a dreamer, it is the secret of infinity in these garments. He who would truly be a match for them must approach them by means other than the eye, with greater reverence yet with more daring. And still, it is the eye that would have to bid him, beholding, absorbing, but then drooping, growing dim as with one overwhelmed.

My eye did not droop, but a figure sank down over the knees of the priestess, someone rested his forehead on the foot of a statue. I know not whether I thought this or if it happened. There is a sleep in wakefulness, a sleep of but a few breaths that holds in itself a greater power of transformation, and is more closely related to death than the long deep slumber of the nights.

. . . .

ONCE more I return to myself. Maybe, I tell myself, it is from these statues that my soul received its direction, maybe it is something else of which these statues standing about me are messengers. For it is strange that again I do not really embrace them as something present, but that I call them to me from somewhere with continuous wonder, with a feeling anxiously sweet, like memory. It would be unthinkable to want to cling to their surface. This surface actually is not there—it grows by a continuous coming from inexhaustible depths. They are there and are unattainable. So, too, am I. By this we communicate.

And while I feel myself becoming stronger and under this one word "Eternal" forever losing more and more of myself, vibrating like a column of heated air above a conflagration, I ask myself, slowly fading like the lamp in bright daylight: If the Unattainable feeds on my innermost being and the Eternal builds out of me its eternity, what then still stands between me and the Deity?

3

Journey in Northern Africa

FEZ

T HE HOUSE I live in lies on the periphery of the town, hardly a hundred steps from the high old town wall which, crenelated throughout, with a tower every thousand feet, encloses the whole multitude of houses stretching over two hills. It is just this wall that makes the town a town, a powerful one, fortified for a thousand years against the bare hilly country which exists for roamers and travellers—open and deserted with here and there the round white cupola of a saint's tomb or an isolated tree, or a few earth-coloured nomad tents, and in the distance the white-shimmering range of the high Atlas. Yet at such a distances does this range lie on the horizon that the stripe of grey and silver with its burden of billowing white clouds resting lightly upon it steals nothing of the sky's purity and emptiness, nothing of its height from which the clear, cool north-east wind blows down incessantly, cut through by the silent flight of many storks or the fluttering of white pigeons over which circle rust-coloured falcons, pressing them down. But as soon as I leave the uppermost terrace of my house and descend the steep narrow staircase whose steps are of multicoloured tiles framed by a marble rim; as soon as I stand in the courtyard of my house, or rather in the garden, between orange-trees, rose-bushes, and stone basins in which the water continuously wells up from within and, dripping over the rim of the basin, flows away below as in a tiny river-bed of blue tiles—then I see but a small section of the endless transparence and wideness of the sky, almost severe in its clarity; for my house is also surrounded by a yellow-red wall rising to the height of two floors and crenelated like the wall of the town. And this home which a wealthy and distinguished man built for himself a hundred or a hundred and fifty years ago; this small charming terraced garden with its colourful little staircases and its rising and falling waters, the main house above with its one huge, magnificent grated window and the five pavilions with their flat snow-white roofs framed in dark green, from one to the other of which one can descend, for the terracing of the roofs repeats that of the garden—this whole world of the powerful sensual individual is enclosed in a fortress.

When I enter the lowest pavilion, close as it is to the town wall and containing only my room and a small anteroom, then I hear through the wall beside my bed the muffled noise of the town, to which I feel in this place as tangibly near as in the upper part of the garden I felt distant and lifted above it. And standing by my bed, arranging my books and travelling things, I hear, above all, the sound of trotting and even lightly cantering horses and mules so near my ear that I can imagine nothing else but that someone is riding over the beaten loam floor in some room of the house itself. I descend the narrow staircase which again, as in all these Arab houses, is built of multicoloured tiles and is very steep—so steep that one invariably thinks of that "pushing down the staircase" that appears so often in Arabian tales—and there is a little ante-room; a few young Arab servants are sitting on a divan, the one delegated to me rises and, politely showing me the way, moves out of the small room, where it has begun to grow dark, over a step into another room which, roofed in by ancient beams, is open on two sides; and here in this sort of vestibule, with narrow benches along the sides on which there sits a blind beggar, I am still in my house. To the right and left there are also doors with thick panels of wood, whose age gives them the appearance of stone, so that the room can be closed. But here I am already on the street. *"Balök!"* a voice calls behind me. *Balök!* Look out! a word uttered by the rider *sotto voce* and carelessly as warning to the pedestrian in his path; and along there comes, riding leisurely on his small donkey, an old man, who throws me, while I am stepping out of his way, a sharp contemptuous look—perhaps because I am on foot (although with a servant), or maybe this contemptuous glance, this turning quickly away, is reserved for encountering a "Rumi"; for to this holy town, the Mecca of western Islam, the European is still exceedingly strange—so strange that he can be met only by such a look. (The French protectorate, administered with great reserve, surrounds the individual with a sense of complete security; yet it is no more than twelve years since here in a single day all "Nazarenes" met their death; and a trembling recollection thereof is still in many eyes that pass us by.) But now there emerges from the opening of a house—or is it a yet narrower, darker alley than that in which I follow my guide?—an even smaller donkey carrying two laughing little children each in blue linen burnous, and now I am overtaken—so that again I have to step aside quite close to the wall—by a very light and fast-moving horse, a Berber horse, Arab in appearance, unusually thin and fine-limbed; a young Negro is riding it without stirrups on a tattered straw saddle and a bridle of straw; how indescribably light and free the wrist of the left hand controls the wretched reins, how light the pressure of the hanging naked legs with their well-formed toes and elegant heel!

But now my guide, turning sharp to the left, has entered

a house; no, it is not the entrance to a house but an alley, another such shaft formed by the windowless walls of high ancient houses; at the top they veer towards one another so that the sensation of being in a closed room is enhanced; at the same time this alley rises; and from above, where it turns once more and seemingly loses itself in another, even darker interior of a house, a veiled woman on a beautiful strong mule comes towards me. The street is so narrow that her stirrup all but touches me, nor does there seem anything to prevent the shawls and veils in which her figure is shrouded from brushing against me. No part of her face is visible save the narrow strip from which the two eyes darkly gleam; of the body, clothed in the flowing disguise of her white veils, nothing is recognizable; wonderful the strong youthful gesture wherewith she straightens herself in the saddle to counteract the downward pacing of the animal. But already between her and myself there comes on one of those soundlessly padding donkeys a sturdy Negro sitting side-saddle, both feet on one side just above the ground; tumid giant-lips, a bulbous nose, an enormous mop of kinky hair, and right across one cheek a scar—deep, ghastly, and, like the whole face, larger than life; and there again, from the other side, on a big, calm-looking, cream-coloured mule, comes a distinguished old man on a blue-green saddle; looks me over quite unperturbed from out of his purple garment that also envelops his handsome face; at each stirrup walks a servant, one black, the other white. And thus I arrive, after no more than a few yards, right in the centre of this town; how much and how soon is one right in the midst of it; how quickly it surrounds one, so multi-valvular, so closed, so exitless, as though one were inside the core of a pomegranate.

For now, from the cellar-like shaft of this second or third alley, I have arrived at a cross-roads, a kind of small square, with old women squatting on mats selling salted fish, but this square is roofed over by open woodwork covered with rushes so that here again is that sensation of being in a shell, of all this being connected and one's moving from one into the other without knowing how. And this feeling will persist throughout the days one spends in Fez, will accompany everything one sees and experiences, and, as time passes, will tend to grow stronger rather than weaker.

And now the servant pushes open a very small door in one of these windowless walls which through age look not like something built but something grown from Nature, and one enters the vestibule of a palace; there on the carpet sit the four sons of the master of the house, reading from the Koran which the eldest in the centre holds in his hand, all reading aloud at the same time, their heads swaying while they read, and between their moving heads the open court-yard with the playing fountains can be seen, the delicate columns of the open gallery, the colours, the tarnished gild-ings, the whole splendour of the Arab house; and fifty yards further, on pushing open another little door, quite as old, quite as low, and taking two steps down, one arrives in the prison of the Pasha. On a mat, his babouches before him, sits the kindly old guard, reading the Koran. A Berber, with wild hair and the shy expression of a captured animal, squats half-submerged in semi-darkness behind stout iron bars. One moves on past this dungeon along a wall, like everything here as old as the hills; the guide pushes open another door and one enters a low room in which something is quietly, pleas-antly whirring and treading. In a delicate yellow-grey half-light five looms are working; at each loom sits a man weaving a wide belt: the ribbons of the lilac-coloured silk threads shot through with silver, or of flaming yellow with red, coral-like designs, grow broader almost visibly under the soundless motion of these busy hands, the soft treading of these naked feet, the muffled whirring and stamping of these looms which again appear excessively old, everything about them polished by many centuries of wear and as noble as ancient ivory.

From the belt-weaving factory one steps into the street of the spice merchants—I might as well have said into the hall or arbour, for it too is covered over with lattice-work of wood on which grows an age-old vine with a thousand shoots. Here, however, the wave of the walking and riding population, the little donkeys that shove me out of their way, the begging hands of children that softly touch me—this wave carries me into a room completely closed in and packed to capacity with mankind and merchandise; the tiny shops, one next to the other, none wider than a cupboard, reaching up to the vaulted stone ceiling (or is it again a ceiling of wood so old as to resemble stone?); and atop the goods, on the spices, the dates and bananas that fill each of these open cupboards, high up there, with his scales and his big wooden spoon with which he ladles down his wares, the merchant sits enthroned. And this completely closed, large, long shop, so crowded with human beings and merchandise that one wonders how the patient little donkeys squeeze their way through or how that nobleman sitting in his blossom-white burnous on the iron-grey mule, his gentle, contemptuous smile raised with infinite superiority above the throng, manages to steer his way through—this overcrowded room, is a bridge; and through a crack somewhere in the wall I see beneath us the wide, yellow-brown water of the Qued; I see a stretch of the shore, sinister walls of houses, windowless save for an iron-barred slit, a peephole here and there, and below, at the foot of one of these house-walls, even reeds, pale green and strange here in the midst of this town and swaying from the turbulence of the water.

Thus one thing merges into the other and everything seems as though it had been like this since time immemorial. Yes, even this small niche in the wall of a particularly dark sinister-looking house seems always to have been meant for the body of that beggar squatting there, two terrible arm-stumps outstretched before him, his eyes closed or blind, mumbling endlessly to himself with fanatical zeal the same prayer, petition, or song of praise. And this relation of all things to all, this concatenation of dwellings and places of labour, of markets and mosques, this ornament of the intricately interwoven lettering that is everywhere repeated a thousandfold by the life-lines entangled one with the other, all this surrounds us with a sensation, a secret, a scent, wherein there is something primordial, a memory of pre-existence—Greece and Rome, the Arabian fairytales, and the Bible; yet at the same time it has clinging to it a touch of something quietly threatening, the true secret of the exotic, and this scent, this secret, this being in the core of the tangle and the faint awareness of the Forbidden that is never entirely absent, this today is still and maybe still tomorrow— Fez. Fez, until twenty years ago the great untrodden, the austerest, most forbidden of all Islamic towns, whose aroma has not yet completely evaporated.

A Memory of Beautiful Days

A S WE ARRIVED the sun still stood quite high, but I asked at once to be steered into the dark narrow streets. While we glided soundlessly along, Ferdinand and his sister sat close to one another, their eyes passing over the ancient walls whose red and grey reflection we divided, over the portals whose thresholds lay washed by the water, over the stony, moist, shimmering crests and the powerfully barred windows. We passed under small bridges, their damp arches close above our heads, bridges over which little old women and bent old men limped along and from which naked children lowered themselves sideways in order to bathe. In front of a small quiet square I asked the man to stop. Steps led up to a church. In the walls stood many stone statues that seemed to step forth from niches into the evening light . . . Brother and sister wished to remain but I pulled them along behind me through even narrower alleys that had, instead of water, a stone floor, finally beneath a damp dark archway out into the great Square that lay there like a hall of pleasure, with the sky, of an indescribable colour, forming a roof: for the naked blueness, vaulted, carried no cloud, yet the air was as though saturated with dissolved gold, and, like a sediment from the air, a hint of twilight-red hung on the palaces that formed the sides of the great Square. Brother and sister, seeing this for the first time, were as though in a dream. Katherina gazed to her right, towards the Palazzo Sansovino, towards those pillars, balconies, loggias, whereof the shadows and the radiance of the evening fashioned something unreal—the mute beginning of a feast to which day and night were invited; to her left she saw the older Palazzo, whose red wall seemed to be alive, the fantastic tower with the blue clock; she saw before her the fabulous church, the cupolas, the bronze horses high up, the open-work shrines of stone in which stood sculptures, the golden gates, the interior mysteriously shining forth, and again and again she kept asking, "Is this true? Can this be true?"

Ferdinand continued to hasten ahead. "Can there be more?" he asked. "Does this go on?"

Now he stopped and saw the open sea and gondolas and sails and pillared portals, new cupolas on the other side, and beyond the islands the triumph of the evening on clouds like faraway mountains of gold. Now, as he turned to call us, he noticed behind him the bulk of the campanile rising straight as an arrow so that the luminous arch above seemed to fall away from it.

"I'm going up there!" called Ferdinand, who rarely left a tower, be it that even of a village church, unclimbed.

But Katherina took him vehemently by the hand so that he had to turn round, and with both hands pointing in front of her she didn't stop but continued to walk ahead towards the water, in which a stream of golden fire seemed to pour out a deep blue glitteringly metallic substance. Ferdinand remained beside her; now they were close to the edge; the men in the gondolas, in the blinding dreamlike light looking completely black, waved at them; one of them rowed nearer, they lowered themselves down into his black boat and glided out into the fiery street. Many gondolas were out there, and between them dark sailboats cut their way through; everything was laden with life, everywhere faces wanting to move towards one another and the paths crossing one another were like magic signs on a fiery tablet, and in the air flew small dark birds whose paths were also similar magic signs.

Standing there on the bridge, leaning over the smooth ancient stone and watching a couple of barges steering towards each other, I found myself thinking of lips and how they find their long-lost way, easily and as though in a dream, back to beloved lips. Although I could feel the painful sweetness of the thought, I was swimming too lightly on the surface of my thinking, I could not dive down to discover of whom I had been thinking in my innermost soul; the thought came like the glance from a mask and I had a notion that it was the eye of Katherina, whose mouth I had never yet kissed. Now everything was on fire, behind the islands the clouds seemed to dissolve in golden smoke, the winged lion glowing on his globe of gold: it struck me that it was the sun not only of this moment but of bygone years—yes, of many centuries. Sensing that I could never again lose this light, I turned round and came back. Girls brushed past me, one pushing the other and pulling her black shawl down from behind; whereupon I caught sight of the nape of her neck between the black hair and the black shawl, which she immediately pulled up again: but the gleam of this tender neck was the shining forth of light that existed everywhere and everywhere was being covered up. The half-grown girls with the shawls had promptly disappeared again, like bats in the crack of a wall; an old man passed by, and in the depths of his eyes, the eyes of a sad old bird, shone a spark of light. Without meaning it, for I felt too well to mean anything, I walked round in a circle and, stepping once more through the archway back into the great Square, wandered along under the arcades. But the golden

light of the fire was no longer in the air; only in the illuminated shops that were everywhere and under the dusky arcades lay things that gleamed: there was a jeweller's shop with
rubies, emeralds, pearls, small ones on strings and large ones
each of which wore round it a lustre like the moon. I halted
before the booth of a dealer in antiques, where lay old silken
materials shot with gold and silver flowers: everywhere in
these silks was the life of light and I know not what memories
of beautiful figures from whom these stiff wrappings had
slipped off during nights of festivity. Opposite, in a small shop,
sparkled blue and green butterflies and shells, above all nautilus shells that are mother of pearl and have the shape of a
ram's horn. I stood before each shop, walking to and fro from
one to the other of these creations whence the life of light vanishes not even at night, and I was filled with desire to fashion
something like them with my own hands, to produce something out of the fermenting bliss in me and to cast it out. As
the moist fiery air of an island-shore forms a sparkling butter-
fly, as the sea with its demonic light buried beneath its might
forms the pearl and the nautilus and casts them out, so I
longed to give shape to something that sparkled with the inner
joy of living and cast it behind me, when the impetuous and
enchanting cascade of existence carried me along.

Although aware of the dark powers, I still did not know
what it was that I should create. So I returned to the inn and
realized that I had not yet seen my room. As I mounted the
dark staircase a young woman passed me. She was very tall,
and wore a light-coloured evening dress and pearls round her
bare neck. She was one of those English women who resemble
antique statues. Wonderful the youthful glow of her almost
severe face and the arch of her winglike eyebrows! Passing me
on her way down, she looked at me neither cursorily nor over-
long, neither shyly nor too self-assuredly, but quite calmly.

Her glance was one with her beauty, charged with a poise that lay precisely between the grace of a young girl and the all-too-conscious splendour of a great lady. In a masquerade she could have played Diana being surprised by Actaeon, but one would have said, "She is too young." She waited downstairs and looked up (this I felt rather than saw), and now her husband or friend passed me—also a young, very tall, handsome person with dark hair and a mouth that at some future date would look like the mouth on the bust of a Roman emperor, a Nero.

I LAY on the bed, still half-dressed, and heard through the paper-covered door the voices of the couple in the neighbouring room. Down below something murmured softly, probably the well in the street—no, this was no village street, it was the sea lapping against the marble steps of the house. From afar came the sound of singing; by now they must have arrived at the islands on the other side, their gondolas hung with Chinese lanterns; perhaps they had landed and hung their Chinese lanterns in the branches of the convent garden and sat close to one another in the grass amidst five thousand blossoming lilies and shrubs of rosemary, and begun to sing. The voices sounded like high-flying birds, so high that they still held the light that had plunged beyond the world—would hold it until it began everywhere to live again. Now the singing died down, but of a sudden it rose once more to the surface, quite near, sounding deeper, fuller, like the soulful sound of a bird it was, so near to human speech, more human than speech, saturated with dark gushing life, not overloud yet still quite close to me. There behind the paper-covered door it was: it was no singing, it was the low, deep laugh of that tall, handsome woman: oh, how utterly herself she was in this laughter, her beautiful proud body, her commanding shoulders! Now she was speaking: she spoke to him who was her husband or her friend. I could not understand what they said. Was she refusing him what he whisperingly begged? She might yield, she might refuse, she might do anything. There was such a swelling sense of her own self in the sound of her low laughter. Now a door opened in the next room and steps sounded outside in the corridor. Then everything was still. So she was alone. At this moment it seemed more wonderful to be wrapped about by solitude, alone and next to her, than with her. It was like a domination over her out of the darkness. It was Zeus to whom it had not yet occurred that he could throw Amphitryon's body round his divine limbs like a cloak and appear to her, who would be doubtful and doubt her doubts and with these doubts transform her face like a wave. But the darkness tried to pull me into it, into a black boat that glided along over black water. Light existed no longer anywhere but here near this woman. My thinking must not fall entirely into darkness, else I too shall sleep: like a sparrow-hawk it had to circle about the Luminous, above reality, above myself and this sleeping woman. Rapture of the stranger who comes and goes . . . (thus my thinking nourished itself on the Luminous and continued to circle) . . . to possess the rights of the master and still remain a stranger . . . Thus he must feel who today is not allowed to sleep next to his beloved. So it has to be. Coming and going. Abroad and at home. To return. At times Zeus returned to Alcmene. Our deepest desire aims at transformation. From this enchanting truth, thought burned as bright as a blazing torch. No, four blazing torches, one over each bedpost. It is the old sinister torch-cart; now the horses pull hard, it drags me into the night. I must lie, lie still, as one asleep, for it goes mountainwards, up into the mountains over stone bridges, across raging streams, all the way up into the old village. Here the stream flows quiet and deep between the old houses. I must hurry: for I must catch the fish before the break of dawn. In the dark, where the mill-race flows deepest and swiftest, above the weir, there in the dark lies the huge old fish which has swallowed the light. Stab him I must with the trident so that I can take the light out of his belly with my hands. The light he has swallowed is the voice of the beautiful woman, not the voice wherewith she speaks but her most secret laughter with which she surrenders herself. I must search for the trident further upstream, amongst the juniper bushes. The junipers are small but they are powerful when they grow close together: they are faithful, that is their strength. Should I fall amongst them, I shall never again transform myself. I merely want to thrust my hand between them to seize the trident when something quivers—that's Katherina's never-kissed mouth! So I stand again, and dare not. But I no longer need what I was seeking, for it is almost morning. I hear bells and the sounds of an organ. No doubt Kathi has already gone downstairs and is praying in St. Mark's—offering up a lip-prayer like a child, then dreaming to herself without words in the golden church.

It WAS a slumber and continually a new waking, merging into new dreams, a possessing and losing. I beheld my childhood afar, like a deep mountain lake, and walked into it as into a house. It was a self-possessing and a self-not-possessing, a having-all and having-nought. Morning air of childhood mingling with premonition of being dead, the globe of the world floated past in a blue fixed light, while a dead man sank deeper and deeper into the dark, and then it was a fruit that rolled towards me, but my hand was too cold and rigid to seize it: now I myself as a child leapt from under the bed on which I had lain with cold rigid hands, and tried to snatch it. From each dream-vision sprang forth harmonies as from an Aeolian harp, a reflection of flames fell on the white quilt, and the early sea-wind rose and moved the white paper on the little table. Gone was the slumber, gaily the naked feet touched the stone floor, and from the water-pitcher leapt forth water of its own will like a living nymph. The night had poured its power into everything, everything looked more knowing, nowhere was there any dream but everywhere Love and the Present. The white pages gleamed in full morning light, they were asking to be covered with words, they wanted my secret in order to give me back a thousand secrets in return. Close to them lay the beautiful big orange that I had put there the evening before; I peeled it and hastily ate it. It seemed as though a ship were weighing its anchors and I had to leave in a hurry for a foreign world. A magic formula pressed and quivered in me, but I could not remember the first word. I possessed nothing but the transparent colourful shadows of my dreams and half-dreams. When, filled with impatience, I tried to pull them towards me, they retreated, and it seemed as though the walls and the peculiarly-shaped old-fashioned furniture of the inn's room had absorbed them. The whole room still looked knowing, but mocking and void. Yet the moment the shadows reappeared there, and while my heart pressed against them and I let my wish—which was directed towards fidelity and infidelity, towards departure and remaining, towards here and there—play against them like a magic wand, I felt how I could draw forth from the naked floor real characters, and how they shone and cast physical shadows, how my wish moved them against one another, how they were actually there for my sake and still took notice only of one another, how my wish had formed for them youth and age and all masks and fulfilled itself in them, and how they were yet detached from me and lusted one for the other and each for itself. I could move away from them, could let a curtain fall in front of their existence and raise it again. Yet all the time, as the slanting rays of the sun beyond a voluptuous thunder-cloud fall on a livid-green garden landscape, I saw how the splendour of the air, of the water and the fire, streamed into them as it were from above in slanting, spectral rays, so that they were, for my mysteriously favoured eye, simultaneously human beings and sparkling incarnations of the elements.

Encounters

T HE FLIGHT of birds is marvellous these radiant days, and I can perfectly well understand how I once jotted down these lines: "Je me souviens des paroles d'Agur, fils d'Jaké, et des choses qu'il déclare les plus incompréhensibles et les plus merveilleuses: la trace de l'oiseau dans l'air et la trace de l'homme dans la vierge."

These lines are scribbled in pencil in the margin of a travel book. I ran across them three days ago while looking for a road that would take me by carriage from Urbino across the mountains to Assisi or the Lake Trasimeno. I realize that these lines are in my own handwriting, that they are written falteringly, in a carriage perhaps, or possibly in a train; but no reflection can suggest whence they come. Very likely from some old French book. But was I reading rare and unusual books during those days in Umbria? I don't remember doing so. Who is Agur? And who is the writer who remembers Agur? At all events, it was I who wrote the lines; everything else is now obliterated; only this remains. And somewhere within me, among the things I experienced before the age of three and of which my conscious memory has never known anything, among the secrets of my darkest dreams, among the thoughts I've thought behind my own back, this Agur now lives. And one day perhaps he will rise like a dead man from a vault, like a murderer from a trapdoor, and his return will be strange, but actually no more strange than when, yesterday afternoon, the returning young swallow plunged down through the air, striking down like a dark streak of lightning through the half-open front door into the old nest. And an instant later, like a second dark flash from the zenith of celestial space, came the little hen, the young sister, and now the mate. For they are siblings, hatched out last summer in this nest behind our front door. How did they know the way, diving down from the infinity of the heavens? Out of all the countries how could they know it was this country, out of all the valleys this small valley, all the houses this house? And where within me dwells Agur, who marvelled at this wonder of wonders, and found nothing more mysterious than the trace of this wonder, the invisible trace of the bird in the air?

But certain it is that the going and the searching and the meeting belong in some manner to the mysteries of Eros. Certain it is that on our winding path we are not only propelled forward by our deeds but lured on continuously by something which seems to be constantly waiting for us somewhere and is invariably veiled. It is the yearning of love, the curiosity of love in our forging ahead—even when we are in search of the solitude of a forest, the silence of a high mountain or a deserted beach where the silver fringe of the sea dissolves in softest sound. A most delicate fragrance encompasses all lonely encounters, be it merely the encounter with a great tree standing alone or the meeting with an animal of the forest which halts without a sound and eyes us from the gloom. It seems to me that it is not the embrace but the encounter that is the true, decisive erotic pantomime. At no moment is the sensual so close to the spiritual, the spiritual so sensual, as in the encounter. At this moment everything is possible, everything in flux, everything diffused. The yearning towards one another is

still without lust—a naïve combination of intimacy and shyness. Here is the deerlike, the birdlike, the animal-dumb, the
angel-pure, the divine. In a greeting there are infinite possibilities. Dante dates his *Vita Nuova* from a greeting bestowed
on him. Marvellous is the cry of a great bird: the strange,
unique, primeval sound at the break of day from the tallest
fir-tree, that sound to which the hen is somewhere listening.
This obscure yet passionate desiring, this crying of the unknown for the unknown, is its true power. The encounter
promises more than the embrace can keep. It seems, if I may
say so, to belong to a higher order of things—to that law according to which the stars move and thoughts fertilize one
another. For a very daring, very naïve imagination, however,
wherein innocence and cynicism are inextricably entangled,
the encounter is already the anticipation of embrace. Such
were the glances the shepherds turned on a goddess who suddenly appeared before them, and in the glance of the goddess
there was something which kindled passion in the dull eyes
of the shepherds. And Agur is right—whether he was a king
or a great sheikh in the desert, a wise and magnificent merchant or a seafarer among seafarers. He is right when in the
evening of his days, sitting in the shadow of his wisdom and
experience, his lips weave into one these two miracles: the
mystery of embrace and the mystery of flight. But who, really,
is Agur, whose living words dwell within me? Should I not be
capable of seeing his face within me? His experiences are rich
and plentiful, the tone of his speech, though casual, is the tone
of an experienced man. He disdains to play the preacher, rather
drops here and there a word that sinks down significant and
mellifluous into the ear of the listener. I imagine him to be like
Boaz, with a beautiful white beard and a sunburnt face, a man
who dressed in fine linen and on whose wheatfields the poor
were not forbidden to glean the ears. But did I not once see

his face? True, it was only in a wordless dream, and he whose face I saw bore no name. Now, however, it strikes me that this was Agur, and I have to put the speech, handed down to me in my own writing, into the mouth of one of whom I once dreamed, and who, as the dream described him, was a patriarch among patriarchs, a ruler over a powerful, a nameless nation of nomads.

Here, then, was the dream. I lay down, tired from a long climb over the mountains. It was still summer, though towards summer's end, and when in the middle of the night a storm blew open the balcony door and the lake beat in furious roars against the piles, I said to myself half-asleep, "These are the autumnal gales." And between sleep and waking I was filled with an indescribable happiness about the vastness of the world (over whose semi-illumined lakes, mountains, and valleys the storm was now raging). I sank into this sensation as into a soft dark wave and was promptly in the midst of a dream, was outside and above, in the livid twilit night, in the storm, on the wide slope of a high mountain. But it was more than the slope of a mountain, it was an immense landscape, it was—I could not see this, but was aware of it—the terrace-shaped rim of a gigantic plateau: it was Asia. And all round me, more violent than the storm and filling the pale, dim night with a mighty commotion, was a vast decampment. A whole populace surrounded me, and the whole populace busied itself in the dark, striking tents and loading their possessions on to pack-mules. Groups of silent people stood quite near to me, hastily loading camels and other animals; but it was very dark. I lent a hand with a tent that had not yet been struck. Alone in the tent, I pulled the pegs out of the ground, and in the dim light I could see the magnificent embroidery decorating the lower border of the tent—a highly artistic design of dark-brown leather strips sewn on light beige-

coloured leather. With the rumbling motion of the great departure constantly in my ears, I was aware that everything
was under the sovereignty of one command—a command that
could not be disobeyed. And mysteriously I knew that the tent
on which I was working was part of *his* tent, the tent of him
who had ordered the departure and from whom all orders
came. And as though under a spell I climbed on to a heap of
folded mule-rugs, pushed the flaps of canvas apart, and peered
into the main tent. It was darker within than where I stood.
Only by degrees could I see, then all of a sudden quite clearly.
The tent was bare of furniture or decoration, nothing but
dark walls. Along one side, on a large, deep red or purple
rug, lay a young woman of dark pallor, of an indescribable
dark pallor and beauty, from whose arms a man detached himself, a tall thin man who rose and moved beneath my eyes
across the empty tent to the opposite wall. The young woman
—wearing nothing but wide bracelets—raised her arms
silently towards him, as if to call him back, but he did not turn
to look at her. Though I had barely seen his face, I knew he
was old, old and powerful, with a flowing forked beard and
round his head an earth-coloured turban. But his exceedingly
thin body, naked to the waist, his long lean arms, were as those
of a young man, all lightness and daring. From his loins hung
a long skirtlike garment of a quite indescribable yellow. This
shade of yellow I shall recognize where and whenever it
should cross my vision again. It was more magnificent than
the yellow of ancient Persian tiles, more radiant than the yellow of yellow tulips. He stood now against the opposite wall
of the tent, the darkest one, and pulled back a flap, thereby
creating a large window. The breeze came wafting in and cast
his white divided beard over his thin brown shoulders. The
beautiful woman raised herself beseechingly and seemed to
call him tenderly by name, but the air failed to carry the words

[211]

towards me. I looked out through the window which he had torn into the wall of the tent: out there lay the dim twilit night, the endless terraced mountain land and the silent departure of the whole populace. And his mere standing there in the rectangular opening of the tent (which was raised above all other tents) caused a mysterious voiceless uproar throughout the decampment so that even the clouds seemed to chase one another faster over the mountainous landscape under the pale moon. This man and no other was Agur.

4

Twilight and Nocturnal Storm

THE SPARROW-HAWK which the boys had nailed to the barn door twisted itself dreadfully towards the breaking night. Euseb, the eldest of those who had done it, stood in the dusk and stared at the bird, from whose shining eyes fury shot forth while it jerked itself to death on the iron nails that pierced its wings. Then its mate dived down from the darkening air; with a shrill cry she flew as though bereft of her senses in giddy little circles, then hung rigid in the air with outspread wings and glimmering eyes, flung herself upwards, backwards, towards the mountain wall, vanishing, then reappearing in wild flights of frenzy. It seemed as though her screams were intended to attract the night-black storm that lay there, its own body afire with suppressed lightning, and with magic circles pull it down on the village. The boy Euseb could hardly stand on his legs; terror gripped him by the neck so that he dared not move his eyeballs. But when, under a silent flash of lightning, the whole barn blazed out in an ashen light, and when to his right a bearded goat-owl, disturbed by a gust of wind, shot out of a hole in the wall to spear a beetle and to his left a bat tumbled down, then horror seized him and drove him with chattering teeth down into the village. And now right in front of him a fresh flash revealed the cemetery wall with all

its crevices wherein wood-lice lived; under the sudden glare
the crosses seemed to stretch, and on the one fresh child's
grave a bush, its blossoms of bleeding hearts hanging by
threads, began to shake. But as the lightning flickered out
and darkness settled down with the weight of a blanket, a
gleam of light fell slantingly from the rear window of a small
house on to the cemetery wall. In this chamber slept the
butcher's daughter, the most beautiful girl in the village; and
it was common knowledge that here one evening, while she
was undressing and until she blew out the light, one of the
older boys had been able to see the shadows of her breasts
upon the curtains.

So Euseb pressed himself under a projecting roof where
shingles lay piled up high; and his heart beat differently
from hitherto. Facing him, its head dangling, hung the calf
he had seen being led past in the afternoon; warm breath
still seemed to be coming from its soft mouth. To the boy
Euseb the time he spent lying here in wait passed like nothing; the quarter-hours striking almost over his head and
booming on the fearful air he failed to hear. Nor did he heed
the lightning that laid bare in dazzling brightness the bells
in their belfry; he was absorbed only with the calf, absorbed
only with the girl who there in the house would soon be preparing for bed in her chamber. Now she was busying herself
in the parlour, wherein sat two or three men, for the butcher
was pouring out some year-old wine.

Presently two dark figures approached the house; they
were menservants of townsfolk who owned country estates
round about the village and on the slopes of the mountains;
one was in livery and knee-breeches, the other clad as a game-
keeper. While the first remained behind, the other strode
ahead and entered the parlour. Whereupon, from a dark
spot close to a gushing well, a wench stepped forth in the

direction of the man who had remained behind, raised her hands towards him, and tried to take his arm. The lower half of her figure was shapelessly broad and Euseb knew immediately that she was the maidservant to the keeper of the "Crown," a young stranger to the place at whom he and the other boys would steal glances when, with heavy body, she knelt down beside the dammed-up mill-stream to rinse the washing, for all were aware that she was with child. Now the servant shook the pleading woman with such force that she had to support herself with one hand on the edge of the well, while with the other she convulsively grasped her belly, and the sound of her sobbing drowned out the gushing of the water. Soon there appeared on the threshold the other servant with the butcher's beautiful daughter, and the one in livery lent to his speech, while half turning towards the maid standing in the dark, a loud and strangely superior tone. "That was last year," he shouted back. "Now we are in another year. Amen." And when, with a "Joseph, Joseph!" from a mouth stretched wide in fear, she tried once more to come near him, he reproached her with knife-sharp words that actually had the power to strike her dumb—to the effect that a person in her condition should be ashamed of loitering in the streets and outside inns, that he regretted the time he had wasted with her during the bygone year and even now would regret every additional minute, since he had better things to do than hang about here with her.

These knife-sharp words penetrated the boy Euseb in his hiding-place with a kind of cruel delight; the skill wherewith the servant had uttered his words and then, whistling three bars and without turning round, disappeared into the inn, gave him much the same sensation he frequently felt when the dresses of women and girls from the town brushed against him: they cast off a subtle, benumbing fragrance which, as he inhaled it, filled him with a divided feeling of sinking down, gently surrendering, while at the same time something within him violently revolted. The twofold sensation now seized him again; it seemed as if, like a door in the dark, the secret splendour of the life of the townsfolk and their servants opened up to him and he was driven to prowl after the maid who stumbled away before him, moaning to herself, hand in mouth, face distorted, to continue following her unobserved and to play a cruel game with the unsuspecting girl. As she walked in heavy despair down the middle of the road, he slipped sideways between the hedges hunched in the storm, under the trees shaken by the storm, past barns that groaned in their beams. Though the nocturnal storm flung dust and chaff into his wide-stretched eyes, he paid no heed; he had lost consciousness of his body, for minutes on end he felt no bigger than the weasels, the toads, or any of the other things that lay in wait and rustled on the trembling earth; an instant later he was of gigantic stature, he stretched up between the trees and it was he who seized their crests and bent them, groaning, down; he was the Terrible who lies in wait in the dark and leaps forth at the cross-roads, yet in him was the timidity of a frightened deer, and all the dread that emanated from him he felt rippling down his spine. She who stumbled along before him had become his prey; he was a gentleman from town and had several of her kind; the new ones he had locked into his house and this one he was now driving to join them; he was the butcher who sneaked up on a runaway animal to lead it to its death, but the animal was an animal bewitched; it was this woman here before him. He ducked when the wind ceased and sprang forth again when it roared; between the breath of the wind and his wild secret chase lay an intimate harmony; the wind was his ally and the brilliant lightning illuminated the road with its cart-tracks, cast its light on the chalk walls of the houses and between the hedges, shone into the forest and revealed the roots of the trees—all that he might keep his victim in sight should she try to slip away from him in the dark.

.   .   .   .

The Woman without a Shadow

O N THE EVENING of the third day, the hunt took its way high up along the slope of a deep valley which narrowed down till its sides fell sheer to the torrent foaming in the abyss beneath. Above a high stone bridge which spanned the chasm there stood a lonely village already occupied by the huntsmen. The Emperor came riding across the bridge. He reined in his horse on the road, the men behind him leapt from their saddles, all stood waiting for him to dismount and two of the noblest ran to hold his reins and stirrup, but he stopped them with a careless gesture of his fine, long hand and remained in the saddle. This was the moment the jester had been waiting for to ingratiate himself with the Emperor by a prank, some rude village sport which should mingle with his present cares. He came capering up to the Emperor's horse, dragging behind him, by his long, yellowish beard, a meek and unresisting old man.

"Come, thou chief of an accursed village," yelled the jester. "Down on thy knees and confess that the men in thy village are known far and wide as hawk-thieves, that all have learned to lure hawks and bait them with a blinded bird, that you are yourselves keen hawksmen and poachers from the womb up, and that every one of you, should—which God forbid!—a red imperial hawk fall into his hands, would sell his

[220]

own mother, nay, his very wife, who is cheap to such as you, for a hawk trained at sparrows!"

The old man blinked. It was deadly earnest to him. Death loomed before him. Raising his hands in protest, he seemed to see handless stumps before his eyes. He opened his mouth to speak, but the brazen voice of the jester, and the huge respect it was in him to command, cast the old man to the ground. He raised beseeching eyes, but the man above him on the horse remained unmoved, not deigning to cast him a glance.

"By my eyes," cried the old man in despair, "may I be struck blind where I stand if we be anything but poor herdsmen who know nothing of hawking, and cannot tell a hawk from a crow."

In his terror, he pawed the air too near the horse's eyes; it reared, and the Emperor's hand moved swiftly to the case with the Empress's letter, which he wore round his neck, under his robe. Only then did he gather up the reins and bring his horse to a standstill, but the jester, greedily hanging on his face for a smile and a nod, received not so much as a glance: the Emperor's eyes gazed straight before him, like a drowsy eagle's. It was very late in the afternoon, and here, in the heart of the seven Mountains of the Moon, the air was so pure that he could descry, in the far distance, the source of the torrent foaming beneath him, where it hung on a precipice, a thin thread of waterfall, and plunged into a clump of trees. On the tallest treetop of the clump, a hawk was tearing at a bird in its talons. The Emperor beckoned the head hawksman to him and pointed it out with a flicker of his eyelashes. The hawksman's wide-set eyes had spied the bird long ago, and he knew that the bird at prey in the distance was not the one they sought, not the bird which it was his supreme duty to find and lure back, and as his ruddy face took on a darker tinge above and below the great scar which barred his nose, he turned aside as if abashed. But the Emperor's face darkened; he bent a little towards the hawksman: "On thy head be it," he said in a low voice, "that we find the red hawk in this place and lure it back again, you and I."

The hawksman did not dare to look his lord in the face; his eyes were fixed on the Emperor's breast, his face turned yellowish-white and terror flashed into his wide-set eyes. He hurried away, called for two mules, took one coat of felt and another of leather, and hung two leather pouches on his belt, one of which was pierced with air-holes like a cage. The Emperor had leapt from his horse; without touching the stirrup, he vaulted on to one of the mules, the hawksman mounted the other. He clung to the pommel of his saddle; there was a numbness in his limbs; more than his lord's anger or his ominous threat, he dreaded to be alone with him. Turning helplessly in the saddle, he saw the master of the horse beckoning to one of the grooms. Feigning that this was what he had been waiting for, the hawksman threw the coats to the groom. The lad had been lurking about covetously; he had crept up on purpose, his eyes were shining. Nimbly he mounted a third mule and trotted off after the other two.

Without a word they took their way along the slope. The road rose steeply. They rode in single file, the mules seeking a footing on loose, glossy rocks and tree-roots. With one knee the riders were hanging over the abyss, with the other they swept the ivy which clothed the black precipice. Little birds eyed them from their nests and fluttered away over their heads. The hawksman's eyes were fixed on the Emperor's back; shoulders and neck looked like rock, unapproachable and pitiless. They reached the top, the Emperor leapt from his saddle, the boy was off his mule as lightly as a cat. The Emperor paid no heed to him, but the lad was overjoyed to be alone with his august master, for the hawksman sidled away, his eyes on the sky. The Emperor looked down; mountains and valleys lay bathed in unutterable radiance, waterfalls flashed as they plunged down to the valleys, grey-blue mist was rising from the deepest gorges. In the distance, mountain ridges crossed in their rise and fall, their slopes were clothed with dark forests, above was rock, gaunt and riven. No two of these precipices were alike, yet each merged shining into the other like the characters in the Empress's letter, which were all wonderful and all different, nor was there a beginning to be seen—the end was interwoven with the beginning; it was as if an ineffable humility and chastity had shrunk from a superscription, and a perfume as pure and strong as that now wafted over the gorges rose from the letter to him who was to read it. Lost in memory, the Emperor involuntarily closed his eyes. The boy saw mercy and mildness in his face; pierced with joy, he broke off a twig in his delight, only to throw it away again. They entered the wood and walked between trees along the river towards a pool.

The hawksman remained behind. For the hundredth time he scanned the sky, which was still bright, yet already bathed in the first moonlight. Facing him, the sun was setting between the two pinnacles of the highest Mount of the Moon: its last, deep-black ray swept through the sky and the gorge, then single clouds writhed like snakes out of the mountain clefts. He sighed, for hope had grown faint. He took fresh heart for the morrow, but he was not ready to give up the search yet. Opening one of the leather pouches hanging at his belt, he drew out a little, rust-red bird, which fluttered wildly. Frowning, the hawksman tied it to a thornbush with a little thong.

"Do thy work," he said. "Thy fear sees more keenly than

the keenest eye. Tell me where the bird is for whom I wait, or thine own life is forfeit. For even as he that is behind me is above me, so am I above thee."

A short time passed; the bird tore at its bond like a man in despair and uttered a piercing note of fear. The hawksman was almost beside himself with fear and impatience. He threw himself to the ground behind the thornbush, and imitated the call of the ring-dove three times and more. From the clump of trees by the river, the male doves came, seeking the caller. Soon, at the top of the sky, a bird appeared, growing larger and larger as it approached.

" 'Tis thee!" cried the hawksman, overjoyed. "Thou rememberest thy hawksman, thou comest back to the hand that first gave thee food."

Pulling a little drum from his belt, he beat his own tattoo on it with his knuckles.

"Knowst thou the sound?" he cried. " 'Tis we, thine own, who seek thy pardon. We have offended against thy noble ways, we know not how, but thou art great of heart and hast forgiven us."

The fettered bird, in terror, bored its way into the thicket, the doves scattered; from above, the hawk dropped like a plummet-stone, with outstretched wings he wheeled above the hawksman, then, without a wing-beat, swooped slanting down to the copse. The hawksman's heart stood still. It was as if the hawk had looked at him with imperious anger in its red-glittering, wide-open eyes. Yet it was the hawk he sought; he knew every line of the splendid bird.

He bounded after it into the copse. The mules strained at their tethers. His very life was at stake; he was bewildered and terrified because the Emperor was nowhere to be seen. The waterfall dropped almost soundlessly from the cliff, a piece of sky was reflected in the pool with the hawk wheeling quietly above the treetops. From time to time the bird uttered its piercing call, as if restless because it could not see its master, and spurned the servant's clutch. The boy was crouching opposite the waterfall, as still as an owl; he had little to tell but that the Emperor had gone in there. He pointed to a cave in the rock face, hardly taller than a man. Drops from the fluttering veil spattered its decaying threshold; a few steps led up to it from the river—they seemed to be the work of human hands, but immemorially ancient. The Emperor, the boy went on, had spoken to himself, touched the water with his hand and laid his cloak aside. The boy had felt frightened and sleepy; with the moon looking down from above like a lamp, it was as if he had been forgotten on the threshold of the Emperor's bedchamber. He had closed his eyes purposely, and dozed to the steady rush of the falling water. Suddenly the Emperor had stood before him, had shaken him and asked whether he could hear singing. The boy heard it, quite close at hand, then farther off. The Emperor had turned on his heel and walked quickly to the cave. At first the lad had not dared to follow him unbidden; later he had crept after the Emperor, but had lost sight of him. The cave must have been an ancient vault; its walls were hewn, and there was probably another way out. But he had been waiting a long time now for the Emperor to come back. The hawksman hardly listened; he could not measure the time he had spent trembling for the hawk's return, and now it was mocking him again with its ceaseless cry. Then the splendid bird shot upward, and spied down at him from the topmost, bare stump of a blasted oak which still flourished in rich verdure below. The hawksman stood as if rooted to the spot.

In the end he tore himself away, bent down and crept up to the tree. His hands turned to bleeding stumps before his eyes at the thought that he might climb the tree and stretch out vain hands to the hawk just as the Emperor emerged from the mountain-side, while the graceless bird would soar aloft, to be lost for ever. The boy ran beside him on noiseless feet. The hawk raised its pinions, flew gracefully towards them, soared sideways up with a single wing-beat, then whirred downwards, and with a cry as if of joy and scorn, swept through the spray of the waterfall into the mountain-side. By some mysterious power it must have divined there an entrance veiled by the falling water. The hawksman clenched his teeth in helpless rage, rolling his eyes about him. The boy was bewildered by all these strange happenings, but the hawksman thought he saw cunning in his eyes and struck out at his face. The lad leapt into the thicket and cowered there, but he felt a strange pleasure in the undeserved blows, a gracious, wonderful smile hovered before his eyes, and he waited silently in the thicket for his master to appear.

The Emperor rapidly descended the smooth, steep steps; he paid no heed to the portcullis behind him; the singing, the strangeness, the very place itself held his senses spellbound. Everything in this place sank deep into his soul, for he was in the region of his first meeting with his beloved. That first, unforgettable hour of love was close to him, his heart beat high, and he hardly felt the strange, tomblike chill which poured in upon him from the mountain-side and up from the ground at his feet. There was no room in him for another adventure—yet might there be? who could tell? No thought formed in his mind, yet every vague imagining was deeply linked to his beloved. He could not distinguish the words of the song. At each step he took, he thought the next would make them clear. A refrain was repeated over and over again. He hastened down the last steps and found him-

self in a kind of antechamber, dimly illuminated; the light
came from under a portal facing him, of wood with ornate
bronze bands. He could see neither lock nor handle, but as
he approached the portal, its wings moved in their hinges.
At that moment, he heard distinctly the last words of the
refrain:

What boots all this, for we are still not born.

He had no time to consider the meaning of the words. He
had crossed the threshold and the wings of the portal clicked
softly to behind him. He was standing in a spacious hall
whose walls seemed to consist of the glossy virgin rock. In
the middle of the hall there stood a table, ready laid for one
guest at each end. At either side of the table, six tall lamps
were burning with soft, solemn light. The walls were bare,
yet from the whole there breathed a strange, immemorial
splendour which took his breath away. A server was walking
up and down between the table and that part of the hall
facing the door which lay in darkness. It must have been he
who had sung the words. He brought in dishes which looked
like pure gold, and long-necked flagons set with precious
stones, and placed them on the table. Many of the dishes
were so heavy that he could not carry them in his hands, but
set them on his head, yet he moved like a young deer under
their weight. The page came out of the darkness into the
light; he saw the Emperor standing in the doorway, but
showed no surprise. He folded his hands on his heart and
bowed. A voice from behind cried: "The time has come!"
yet that part of the hall lay in gloom, and it was only later
that the Emperor distinguished a door there, in all respects
like that through which he had entered, and exactly facing
it. The loud cry re-echoed through the hall, revealing its
vastness. The page bowed to the ground before the Emperor.

He said not a word, but with a reverent gesture pointed to the seat at the upper end of the table. Though all the twelve lamps which stood along the table seemed to be burning with equal power, those at the upper end must have been stronger, for they cast a glow over the seat and the splendid utensils set out before it; the middle of the table lay in pure, soft light, but a brownish twilight veiled its lower end. The page's eyes never left the Emperor, but his lips remained firmly closed. It took a moment for the Emperor to realize that he was expected to speak first.

"How comes it," he asked, "that you have prepared such a meal for one whom chance leads this way?"

The boy's firmly closed lips parted, he seemed to be at a loss; he stepped back and looked about him. But the Emperor had already forgotten his question, for three figures issued from some part of the side wall, and the sight ravished him. In the middle was a beautiful young maiden. She glided rather than walked towards the Emperor. The two pages beside her could hardly keep pace with her; they resembled the server in their beauty, but were smaller and more childish.

In her hands the maiden carried a rolled-up rug, which she laid at the Emperor's feet, and then she bowed almost to the ground.

"Pardon, great Emperor," she said, and only when she had risen again could he see that, for all her childlike delicacy, she was almost as tall as he—"pardon," she said, "that, intent on my work on this rug, I did not hear you come. Yet should it be found worthy to lie beneath you at the humble meal we offer, the thread at the end must not be broken, but must return to join the thread at the beginning."

She spoke with lowered eyes. The sweet tone of her voice so moved the Emperor that he could hardly grasp the meaning of what she said. The rug lay at his feet. He could see only part of it, and that the under side, yet he had never seen a fabric like it, for in it the crescents of the moon, the stars, leaves and flowers, men and beasts, flowed into each other. He could hardly take his eyes from it. He strove to remember the duties of courtesy, but minutes passed before he could speak a word to the strangers.

"You would seem to be travellers," he said with great con-descension, suppressing the tone of command in his voice. "Your tents, and those of your retinue, I imagine, are near at hand, and you have entered this ancient vault to seek its coolness. I should not wish to hear that you live in this moun-tain."

The children hung on his words with deepest attention. At the last, which, in spite of himself, he spoke more sternly, a smile passed over their faces. He could see that the three boys were struggling not to laugh aloud. But the maiden soon regained her self-command, and once more her look expressed deepest attention, even gravity.

"Or is your father's house close at hand?" the Emperor asked again, with no sign that he had noticed their unseemly behaviour. The three boys made a yet greater effort to sup-press their laughter, and the server hastily bent down and busied himself about the table to hide his face.

"But who is your father, my beautiful children?" asked the Emperor for the third time, with unmoved composure. Only one who knew him well would have divined his anger by the slight quiver in his voice.

The lovely girl was the first to recover. "Forgive us, great lord," she said, "and do not let your anger rise against my brothers. They know nothing of the art of courtly conver-sation. Yet we must pray you to be content for the time with such poor entertainment as we have to give, for it seems that our eldest brother has not yet assembled all the dishes and garnishings that he holds worthy to be set before you."

She motioned him to approach the table, and indeed, he felt almost faint with hunger, but the bearing of the children, and the inconceivable grace of all their attitudes, even of their ill behaviour, filled him with such delight that he could think of nothing else. The maiden was kneeling at the upper end of the table; she unrolled the rug and motioned him to recline upon it. The web was under his feet, flowers bloomed into beasts, huntsmen and lovers broke through creeping foliage, hawks wheeled above like flying flowers, each thing embraced all others, each was entwined with each, the whole was splendid beyond imagining, but there rose from it a chill that reached his loins.

"How didst thou make this pattern in such perfection?" he asked, turning to the maiden, who had modestly withdrawn a step or two.

At once the maiden lowered her eyes and answered without hesitation:

"When I weave, I separate beauty from the material, I leave out all that is a snare to the senses and subjects them to folly and ruin." The Emperor looked at her. "How dost thou work?" he asked, striving to keep his attention from wandering. For every single thing his eyes rested upon imprinted itself on his mind with wonderful clarity. He could see many things in the hall, and with every breath he took he seemed to see more.

"How dost thou work?" he asked again.

The maiden followed his gaze with joy. Some time passed before she replied. "When I weave," she said, "I proceed in the same way as thy blessed eye in seeing. I do not see what is, nor do I see what is not, but I see that which always is, and thus I weave."

But he was not listening to her, for his eyes were rapt in the sight of the splendid, lamplit walls. The boys turned their faces to him so eagerly that he knew it was his turn to speak. He was entranced by the beauty of their faces, and the radiance which, it seemed to him, he had never seen on children's faces before, and in the eyes fixed upon him he saw what he had never seen in any eyes.

"Are there more of you?" he suddenly asked the boy standing next to him. He did not know why this question, of all others, should rise to his lips. His eyes clung to their forms. The lust of possession seized him from head to foot, and he refrained from touching them with an effort.

"That is for you to decide," replied not the one he had asked but the other of the two.

The Emperor turned to him, and felt the effort it cost him to put his question in a jesting tone.

"Is the house near or far? Speak. Have you run away for good or evil?"

The boy made no answer, he looked across the table to the server, and again they could hardly suppress their laughter. The Emperor raised himself a little from the pearl-embroidered cushions on which he was reclining. It was strangely difficult for him to move. A chill rose from his hands and feet and reached his heart. He looked closely at the children.

"Did you know that we should meet?" he asked, speaking to none in particular. "Is this the end of a journey or its beginning? Does there lie more before you or behind you?"

His voice rang harsher in the high vault than he had wished, and his questions followed hard one on another.

"Thou liest before us and thou liest behind us," cried

the server aloud, making deep obeisance before the Emperor, stretching his hands, which still held the golden soup-ladle, to the ground. One of the boys ran to the Emperor, came to a standstill close beside him, and, looking him steadily in the eyes with feigned gravity, said slowly and emphatically:

"Thy questions are senseless, great Emperor, like those of a little child. For tell us this: when thou sittest down at table, is it to remain fed or to know hunger again? And when thou settest forth on a journey, is it to stay away or to return?"

"What mean these words?" cried the maiden, with widening eyes. "Come, stand behind me."

The boy ran back to her side and kissed her hanging sleeves with reverence and compunction, and the other did so too, though she had shown him no anger. She gave them not a glance, and raised her hands towards the Emperor in anxious supplication.

"O, how can we content thee, we who are so imperfect?" she cried in fear.

The Emperor saw nothing but her hand; it was inexpressibly beautiful and translucent as alabaster.

"It is you whom I must possess and keep," he exclaimed, "whatever be the way."

Her hand fell, her eyes rested on him with ineffable modesty and awe, he repented his haughty words, still more the naked violence of his tone, and hastened to add, in a gentle, beseeching tone, "How can I be united with you all for ever? For that is what I will, though it cost me my heart's blood."

Again the maiden shrank visibly. It seemed as if the question were too great for words, so that she could answer it only with her eyes.

"I am wont to attain what I desire," exclaimed the Emperor.

Her soul leaned out of her eyes, and she bent on him a long look blent of awe, tenderness, and nameless dread, which had such power over the Emperor that he lowered his eyes to collect himself for a decisive question; it seemed to be hovering on his lips, but he forgot it, for when he raised his eyes again, he saw the whole table covered with flowers flashing in the light of the lamps like a heap of jewels, saw how, under the maiden's hand, the last flowed to join the first, how they poured out of her hand, arranged themselves, and at last lay all in due order like a splendid embroidery wrought with skill. He saw her face shine, saw how she beckoned lovingly with her eyes to one who had not been there before, and who resembled her in stature and slenderness, while at the opposite end of the hall he saw a door at all points like that through which he had entered not long before, whose wings now stood open and through which half-grown children were entering two by two, with covered dishes in their hands.

"Who is he?" the Emperor asked the maiden, glancing towards him who had not been there before. "Is he the master cook?"

"The time has come!" cried the newcomer, as if wishing to proclaim himself to the boys carrying the dishes, and they approached two by two, noiselessly and with speed, and brought their dishes running, one hurrying to the top of the table and the Emperor's seat, the other to its opposite end.

"What means this saying that I have heard twice?" exclaimed the Emperor, "and why must all these things happen with such speed that I can hardly collect myself? Tell this man to take the time he needs."

"Time?" said the maiden, looking at him bewildered. "We know not time, but it is our great desire to know it and be its subject." Her bewilderment only heightened her beauty. The Emperor feasted his eyes on her, but in his delight there was no desire.

The master cook clapped his hands, the servers sprang aside in two rows. Like a lightning flash a horseman rode between them with a second on his heels, the first on a steel-grey horse, the second on a horse the colour of fire. Each carried before him on the pommel of his saddle a covered golden dish set with precious stones; they pulled up short, one after the other, a carver ran to each, took a dish and presented it kneeling, with deep solemnity, to the Emperor. The horsemen unsheathed their swords and saluted the Emperor by riding up to him, bending from the saddle with a lightning-swift movement and touching the ground with their ringing sword-points to right and left of the table. The Emperor was rapt in the sight of them; what most delighted him was the family likeness between these youths and the boys who had surrounded him before. Above all things he desired to speak to the newcomers. He beckoned them to him with a look of the utmost condescension and graciousness. But in vain. Not seeming to understand that he desired their company, they backed their horses along the smooth stone floor, grasping the reins with an enchanting grace, farther and farther back until the horses' hind hoofs almost touched the wall. Then the horses reared aloft at a slight pull in the reins, their forefeet pawed the air, they looked like birds, so supple were their necks, and they played with their own burdens like scaly fish in the moonlight, the one on the left, the other on the right of the hall. There was a look of strain on the youths' faces, but a silvery smile lay over them which they kept turned towards the Emperor; it was clear that the youths' task was done, and that they would vanish from the hall again, but that they did not, in their reverence, wish to turn their backs on their guest. They glided into the wall, though no eye could see where the wall opened; their smile was the last thing to flash like reflected light.

A pang pierced the Emperor. "Where have they gone?" he cried. He could not believe that a sight he had come to love so soon should so soon be past.

The maiden's eyes rested on him with delight. She seemed to be drinking in the wonder in his face, and she cried, "Great Emperor, is this not like my rug, and the curves and loops that found favour in thine eyes, and art thou content with the spectacle which my second and third brothers have presented to thee?"

"In truth, it is the same," replied the Emperor, and his breath came hard. "But why this haste?" he cried, and without his will, a deep sigh rose in him. "These infants are no company for me. Those two should have sat at my right hand and my left, and I must see them again, for each has carried away a piece of my body."

There was no answer. The young creatures hastened to serve him, the server placed the dishes before him, others entered, they handed their dishes to the carver, and though each crossed the other's path, non jostled the other. The master cook directed them all with his keen, dark look. There were others there, invisible, mere shadows who handed dishes out of the dark; no one could have told who was in the hall and who was not. They knelt in turn with their dishes to right and left of him, and once there came a little girl. The child was carrying a heavy golden dish she could hardly hold; with solemn effort she forced herself not to tremble.

"How canst thou do that, small and tender as thou art?" asked the Emperor.

"Service is the road to rule, there is no other, great Emperor," said the child, and, over the dish, she gave him, from under the clear arch of her eyebrows, a look far beyond her years. He sought for an answer, but had to turn again, for on his other side, there was kneeling one of the boys who had been with the elder girl before, offering preserves in a deep dish set all over with jewels. He could not but show all these lovely beings the feeling which ran through all his veins; he meant to keep them beside him, though the orderliness of the table and everything else should be destroyed. On either hand he dipped into the dishes, which contained a sweet food aromatic with spices and fruit.

"Set your dishes on the ground," he commanded, "and turn your faces to me," and he would have filled their mouths with the delicious food, but they bent backwards and warded him off with a beseeching gesture. He stretched out his hands to lay hold of them; his hands grasped the void, but a breath of icy wind, as if some door to the outer air had opened, swept over his outstretched hands and face. The children were already far off, and the look they bent on him was severe. Their faces, seen now in profile, looked much older, the maiden's eyebrows more clear-cut and strange, as if every breath was a year to her. They glided into the crowd of servers and, mingling with them, once more became children like the others. Never had the Emperor been so dismayed.

"Who am I?" he asked, "and where am I?" His throat grew dry. His hands moved to the heavy golden goblet standing in front of him, a cool, faintly aromatic drink he had never tasted before met his lips, he drank thirstily, but was soon master of himself again and, raising his goblet, he cried:

"I drink to you! This banquet is served most skilfully. Praise to our meeting and to those who taught you this wondrous skill!"

"Everything is wondrous in thy presence," replied the maiden, who was standing motionless behind him. "And this moment, when thou art our guest, is for us the moment of moments," and her face took on an expression of joy so great that her eyes dilated as if in fear. The Emperor beckoned her close to him. A feeling of happiness and security such as he had never known overcame him, blotting out the chill which rose to his shoulders and gripped his loins like an iron band. Understanding, he raised and lowered his eyes more than once, then spoke:

"You have some secret, and it might be bliss to me to share it with you."

"Between us and thee there is only one secret, perfect reverence," replied the maiden. The Emperor's eyes rested on her without understanding, but with delight, and he kept his face turned towards her; at the same time he saw, without looking, that another was already kneeling beside him with another dish, while yet another was raising the lid. His mind was still full of the maiden's answer, which seemed to him to contain more than mere courtesy, and he put his hand into the dish without turning his eyes to it.

"Thou speakest of what we are to thee. Why dost thou never ask what thou art to us?" said the maiden, rapidly, in a voice like a sigh.

The Emperor's face changed, and his mouth, suddenly opening and baring his teeth for a moment, betrayed the impatience he could no longer curb.

"I demand to know from you how I can take possession of you for ever," he cried imperiously, hardly recognizing his own voice. Suddenly the maiden was at his shoulder, like a bird, bending down to him; the beauty of the flashing movement entranced him.

"At the moment when we tell thee that, thou wilt drive us from thee for ever."

The master cook looked at her over the table; she went to

him obediently and took her place beside her brother at the middle of the table. The Emperor raised his eyes to watch her. He was angered by the answer he could not understand, his brow darkened that she should obey another in his presence, he was about to push the table from him and rise from it. At that moment, the little girl passed by. She smiled at him, and the words "True greatness is graciousness, great Emperor" came softly from her lips, so soothing him that he sat looking straight in front of him like a guest who sits at table unconcerned. Thus it came about that, for the first time since the beginning of the banquet, his eyes rested on the dark end of the table facing him, and to his amazement, he saw something going on there that he could understand still less than anything that had yet happened.

He saw the same children who had served him with their radiant smile kneel down to left and right of the empty chair and solemnly present each of the dishes to a guest who was not there. Those who were standing removed the covers, waited awhile with the same reverence as they had shown himself, and replaced the covers. When those who were kneeling rose and went away, their faces were bathed in tears, tears flowed down the faces of those who were standing, and sighs rose ceaselessly from their breasts. Others joined them, and when they had served the guest who was not there, they wept and sighed like the others. Their sighs and smothered weeping filled the hall.

At the same time he saw the light of the lamps suddenly die down as if it would go out. He looked at the master cook and was about to make a sign for him to attend to them. Then from the eyes of the master cook, a look struck him, from above and sidelong, which he had endured once in his life and thought he must never endure again; it was the look which the bleeding hawk had bent long and piercingly upon its master from a high rock for the last time, before it disappeared in the dusk with heavy, twitching wing-beats. With his utmost strength, the Emperor endured the being's look.

"Who art thou?" he cried. "Hither to my feet!"—and would not cast down his eyes.

The master cook turned his own slowly, as if in contempt, and made a single sign. The running and handing of dishes, the lifting of covers and the carving stopped. The hall stood full of silent figures. Through them he strode noiselessly towards the Emperor. The princess took a step as if to come between them, then stopped as if spellbound.

"Who is this man?" cried the Emperor to her over his shoulder. "What is this insolence in every step he takes? Who has set him up to be my judge?"

He felt the heavy beating of his heart. Meanwhile he had risen slowly to his feet—he might have been lifting some strange burden from the ground. He turned, and over his shoulder saw the maiden standing near by. Behind her, two youths had issued from the wall and approached him, one carrying a golden basin, the other a little ewer. When they had reached him and were preparing to pour water over his hands, he recognized in them the two wonderful youths who had appeared in the guise of seneschals and had vanished with their horses into the wall. The Emperor signed to them; he opened his hands towards them, glad and smiling, but they did not seem to know him. He opened his mouth to speak to them, but the words died in his throat. With strange and mournful faces they looked at him, one held out the basin, the other raised the ewer. The water leapt from the ewer; it struck hard against the Emperor's hands, pouring over them as over dead stone. The Emperor looked across to the maiden, as if seeking comfort; she had raised both hands, her face shone like a jewel, she seemed to be pointing him to where there was comfort and help. The Emperor sought for the meaning of her gesture as one in darkness struggles towards the light, but he could feel nothing within him but a dark tumult of changing feelings. He was deeply aware that the other, drawn up to his full height, was approaching him with slow, and it seemed, stern steps; measured by the dull beating of his heart, the time seemed unendurable till the other had covered the short distance that lay between them. But now, without raising his eyes, he felt the other close at hand; a chill blew upon him from his temples to his feet. Through his eyelashes he saw that the being had grasped at the empty air, now held a white linen towel in his hands, and was drying his own with reverence. But his flesh crept at the fluttering touch of the linen.

"O Emperor," said the voice, so close to his cheek that he felt the cold breath on his cheek and trembled with offence at a familiarity such as he had never known before. "Dost thou not regret that we have set her place for her in vain?"

The violence of the reproach in the simple words was beyond belief. The Emperor's heart was wrung, cold tears ran down his face, they froze on his cheeks. As a sign that he would suffer no one to speak to him of his wife, that no one should force him to yield up that which belonged to him alone, he gazed fixedly in front of him. The chill about him soothed him for a moment; nothing could reach his heart. Forthwith the children standing in the hall opened their mouths:

"She would fain come, but cannot," they called to him. "O that we might see her face," they cried on all sides, and began again to sigh and weep.

He strove to speak sternly: "What is this mourning?" But the words died in his throat. A wind, ghastly in its chillness, rose from the middle of the hall. At the same moment, the voice of him who showed so little reverence reached him, low, but close at hand: "Poor is the reward of him who helps thee to thy heart's desire! That thy red hawk knows."

To hear that first hour of love which had had no earthly witness but the dumb bird thus spoken of, the Emperor ground his teeth till the sound was audible. The silence had grown terrible. The wind had fallen.

"Dost thou not know my eldest brother?" the maiden whispered to him. "It was he who beat her eyes with his wings and helped thee to win her."

The Emperor gave no answer.

"She is seeking her way to us!" cried the children. "Do thou bless her way. That is all we crave of thee."

"What way is that?" the Emperor cried back, and at once felt a pang of compunction for the words, but it was heavy and dull, and he could not tell what it was.

"What boots it for us to tell thee what thou canst not comprehend?" replied the children. "Her letter lies on thy breast and thou canst not read it."

"What does this mean?" cried the Emperor, and felt the chill about his heart as he spoke.

"If thou couldst read it, thou wouldst know her anguish and understand her lamenting," they replied.

The Emperor's hand moved to his breast, but he felt there was no help for him there, and he let it fall.

"Thou hast not unloosed the knot of her heart. That is why we must mourn. So she must be taken from thee and given to him who can unloose the knot of her heart."

The wind had risen again and was blowing on him.

"Who has told you these things?" burst from his lips.

"Twelve moons are past, and she casts no shadow," cried the children.

"Then you know all?" asked the Emperor.

"We know that which must be known," said the children. "Thou hast surrounded her with walls," they chanted in antiphon, "therefore she must creep out like a thief. Like a thirsty gazelle, she steals away to the dwellings of men."

"How dare they say such things to me?" thought the Emperor. He heard the children's voices change. "That is the song I heard as I stood outside," he said to himself.

"She does the service of a handmaid," sang the lovely voices again, "but she rues it not. She does it for our sakes, and hardly has the light of the sun arisen when she sits upon her bed and cries with longing, 'Where art thou, Barak! Come in to me. For I owe myself to thee, Barak.' "

"To thee I owe myself, Barak," they all repeated, in radiant voices which resounded in the vault above.

"What words are these?" cried the Emperor, his eyes wide opened, with the last breath in his breast, which had grown heavy as stone.

"The last!" replied the children.

His chin dropped heavily upon his breast.

"Woe!" he said to himself. "Woe that my jester ever dared to speak of my sadness before I knew this hour."

"Hail to thee, Barak!" cried the children, and their voices rang with beauty. "Thou art but a poor dyer, but thou art great of soul and a friend of those who are to come, and we bow to the earth before thee."

The Emperor stood unheeded in their midst; they bowed before one who was not there, their lovely faces bowed so close to the ground that it shone like water. The maiden stood apart. Her eyes were bent unmoving upon the Emperor with an indescribable expression of love and dread. He turned his eyes upon her once more.

"Answer me," he said. "Who is this Barak, and what hath my wife to do with him?"

"O, but a grain of greatness," chanted the children in piercing voices.

"What?" he asked again, sternly, looking at her through half-closed eyes. His eyelids were growing heavy as lead. He neither expected nor wished for an answer. The maiden left the others. She glided towards him, it seemed on folded feet. Her troubled gaze seemed struggling to impart some wonderful secret to him.

"Only a grain of greatness," called the voices.

In horror, he saw that the maiden now mysteriously resembled his wife. There was a look of utmost dread and devotion in her eyes; she was the image of the gazelle in its mortal terror. In that look he could read nothing but the confession of that which he never wished to hear, and the prayer for a pardon he could not bestow. He hated the message and her who brought it, and felt his heart like a stone within him. Silently his hand sought the dagger at his belt to cast it at her, since he could not cast it at his wife. The fingers of his right hand were numb, his left hand moved to help them, but both refused their office; the stone arms lay stiff along the stone thighs, and no sound came from the stony lips.

"The time has come!" cried the eldest brother aloud. The lamps and the covered table vanished.

"Only a grain of greatness, O our father," fervently chanted all the lovely voices again, but the statue which stood tall and dark in their midst had ceased to move. The children flickered up and down like flames; a mild radiance shone from their faces. The eldest sister was the last to fade; her eyes clung to the statue. The walls drew in, the doors vanished, the chamber was a circle. It opened above, the stars looked down, the figures had vanished, and in the midst of the chamber the Emperor's statue stood alone.

5

Shakespeare's Kings and Noblemen

ADDRESS TO
THE SHAKESPEARE SOCIETY, WEIMAR, 1905

I THINK I know why you called me here to speak before you. It was certainly not the desire to learn something new; you certainly could not expect my handful of observations to add a substantial weight to the load of knowledge about Shakespeare with which your warehouses are overcrowded and your ships overburdened to the point of sinking. None of the obscurities (in so far as there are any left for you) could expect an illumination from me; none of the findings that you have received from preceding generations and will hand on, purified and deepened, to the generations to come, could want confirmation from my lips. But perhaps you feel a trifle oppressed, even overawed, at so much accumulated wealth; perhaps you sometimes feel stupefied by the immense flood of tradition in whose tumultuous roar the voice of Herder mingles with that of Sarah Siddons. And an inner voice—was it memory or intuition?—told you that beyond the pure passion of understanding, a less rational, less pure, more heterogeneous instrument is still needed to work the true magic. So you stepped out of the silent study of the scholar into the forest of life, and as the magician reaches for the mandrake you reached for someone alive; you reached for me and set me down in this circle. Accustomed to dissect the marvellous phenomenon into its elements and to dwell with your thoughts in the streaming rays of its divided light, you sometimes desire to call in from outside a living person at whose soul Shakespeare, as an undivided Whole, knocks like Fate demanding to be admitted, and for whose eyes this undivided light illuminates the depths and summits of existence. In your memory, which harbours an almost boundless tradition, there stirs an old saying occasionally obscured but never quite forgotten: the true readers of Shakespeare and also those in whom Shakespeare is truly alive are those who carry within them a stage.

"The gift of imaginary performance . . . this very specific creativeness: to produce within oneself action as it is on paper as the most personal experience." For this reason—and the words with which I try to convey it are from one out of your midst—let me believe that you called me here; for this reason, and because, to continue quoting Karl Werder, "Shakespeare's work is action, not mere description. Whoever wants simply to be told stories misunderstands him. Whoever only listens while reading him reads him only half and therefore mishears him. Shakespeare needs to be played, because only then can we hear and see what he does not and cannot say. If he were to say what would be necessary to make uncreative readers understand him without seeing him acted, then he would cease to be Shakespeare."

When I ponder these words and realize that with you they are a tradition—a tradition as unlikely to be lost as anything essential and intelligent ever said by a scholar in your field; and when at the same time I remember a paragraph from Otto Ludwig's essays whose first line runs: "Shakespeare wrote his plays from the core of dramatic art," then it is fully transparent to me what persuaded you to call me here: you presumed I know how to read Shakespeare with imagination. It is with the reader of Shakespeare that you are concerned, with the reader from whom you can assume and demand this "very specific creativeness"; and I feel that if I am not to dissipate your indulgence I must speak to you only of what is a pleasure and a passion, a conscious talent, an imagination, an innate art perhaps, like playing the flute or dancing, a shattering but silent inner orgy—the reading of Shakespeare.

I am speaking not of those who read Shakespeare like the Bible or some other true or great book; not of those who lower their faces, tired and wilted by life, over this deep mirror in order to realize that "life has always been like this," and who "cleanse the stuff'd bosom of that perilous stuff"; not of those whose heart is filled with "the ignominy that weighs upon the poor man's shoulder," with "the law's delay, the insolence of office," and all the other terribly real evils of Hamlet's monologue. I am speaking not of those who turn to the wisest of all books, seeking solace when before their outraged eyes the course of the world looks hopelessly out of joint—although it seems to me that it is on them that the marrow of Shakespeare's work continually renews itself. But the readers about whom I wish to speak are those on whom the skin also feeds, retaining forever the brilliant bloom of youth. These are the readers whose passion sees each of Shakespeare's works as a Whole. Those others, driven to Shakespeare by tragic experience, offer their soul—cruelly bent by the pain and harshness of life, like the body of a musical instrument—as the sensitive sounding-board for the fall from grandeur, the degradation of the good, self-destruction of the noble, and the ghastly fate of the tender spirit exposed to life. Those of whom I wish to speak are the sounding-board, however, not for this alone, but also for a thousand more delicate, more hidden, more sensual, more symbolic things—which, with their intertwining diversity, form the mysterious unit whose passionate servants they are. For them it is not only the great destinies, the sudden turning-points of Fate, the tremendous tragedies, that exist. The scene, for instance, where Lear's daughters enter the castle at the approach of rough weather: the heavy door groans to a close behind them and the old man stands there, his white hair exposed to the drenching rain, his heart to the sinister night and the frenzy of his impotent rage. Or the scene in the gloom of the castle yard when Macbeth and his wife, their glances locked in complicity, exchange muttered words. Or that in which Othello steps from the door into the yard, from another door on to the rampart, Iago always one pace behind him, words pouring from his mouth like corrosive poison, a devouring, inextinguishable fire-poison eating through the bone into the marrow, Othello listening all the time and protesting, his tongue twisting in his mouth like that of an animal about to be slaughtered, his rolling bloodshot eyes as helpless as a tortured steer's; and Iago, his fangs always in the other's entrails, dragging him, the dog the steer, through rooms and corridors, doors and courts, letting go only in the final death struggle. . . . Although nothing created by human beings can be compared with these scenes, it is not for them alone that the readers about whom I wish to speak lose themselves in a world built by a genius. For them there are innumerable encounters during which the soul does not have to hide fearfully in the dark and cry out to itself: *Guarda e passa!*

These dramas are not exclusively filled with events whose aspect is of the same order of things as the maelstrom, the surging sinister sea, the landslide, or the human face frozen in death. Not everything in them emanates the dread loneliness that hovers round the monstrous fates as it does round the summits of icy mountains. At times in one of these dramas the human destinies, the dark and shining, yes, even the torments and degradation and bitterness of the death hour, are so well woven into a Whole that their being side by side, their merging and disappearing into one another, creates something like a deeply moving, solemn, and woeful music. In *Henry VIII* Wolsey's fall and his calm acceptance of it, the clear sound of his great, resigned words, and again the dying of Queen Katharine, this fading away of a gentle, suffering voice, the festive music surrounding the King and the new Queen, all merge inextricably into a melodious Whole, which, in its heroic elements and the recurrent theme, is reminiscent of a Beethoven sonata. In the romantic plays, in *The Tempest*, in *Cymbeline, Measure for Measure, As You Like It,* and in *The Winter's Tale,* the Whole is interwoven by this music. Or rather everything joins into it, everything surrenders to this music, everything which is placed side by side, everything breathing at the other, mingling love and hatred in their breath, everything that glides past the other, that delights or terrifies, all that is sublime and all that is ridiculous—yes, all that is there and not there, in so far as in each work of art those things which do not appear in them also play a part by spreading their shadows round the Whole. Only the combination of all this can produce the unutterably sweet music of the Whole. And it is precisely of the reader who can hear this music that I wish to speak to you—because he is the person who reads Shakespeare with all his heart, with all his soul, with all his strength. And of him in whom this passion dwells let me speak to you as of a figure, as Milton in his verse speaks of L'Allegro and Il Penseroso, or as La Bruyère speaks of the Distracted and the Ambitious. I feel that such plays as *Cymbeline, The Tempest,* and the others possess the power to produce again and again in the imagination of the creative reader an inner stage on which their magic can live and their music be heard as a Whole.

In the same way the figures of Lear and Shylock, of Macbeth and Juliet, overpower the body of the great actor in order to live and die in it—for there is no doubt that Shakespeare's reader and Shakespeare's actor are closely related. The difference is that round the actor a single figure wraps itself like a skin, whereas in the reader all figures want to live simultaneously. The former is beckoned aside by a phantom: "Give me all your blood to drink," while the latter is surrounded by a host of phantoms. I do believe that with this mysterious awakening of a "specific creativeness" on a day unlike other days, under a wind and weather unlike other wind and weather, the figure will demand to be played by the actor (who is powerless to refuse) and the drama demand of the reader: "Today you read me, and I live in you." I don't believe that the reader who "carries within him a stage" could have read *Romeo and Juliet* on the day he was destined to read *The Tempest.* Perhaps he reached out for *Romeo and Juliet;* he leafed through it, but the play left him cold. It didn't tempt him. The lines of verse whereon his eye fell today seemed to him indifferent, not like eyes, not like the calyx of a flower through which one can peer into its depths. The stage directions for the acts and scenes did not seem like little hidden doors in a mysterious wall, not like narrow clearings which open and lead into the dusky heart of the forest. So he laid the volume down and was about to go off without Shakespeare when his eye fell on this title: *The Tempest.* And in a flash he knew: "I can, after all, create life. Today I am able to revive within myself Prospero and Miranda, Ariel and Caliban, more effectively than water can revive wilted flowers. Today or never am I the island on which all this has happened. Today or never I carry within me the cave before whose entrance Caliban suns himself, the thicket of high fantastic trees round whose crowns Ariel glides like a miraculous bird: within me also is the air of this island, a southern evening breeze of gold and blue wherein Miranda's beauty swims like a wonder of the sea in its element. Today or never am I all these things at once: I am Prospero's magnificence and Ferdinand's youth, Ariel's elflike devotion and Caliban's hate; I am Antonio the evil, Gonzalo the honest, Stephano the drunken villain. And why, pray, should I not be all these beings? In me there are so many. In me so many meet one another."—True, in each of us there live more beings than we care to admit to ourselves. Somewhere lying dormant within us are the shadows and fears of boyhood's twilight hours forming a cave for Caliban. There is so much space within us. And over many things drifting about in us we have no more power than a shipowner over his vessels tossing about at sea.

So the reader walks off with *The Tempest* in his pocket. The meadow is too near to the highway, the forest already too dark. For a while he strolls to and fro unable to decide, until he settles down on a tree trunk between gossamer threads and mossy branches, and projects his magic theatre. It requires a supreme effort of imagination; he has to efface himself, become completely empty, become the scene of action, that island, become completely a stage. Then Prospero emerges from the cave, a shadow of tiredness on his noble face, and Miranda's flowerlike hands reach for the clasp to loosen the dark magic cloak from his shoulders. And now he, the reader, is nothing but an instrument: now the book plays on him.

You will tell me that my reader's name is Charles Lamb or Théophile Gautier, that he is a poet in whom the poems of others come once again to life. But that should make no difference. What matters is Shakespeare's music, and that again and again there must be someone to whom it is granted to hear the whole music of these poems. But it must be as a Whole.— Take *Measure for Measure*, a play full of harshness, with sombre passages, with a strange, tart blending of the high and the low; more difficult in language, its motives moving us less quickly than the others—a play that begins to live only after we have heard its whole music. It resembled the faces of certain rare women whose beauty is known only to him who has been happy with them. How frightful is this action in itself, this story of the disloyal judge, disloyal to his profession, disloyal to the wretched convicted, disloyal to the good sister —how harsh and sinister, how heart-constricting, how outrageous, repulsive, and revolting all this is! How harsh and sinister, how painful is Claudio's fate, his fear of death, his clinging to the straw that can save him! And all this only because of a senseless law, because of something no better than a trivial coincidence, a "blank in the lottery"! And grafted on to this misfortune which so outrages us, more misfortune. What a wonderful composition it is! what lights thrown on darkness! what life these lights give the shadows! In the mouth of the one who has to die and is afraid of dying, what a voice, what eloquence, what language, wiser than himself, more profound than his shallow virtue—how death squeezes out of him the best sap! And in the mouth of the girl who is helpless, who is betrayed, what strength, what a sword of God suddenly in her hand! And the others! See how their lives intertwine, how their very presence changes the air: the presence of the old murderer Barnardine, who has been condemned to death for seven years, next to the boy Claudio, who was condemned twenty-four hours ago. Friar Thomas and Friar Peter in the quiet monastery with its peace and seclusion, next to the prison, next to the palace wherein the evil Angelo lurks like a poisonous spider in the masonry. Then all of a sudden we are out of town and there sits Mariana before the "moated grange" and a boy's voice singing that sweet song "Take, O take those lips away". . . And between this world and that, combining everything like a chorus, the disguised Duke, who now sees at close range those whom he has formerly seen only from

above, from afar, he whose presence calms our heart as during
a nightmare does the deep knowledge "It is only a dream!" and
from whose lips fall those incomparable words about life and
death. Between these figures, so that life and light shall play
everywhere over living flesh, the shadows emphasizing life,
there is still this company of commoner, lower beings, even the
least among them not completely denuded of some goodness
or wit, some grace or courtesy, not quite incapable of showing
goodwill, of saying something kind or uttering an apt analogy.
And between all these human beings, what an atmosphere,
what a co-existence on this earth, what little yet immeasurably
deep and tender gestures toward one another, what looks of
pity or mockery exchanged between them! What a Whole, not
of calculation, not of reason, not even of emotion, a Whole
not so much from the point of view of colours alone or from
that of morality, not from the contrast between heaviness and
lightness, sadness and gaiety—but from a combination of all
this, what a Whole "before God"! What music!

In the performance of *Twelfth Night* by Beerbohm Tree
and his troupe, the play ends—and it is said that this was not
the director's brilliant idea, but an old English tradition—with
each gentleman offering a hand to his lady, and thus, in
couples, the Duke and Viola, Olivia and Sebastian, and behind them their retinue dance across and off the stage. Hand
in hand they dance, those who had inflamed and tortured one
another, sought and deceived and enchanted one another.
Thus these figures become figures of a dance, pursuing and
not finding, chasing the Wrong and fleeing the Right. This is
now the final figure, and for an instant something wafts past
it like a shadow, a fleeting memory of the Dance of Death
which also makes everything equal, as everything here is equal
and together, hands in hands, is creating a double chain, a
"figure" wherein the single destiny has as much value as

a single spot of colour on an ornament, as a single theme in a symphony. Even if this idea were re-created out of an old tradition, it was nevertheless once, the first time, a stroke of genius on the part of one director who invented this perfect symbol of binding together the human bodies (in whose gestures he has expressed for five acts the experiences of each single character), of binding them together at the last moment by a rhythm and expressing in them the wholeness of the Whole. You will say that this director was also a poet. But every creative stage director is a poet. Again and again throughout history Fate chooses one man from among those who "carry within them a stage" and who, in luxurious solitude, play Shakespeare for themselves—chooses the man and gives him a real stage.

And thus, among the hundreds of stages on which Shakespeare is played for show—where he is played, I mean, for tradition's sake, because he constitutes part of the repertory or because his plays contain fine roles—there shines out one stage where he is performed out of sheer passion. Just as Macbeth and Shylock, Othello and Juliet, continue to overpower the body and soul of an actor of genius, so the music of the dramas continues to overpower the soul of a creative director and his whole stage, and lives anew. For everything alive lives only from the living, and the flame only from that which wants to burn.

On announcing that I was going to talk to you about Shakespeare's kings and noblemen, it was agreed that I would not speak of anything but the Whole in Shakespeare's work. It's as though I had said I wished to talk about the solemn and sublime sounds in Beethoven's symphonies, or of light and colour in Rubens. When I say "kings and noblemen" your memory is inundated with a flood of figures and gestures incomparable to any vision unless it be that which was granted

to the old men on the walls of Troy when before their eyes
the dust-clouds parted, and the sun was seen gleaming on the
armour and faces of the countless heroes so akin to the gods.
More figures, images, feelings, surge up in you than you can
grasp. You are reminded at once of Lear, who is a king, every
inch a king; of Hamlet, who is a prince, a prince to his fingertips; of Richard II, that elder "brother" of Hamlet who talks
so much about his royal blood, round whose shoulders hangs
the royal cloak as agonizing to wear as that garment immersed
in the blood of Nessus and which, when finally torn off, spells
certain death. And the face of Henry VI, pale as though his
head had been cut off and stuck on a pike, rests for an instant
in you, and the face of gentle Duncan, too. In a flash you see
the royal, commanding gestures of Antony and feel a breath of
the spirit-kingdom on Prospero's island, of the fairy-realm of
those idyllic kings in long red cloaks and sceptres in their
hands—Leontes of Sicily, Polixenes of Bohemia, Cymbeline,
and Theseus. But this flood of visions continues to rise, and
you look into an imbroglio of noble gestures until your head
begins to swim. The gestures of command and contempt, of
haughty defiance and magnanimity, glitter before your eyes
like a thousand flashes of lightning. The words "kings and
noblemen" have the power to make continuously fresh floods
rise from the well of a memory steeped in Shakespeare.
Swamped by a vision and figures almost impossible to grasp,
you will search within yourselves for a word that can compress
in one idea this whole imaginary world of spirits. You sense
that these words conjure up not only three-quarters of all
figures created by Shakespeare, but also what happens between these figures as well as what happens between them and
those of less importance who stand beside them; you sense
that these words apply not only to these figures but also to the
empty space around them and to what fills this empty space—

what the Italians call *l'ambiente.* You slowly realize that in this world of Shakespeare there really exists a line leading from one point to another, some true relation between the scene in which Kent, the unrecognized, offers his services to Lear because he had something in his countenance which "he would fain call master," and the sylvan idyll of King Cymbeline's sons who grow up in a cave, unfettered, like beautiful young animals although of royal blood; between the sullen feuds of the English barons in the dramas of the kings and the benevolent master's tone in which noble Brutus speaks to Lucius, his page; between the tone of proud Othello, yes, between Cleopatra, a queen, and Falstaff, who is—after all—a nobleman. You feel, as I do, this imponderable, this intangible element, this Nothing which is nevertheless everything, and from my lips you take the words wherewith I wish to name it—the Atmosphere of Shakespeare's work. This word could not be more vague, yet it belongs to those of which we may have to make a very definite, very productive use.

At no other time of the year, however, would I have dared to speak of something so vague and in it to seek something so great than now, that spring has come.

"Now with the drops of this most balmy time/My love looks fresh" . . . and now greater than ever is the courage to see all beautiful things afresh, to dismiss all those clearly defined subjects which are usually discussed—characters, actions, ideas—and to follow this fleeting, barely palpable truth which pervades all of Shakespeare's work.

The moment itself has so much atmosphere. I mean this very moment in the life of Nature, this moment of the not yet fully awakened, not yet luxuriating, still-yearning spring in which the death-anniversary of a human being unites us here, a human being who has become almost a myth to us and of whom we can scarce believe that he ever was a presence among mortal men. It does not appear to me as something essentially different whether we sense the atmosphere of spring, the atmosphere of a Shakespearean drama, or that of a picture by Rembrandt. Here as there I feel a gigantic *ensemble*. (Let me take this sober word from the technique of painting rather than any other. There are many at my disposal: I could speak of the music of the Whole, of a harmony, of a spiritualization, but all these words strike me as somewhat wilted, slightly soiled by the touch of human hands.) An *ensemble* wherein the difference between great and small has been cancelled in so far as one lives for the sake of the other, the great for the small, the dark for the light, where one seeks the other, emphasizes and restrains the other, colours and discolours, and where finally for the soul there exists nothing but the Whole —the indivisible, intangible, imponderable Whole. To dissect the atmosphere of spring was always the passion of the lyric poet. But its essence is nevertheless the *ensemble*. Everywhere the world is burgeoning. The far and the near whisper to one another; the tepid breeze gliding over the still-naked earth breathes an air of oppressive sultriness. Light, like water, is melting everywhere, but no moment is more pregnant with the abundance of spring than that of noon, when darkness falls and heavy, sinister clouds brood over the earth-brown hills and the clamour of delirious bird-voices rises from the bare branches into the gloom. And as in a phantasmagoria, everything has changed. The naked landscape, hitherto so sad and deserted, is full of voluptuousness. The darkness doesn't oppress, it exalts. The near is as mysterious as the far. And the voice of a single bird contributes no less to the Whole than the dark forest which lends to the wind the scent of moist earth and budding green.

I could continue to offer you this notion of Atmosphere were I not sure that you have understood me immediately and completely, and were I not afraid to tire you. The death of a human being has its Atmosphere, like spring. The faces of those in whose arms a man has died speak a language that defies words. And in their presence inanimate objects join in this language. A chair that has always stood elsewhere, an open cupboard that has never remained open for long, and a thousand trivial signs appearing at such a moment like traces of ghosts' hands: this is the world which ends at the window panes. But the outside world, too, in a mysterious way, shows this fateful, deeply knowing face: the street lamps are burning as on any other day; the passing of the unsuspecting strangers, turning a corner, passing the house, turning another corner— all this condenses itself into something that drags along like an ominous iron chain. These are the moments when the long-forgotten friends return: the emergence of those whose be-haviour has become queer, who are embittered or utterly estranged, and out of whom now break forth words and looks never heard or seen at any other time. The sudden astonish-ment: how did we part? how did all this happen? The quick realization: how futile everything is! How alike we all are, how similar to one another!—This, too, is Atmosphere. Here, too, something indefinable connects the near with the far, the great with the small, one moving the other into its proper light, intensifying and subduing, colouring and discolouring one by the other, annihilating all borderlines between the seem-ingly important and seemingly unimportant, the common and the exceptional—and creates the *ensemble* out of the whole existing material, considering no elements to be incom-patible.

The Atmosphere in Shakespeare's work is nobility: the king is merely the greatest nobleman among great noblemen, and each of them has in him something of a king—nobility in

the sense of the Cinquecento—that is, infinitely freer, infinitely
more human, more colourful than anything which we are accustomed to associate with this notion. It is not only the characters and their feelings born out of Shakespeare's soul which
are imbued with this nobility, but precisely and above all the
Atmosphere, the air of life, *ce grand air* pervading everything.
All these characters (the duller few who do not belong
to them exist only to create contrast) are steeped in the element of nobility as the figures in the paintings of Titian and
Giorgione are steeped in the golden, luminous element of
colour. It's in this element that such groups as Romeo, Mercutio, Benvolio, Tybalt, as well as Antonio the noble merchant
and his friends, move. The banished Duke in the Ardennes
and all those who belong to him, above all Brutus and his
household, are surrounded by this aura. This light, this air, is
around them in such abundance and with such intensity that
it cannot be ignored. A noble consciousness—nay, deeper than
that—an existence of almost conscious nobility, a noble
breathing, and closely connected with it a remarkable tender
and strong feeling for the other person, a mutual almost im-
personal affection, a tenderness, reverence for the human.
Have I not recalled to you with these words—too weak to
express what is ineffably alive—what all these different young
people have in common: the melancholic Jaques with the
light-hearted Bassanio, the passionate Romeo with the shrewd,
shy Mercutio? The element in which these beings are bred is
delicately suspended between arrogance and courtesy. It is the
youthful attitude of defiance which is nevertheless shocked at
the thought of having offended—a readiness to open up and
form attachments, yet at the same time remaining detached
and complete. Their equilibrium is one of the most beautiful
things I know. Like graceful, well-built ships they lie rocking

to and fro above their own shadows on the flood of life. Round them there is something exultant, something expansive over-flowing into the air, an abundance of life, a glorification of life itself, something definitely welcoming life, something that evokes the Pythian and Nemean odes of Pindar, those radiant salutations of victors. Not only is Prince Henry ultimately their brother, but so, to a certain degree, is Falstaff. They are youths, but Brutus is a man. They are without any other des-tiny but the destiny of love; they seem to be placed in this picture only as a glorification of life, like glowing reds and resplendent yellows in a painting. Brutus, however, has a lofty destiny of his own. He is modelled of the same clay as they, but he is a more mature person. It is not the manner in which his soul interprets life, but his attitude in life, this nobility without harshness, full of generosity, of goodness and gentle-ness, this tone whose harmony could shine forth only from a soul in whose depths the profoundest self-respect is rooted. Apart from his destiny which fulfills itself in him—"the genius and the mortal instruments are then in council"—and drives him to the great deed of his life which is then followed by everything else, even by death, as water follows water when a dam is opened; apart from his inner destiny this tragedy (whose hero is Brutus) is illuminated almost exclusively by the light of this noble being in whose ray all other characters mould themselves by coming closer to him. What occurs be-tween Brutus and Cassius is nothing but the reaction of Cas-sius (who is less noble and knows himself to be less noble) to the atmosphere around Brutus. In Cassius there is a vain, mute, inner wooing of Brutus, a wooing with every torment of jealousy which Cassius does not admit to himself, which Bru-tus, too, perhaps, if aware of it, does not admit, doesn't want to know, certainly doesn't want to analyse. And in Brutus an amazing forbearance for Cassius; up to the moment of his single outburst he places himself tactfully on the same level; and even then it is his nerves, not his will, which give way. (An hour ago he has received the news of Portia's death, yet refrains from mentioning it.) And then, on parting, once again: "noble, noble Cassius." Imagine him being capable of saying this, the noble one to the less noble! Of feeling driven to say it twice! This is the attitude of Brutus towards Cassius. And Portia! She has but this one unforgettable scene. Enveloped in the atmosphere of Brutus, her noble face is moulded from the light emanating from him. Or does this light emanate from elsewhere? Are both Brutus and Portia moulded out of this light and its shadows? Who, before a Rembrandt, can say whether the atmosphere is there for the sake of the figures or the figures for the sake of the atmosphere? But certain places exist simply to catch the whole light, which is the soul of the atmosphere. I have in mind the scenes with the boy Lucius and the other servants. The considerate tone of his voice when he apologizes to Lucius for shortening his sleep to which his youth has so much claim. And this: "Look, Lucius, here's the book I sought for so; I put it in the pocket of my gown. . . . Bear with me, good boy." And then, as Lucius falls asleep while tuning his lute, Brutus steps forward to remove the lute on which his arm has sunk in slumber: "If thou dost nod, thou break'st thy instrument." I don't know what can bring tears to a reader's eye if not such a detail. This is the man who was Caesar's murderer. He is the general in his tent. He is the last Roman; tomorrow at Philippi he will die. And here he is, bending down, and from under the sleeping boy removing a lute so that it shall not be broken. And at the moment of making this small gesture, this plain, homely, almost feminine little gesture —more natural to a woman, a housewife, a mother—at this moment, so near his death (Caesar's ghost is already standing there in the dark), I see his face: it's a face he has never had before, a second face as though taking form from within—a face in which male and female features mingle, as in the death masks of Beethoven and Napoleon. It is here that we are moved to tears, rather than at Lear's curses, rather than when Macbeth, strangled in his own iron torments as in a hundredweight of armour, turns his eye on us and constricts our heart. From such minor details our admiration for Shakespeare is intensified to the pitch of worship. Indeed, in a work of art there is no difference between great and small. Here, when Brutus, Caesar's murderer, picks up the lute so that it shall not be broken, here as nowhere else do we face the tornado of existence that sucks us down. These are the flashes of lightning wherein a heart reveals itself completely. We are reminded of Ottilie in the *Elective Affinities,* who could never forget the anecdote about how Charles I of England, already dethroned and surrounded by enemies, drops the knob of his stick. He looks round and, dumbfounded to see that no one picks it up, stoops himself for the first time in his life. This incident so engraves itself on her heart that from then on she stoops whenever anyone, even a man, drops something. Again, we think of the howl suddenly uttered by Natasha during the hare-hunt in *War and Peace,* that wild, triumphant howl of a hound from the throat of an elegant young lady. These are the flashes of lightning I have in mind. And in Shakespeare they are legion. They are the cataclysms of his atmosphere.

I know nothing that so grips the heart as the tone of Lear's voice when he speaks to Edgar. To his daughters he talks like a furious prophet or a patriarch drunk with pain. To his Fool he speaks harshly. But to Edgar, that naked madman whom he has found in a cave, he speaks in a tone (wherein, to be sure, there is something of madness) whose keynote is an extraordinary politeness of the heart, an indescribable courtesy, which makes us realize how this king could sometimes make his people happy when in a gracious mood. It is that same politeness whose glow hovers over gentle Duncan when he comes in and suggests that the air round Macbeth's castle ought to be good since swifts nest there. The same light, too, shines over that brief scene between Richard II and the groom (shortly before his death); and the same but stronger, more exotic, more resplendent light in each scene between Antony and Cleopatra, between Antony and his friends, Cleopatra and her attendants. What reverence for themselves and the grandeur of their existence! What "Olympian air," what magnificent style, when the affairs of the world have to wait in the anteroom while they embrace: "The nobleness of life is to do thus . . ." The same light again, as if penetrating dense storm-clouds with furious flashes of lightning, falls on the hundred figures of the proud peers of England whose self-esteem (one of them calls it "our stately presence") shrouds them in wide folds grander, wilder, more real than any ermine-trimmed cloak. But I could continue endlessly saying "It is here! It is there!" for I see it everywhere. I could spend another hour describing how I see in this aura the figures of all these regal, noble women, from Cleopatra to Imogen. I see it everywhere so much, in fact, that I am deeply perplexed when perceiving a figure like Macbeth with almost nothing of this atmosphere around him. This suggests to me that Shakespeare meant to endow him with a peculiar frightfulness, meant to let him be shrouded by an icy air of death. It seems as if the ghastly breath of Hecate had eaten away from the world around Macbeth everything alive, everything that ordinarily unites mankind, leaving nothing of that which surrounds Hamlet as a breath of life. Take the scene with the actors, where Hamlet's whole being expands in a princely, gracious self-indulgence and joy, even delighting others with his self-indulgence. Or the scenes with Polonius,

Rosencrantz, and Guildenstern as a conscious use of his princely eminence, an ironic and grievous demonstration of his superiority—implying that even this prerogative is worth nothing, even this privilege is of no avail save as an instrument of self-torture.

GENTLEMEN! The ideas I have been expounding here seem to me to bind together the whole of Shakespeare's work. They are a mystery and the word "Atmosphere" describes them in as unsatisfactory and almost as superficial a manner as the word "Chiaroscuro" describes a similar mystery in the work of Rembrandt. Were I thinking of the figures alone—and it is the isolated figures, as though standing in a vacuum, that are usually made the subject of observation—then I would have tried to talk of the Shakespearean "attitude." For the important point is to see or to sense the common ground whereon, in life, all these figures stand. Dante's figures are placed in a gigantic architectonic system and the place on which each stands is *its* place according to mystical designs. Shakespeare's figures, on the other hand, are determined not by the stars but by themselves; they carry within themselves hell, purgatory, and heaven, and instead of their place in life they have their attitude. I, however, see these figures not each by itself but each in relation to all the others, and between them not a vacuum but a space mystically alive. I don't see them next to one another separately, like the figures of saints on a painting by an early primitive, but standing out from a common element like the men, animals, and angels in the paintings of Rembrandt.

The drama (I don't mean only Shakespeare's drama) is just as much a picture of the absolute solitude of the individual as a picture of the co-existence of mankind. In the dramas cast out of the volcano of Kleist's fiery soul, this atmosphere, this co-existence of characters, is perhaps the most beautiful part of the whole. His creatures, you will remember, are continually lusting after one another; suddenly, when addressing one another, they change from the distant you to the naked thou, caress one another with amorous glances, seize one another with violence, the one yearning to merge into the other but promptly turning cold, flying asunder in estrangement, then to go all over again in ardent search of one another. All this fills Kleist's space with passionate life and movement and creates something living out of the void.

To sum up: Whatever occurs between these figures seems to me filled with a life flowing from the same mysterious sources as the figures themselves. This mirroring of one another, this humiliating and exalting, restraining and fortifying of one another—all this, for me, is as much the work of a hand of a gigantic genius as the figures themselves. And it is because I cannot, in Shakespeare's work any more than in Rembrandt's, draw or admit a dividing line between the figures themselves and that part of the picture without them that I have seized upon the word "Atmosphere." The lack of time and the urgency of immediate understanding between us has prevented me from employing a word even more appropriate and more mysterious—the word "Myth."

Had I been able with greater intensity than today to evoke in your minds the power of Rembrandt and with comparable intensity the power of Homer, then these three primeval forces —Shakespeare's Atmosphere, Rembrandt's Chiaroscuro, Homer's Myth—would for a moment have merged into one. Grasping this glowing key, we would have descended to the Mothers, and there, where "neither Space, still less Time" exists, have visualized the deepest creating and longing of distant spirits in mystical union with the deepest creating and longing of our own epoch—to generate atmosphere for its existence, to let its figures move in the lightness and darkness of life, to imbue its breath with myth.

Balzac

THOSE WHO KNOW only this or that book by Balzac do not know this great author. No single volume contains the essence of his poetic genius as *Faust* or the *Poems* contain the essence of Goethe's. Balzac has to be read extensively, and to read him does not require any art. He provides the most natural reading matter for men of the world—and I employ that phrase in its broadest sense—from the solicitor's clerk or merchant's apprentice to the *grand seigneur*. The reading of Goethe, on the other hand, requires from men of the world (I am talking here of men of all ranks, of politicians and soldiers, of travelling salesmen, of distinguished and simple women, of clerics, of all people who are neither professionals nor amateurs of letters, of all those who read not from desire for self-improvement but for entertainment or in order to stimulate their imagination) an occasional minor effort, a certain transition. While it is more than possible that Goethe would deny himself to them in the troubled and confused moments of their existence, Balzac will always be ready to open his door to them. I do not mean this in the literary sense, for the first verse of Goethe's they set eyes on will always be something marvellous, as from another world, an incantation; whereas with Balzac they may easily fall upon three or four boring, tiresome pages, not only at the beginning of a story but possibly wherever they may happen to open the book. Nevertheless, while automatically glancing at these indifferent and rather laborious pages, something will begin to take hold of them, something from which the real reader, the alive reader, can never escape—a vast, indescribably substantial imagination, the greatest, most substantially creative imagination since Shakespeare. Wherever they open the book —be it at a digression on the law of exchange or the practices of usurers, on legitimist or liberal society, the description of a kitchen interior, of a marital scene, of a face or a den, they will feel the *world*, substance, the same substance from which the vicissitudes of their own lives are shaped. They will be able to move over directly from their own lives—from their worries and vexations, from their favourite anecdotes and financial affairs, their trivial troubles and ambitions—without intermediary stages, into these books. I have met the banker who, after his meetings and conferences, picked up without transition his Balzac, in which he kept as bookmarker his last quotation from the Stock Exchange; I have met the *dame du monde* who considered *Les Illusions perdues* or *La Vieille fille* to be the only possible literature to find the way back to herself.

In the evenings, after we have been among people or have entertained guests, Balzac seems the only reading matter strong and pure enough to cure the imagination of its sudden and destructive fever of vanity and to reduce all social matters to their human value. This function of delving straight into the lives of human beings, of curing the ill with the ill, of conquering reality with intensified daemonic reality—I ask myself who among the great authors, on whom our intellectual life counts, can in this respect rival Balzac, unless it be Shakespeare? But to read Shakespeare as former generations read the classics—I mean to read them so that we absorb from him the whole of life, to read him from the point of view of living, and to satisfy through him our profoundest desire for knowledge—this not all of us can do. Not everyone can strain his imagination and make it soar across the distance of three centuries, make it penetrate all the guises of a magnificent but utterly strange epoch, and recognize behind them only the eternally true ups and downs of human actions and sufferings. It is not easy for everyone without the help of the actors, without a very specific talent for recreative imagination, to unravel the most brilliant telescoping and condensation ever realized, to spread it out into such a broad picture of the world that in it he can rediscover himself and the manifold entangled threads of existence whose interwoven pattern represents his reality.

In a certain sense Goethe is easier to read, and who does not read him? Although he expressed one of his profound and subtle insights when he said that his writings were not qualified to become popular and that their true content would always reveal itself only to the individual who has gone through similar experiences, there seem to be so many of these individuals nowadays that the truth of his words has almost lost its meaning. He, however, who wants to reabsorb one of Goethe's works, who wants to enjoy *Hermann and Dorothea, Wilhelm Meister,* or the *Elective Affinities,* must approach the book with senses already purified. He must leave much of himself, of the atmosphere of his life, behind. He must forget the big city. He must cut through ten thousand threads of the feeling, thinking, and wishing of the moment. He must try to recall his "spiritual body"—I mean his immortal, his absolute, his purely human essence; he must keep in mind the eternal stars and through them purify himself. Once he has achieved this, however, it is of little importance which of Goethe's works he opens. Everywhere he is enveloped by the same enhanced and transfigured reality; he is truly surrounded

by a world, a spirit in itself a world. The interpretations and
the characters, an idea or the description of a phenomenon of
nature, a verse, a figure like Mignon or Ottilie—all these are
of the same divine radiant substance. Behind each line he
senses the reference to a Whole, to a sublime order. The immense calm of an immense wealth descends almost oppres-
sively on his soul in order to raise this soul again into a state
of bliss. But this arm which can raise to the stars does not
embrace everyone. The living Goethe, too, gave himself only
to a few and to these not at any hour. To him who reaches
out for it with a nervous hand, a creation such as the *Elective
Affinities* snaps shut like the shell of an oyster. To such people
Goethe appears cool, distant, strange. He impresses more than
he captivates. They postpone the reading of his work—for
calmer days or for a journey. Or he creates in them a nostalgia
for their youth, for a higher receptiveness. To them he appears
artificial, he who was himself Nature, and cold, he whose
loving eye penetrated even the impenetrable primitive rock
with warmth. They gaze about in search of something that
will help them enjoy him. They reach out for an interpreter
or for the wonderful letters and conversations in which he
comments on himself, and only in this roundabout way do
they return again to his books.

Nothing is more unthinkable than a reader who would
come to Balzac's works by an indirect route. The fewest of
his innumerable readers know anything about his life. The
littérateurs know a few minor anecdotes which would be of
interest to no one were they not concerned with the author of
the *Comédie humaine*. And they know the correspondence
with one person containing almost nothing but bulletins about
the incessant, gigantic job of writing—an achievement that
cannot be compared with any other in the world of literature.
It is the strongest proof of the immense power of his work

that we are able to read these endless bulletins with a thrill similar to that with which we read Napoleon's reports on his campaigns, on Austerlitz, Jena, and Wagram. His readers know his books, but not him. They say *La Peau de chagrin* and recall a waking dream, an adventurous experience, not the achievement of a poet; they think of old Goriot and his daughters but do not remember the name of the author. Once they have entered this world, ninety out of a hundred readers will always return to it again, after five, after ten, after twenty years. Walter Scott, who once was read with rapture by mature people, has become the reading-matter for boys. Balzac will always (or for a long time, for who can speak of always?) remain the reading matter for all stages of life, for men as well as women. The war stories and adventures, *Les Chouans, L'Auberge rouge, El Verdugo,* are for the imagination of a sixteen-year-old boy the next stage after the tales of Red Indians and Captain Cook; the experiences of Rubempré and Rastignac compose the reading of the young man; *Le Lys dans la vallée, Savarus, Modeste Mignon,* that of the young woman. Men and women around forty, the mature but not effete ones, will keep to the most mature—to *La Cousine Bette,* that magnificent book which, although containing only ugly, sad, and terrible facts, I cannot call sinister because it glows with fire, life, and wisdom; to *La Vieille fille* which combines a plasticity of characterization surpassing all praise with the most profound philosophy of life, and at the same time is intimate, cosy, gay—in every respect an incomparable book that alone would have the power to carry the fame of the author through the generations. I have heard an old gentleman praise the *Contes drolatiques,* and I have heard another old gentleman speak with emotion about the story of César Birotteau, that steady rise of a good man from year to year, from profit to profit, from honour to honour. And if there have been people who cut out of *Wilhelm Meister* the "Confessions of a Beautiful Soul" and burned the rest, then there has surely also been the man who cut Séraphitus-Séraphita out of the *Comédie humaine* and made of it a devotional book. And just such a person, perhaps, was that unknown man who, in a Viennese concert hall, forced his way to Balzac to kiss the hand that had written *Séraphita*.

In Balzac's work everyone finds as much of the great complexity of life as he carries in himself. The more richly a man's experience has been nourished, the stronger the imagination he possesses, the more deeply will he enter into these books. Here no one need leave anything of himself outside. All his emotions, uncleansed as they are, will be brought into play. Here he finds his own inner and outer world, only stranger, more condensed, more illuminated from within. Here are the powers that determine him, here the inhibitions that paralyse him. Here are the diseases of the soul, the greeds, the almost pointless aspirations, the consuming vanities; here are all the demons that burrow within us. Here above all is the great city with which we are familiar, or the province in its peculiar relation to the big city. Here is the money, the colossal power of money, the philosophy of money, transformed into characters, the myth of money. Here are the social stratifications, the political groupings that are more or less still ours; here is the fever of rising in the world, the fever of money-making, the fascination of work, the lonely mysteries of the artists, the inventors—everything down to the misery of the petit-bourgeois life, to the small money-misery, to the laboriously and constantly mended glove, to the gossip of the servant.

The exterior truth of these things is so great that it has been able to continue its existence separate, so to speak, from its object, and to pass on like an atmosphere; the Paris of Louis Philippe has disappeared, but certain constellations, the salon in the province in which Rubempré takes his first step into the world, or Madame de Bargeton's salon in Angoulême have today an astonishing significance for Austria whose social and political condition bears, in a sense, a resemblance to the July Monarchy; and certain features from the life of Rastignac and de Marsay are possibly more significant today for England than for France. But the varnish of this palpable and exciting "truth," the first great glory of the "modern" surrounding his work, will pass. Nevertheless, the inner truth of this world hurled forth by the imagination (which coincides only for moments in a thousand insignificant points with the ephemeral reality) is today stronger and more alive than ever. This world, the most complete and multi-articulated hallucination that ever existed, seems to be charged with truth. Under our reflective gaze its corporeity dissolves into a coexistence of innumerable power-stations, of monads whose essence is the most intense substantial truth. In the ups and downs of these careers, these love-affairs, money- and power-intrigues, rural and small-town events, anecdotes, monographs of a passion, of a soul-sickness, of a social institution, in the maze of close on two thousand human existences, almost everything is touched which, in our cultural life complicated as it is to the point of confusion, ever plays a role. And almost everything that is said about these myriads of things, relations, phenomena, bristles with truth. I don't know if an attempt has already been made—it could be done at any time—to compile a dictionary whose content would be drawn exclusively from Balzac. It would contain nearly all material, all spiritual and intellectual realities, of our existence. It would include cooking recipes as well as chemical theories; details about money and commercial affairs, precise and useful details which would fill columns; about trade and commerce we would learn many facts that are out of date, but we would also learn other facts that are eternally true and valid. And next to these, under arbitrary slogans, we would have to include the most daring prophecies and anticipations of biological facts of later decades; the articles under the headings "Marriage," "Society," or "Politics" would each comprise a book in itself, and each a book which, among the publications on worldly wisdom of the nineteenth century, would know no equal. The book containing the treatise on "Love" would reach in a boldly designed arc from the most sinister, inscrutable mysteries (*Une Passion dans le désert*) through a chaos bristling with all human possibilities to the most spiritualized, angelic love. By the greatness of its conception and the magnitude of its panorama, this volume would put the one famous book we have on the same subject (and one written by a master's hand) into the shade. This dictionary, however, does exist. It is spun into a world of characters, into a labyrinth of events, and we leaf through it while following the thread of a superbly invented story. The man of the world will find in these volumes the whole range of human situations, so specious yet so true, that constitute social life. The thousand nuances wherewith men and women treat one another well or ill; the imperceptible transitions, the unrelenting gradations, the whole gamut from the truly distinguished to the semi-distinguished, to the vulgar—all this modified and perforated in the most splendid manner by the Human, by the Passionate, and for moments reduced to its nothingness. Man in his struggle for existence (and who does not struggle to make a living, to maintain what he has or to suffer privation?) has his whole world here. The great financier, the struggling physician, the starving and the triumphant inventor, the great and small promoter, the rising business man, the army contractor, the notary as mediator, the usurer, the stand-in, the pawnbroker—and of each not one but five or ten types. And what types! With all the tricks of their trade, their secrets, their last truths. Painters among themselves maintain the legend that Delacroix must have been the source of the last intimate details of modelling by light and shade described in *Le Chef-d'oeuvre inconnu;* this truth appeared to them too substantial to be discovered by someone not a painter, and a great painter at that. A thinker who has been handed *Louis Lambert* as the monograph on a thinker may find the biographical part weak and may doubt the validity of the character; but as soon as he reaches the thought material transmitted in letters and notes, he will find the consistency of these thoughts, the substantial power of this thinker, so convincing that any doubt about the character will be dispelled. These are thoughts of a real being, this brain has indeed functioned—no matter to what extent we may reject these thoughts, this philosophy of a spiritualistic dreamer. And the married man who, in a pensive hour, comes across the *Physiologie du mariage* will find in this strange book (which, perhaps, owing to a certain semi-frivolous tone, has lost some favour) several pages whose truths are as delicate as they are deep, and worthy of being taken to heart—truths which, when absorbed, expand themselves and continue to live in us with a gentle, radiant power. There is nothing esoteric clinging to these truths. They are presented in a worldly, sometimes in an almost frivolous tone. Interspersed among events and descriptions, they form the most spiritual element in the body of a story, a novel. They are offered to us as life itself offers us its content—in encounters, catastrophes, in the unfolding of passions, in sudden perspectives and insights, in unexpected vistas opening up the dense forest of human existence. Here we find the most passionate and most comprehensive painting of life, and simultaneously an extraordinarily perceptive philosophy ready to take whatever seemingly obscure phenomenon of life for its point of departure. Thus the whole great work, whose world-image is certainly as sombre as that of Shakespeare's and at the same time so much more bulky, cloudier, heavier through its own volume, is nevertheless pervaded by a spiritual aliveness—yes, a spiritual gaiety, a deep sense of gratification. What else could we call that which—whenever we come across one of these books—makes us turn the pages back and forth, not read but leaf through them, an act wherein lies a far more subtle, nostalgic love? What else could we call that which can turn for us the mere enumeration of the titles of these hundred books or the record of the characters appearing in them into a kind of summary perusal whose enjoyment is complex and violent, like that of a favorite poem?

The amassing of such an enormous bulk of substantial truths is not possible without organization. The talent to organize is as much a creative gift as the merely productive one. Or rather, they are only different aspects of one and the same power. From the truth of the countless isolated phenomena follows the truth of the relationship between them: thus a world is created. As with Goethe, I feel myself here in a definite relationship to the Whole. I find an invisible co-ordinating system by which I can orientate myself. Whatever I read, be it one of the great novels, one of the stories, one of the fantastic philosophic rhapsodies; whenever I become engrossed in the secrets of a soul, in a political digression, in a description of a lawyer's office or a small grocery—never do I lose the sensation of being related to the Whole. I feel around me an organized world. The great secret is that this world surrounding me without any gaps, this other, more condensed, more intense reality, does not affect me as an oppressive burden, as a nightmare taking my breath away. It does not make us stop short, does not petrify us; rather, the sight of it pours fire into our veins. For this world itself does not stand still but is constantly in motion. It is in flux, *infinitis modis,* to use a technical term of medieval thinkers. In this most complete vision to have sprung from a human brain since Dante, the world is conceived not as static but dynamic—observed, moreover, so minutely that it forms a gapless scale, presenting the whole texture of life, from thread to thread. Yet everything is seen in motion. Never was the ancient wisdom of *Panta rei* more magnificently conceived and transformed into characters. Everything is transition. Behind these books whose totality represents, after *Don Quixote,* the greatest epic conception of the modern world, the idea of epic art form seems to come to life. To describe human beings, how they flourish and perish like the flowers on the earth—Homer did nothing else. Dante's world is static. It does not move; rather, he himself moves, and walks past it. Balzac himself we do not see, but we see with his eyes how everything changes. The rich turn poor, and the poor rich. César Birotteau rises and Baron Hulot goes down in the world. Rubempré's soul appeared like an untouched fruit, and before our eyes we see it transformed; we see him seize the rope to put an end to his tarnished life. Séraphita extricates herself and soars off to heaven. Each one is no longer what he was—each becomes what he is not. Here we are as deep in the core of the epic *Weltanschauung* as with Shakespeare we are in the core of the dramatic. Everything is flowing, everything on the way. Money is merely the brilliantly conceived symbol of this constant motion, and at the same time its vehicle. Through money everyone gets everywhere. And it is the nature of the world, conceived in this magnificent and epic fashion, that everyone gets everywhere. We find transitions everywhere, nothing but transitions, in the moral as well as in the social world. The transitions between vice and virtue—two mythical concepts which no one knows quite how to grasp—are as finely graded and as continuous as those between rich and poor. Hidden in the most

far-removed and most contradictory things lie certain secret relationships through which everything is connected with everything. Between a concierge in his basement and Napoleon in
Saint-Cloud, there can flash up for a moment a secret affinity
meaning far more than a mere witticism. Since in the world
everything affects everything, why should this not be conditioned by the most secret analogies? Everything is in flux; no
rigid block remains, either in the spiritual world or in everyday
existence. "Love" and "Hatred" appear sufficiently separate and
clearly enough defined. And there are in Balzac's work characters in whose heart one of these feelings merges as imper-
ceptibly into the other as the colours of glowing iron. Does
Rosalie hate Albert Savarus or does she love him? In the
beginning she loves him, in the end she seems to hate him.
She acts under an obsession that is perhaps both love and hatred at once. And were we able to ask her, she could not in-
form us by which of the two emotions she feels tortured. Here
we are separated by an abyss from the world of the eighteenth
century with its notions (such as "virtue") which are clear,
well defined, and dogmatic, well suited to replace clear and
theological concepts. Here any mythology, even that of words,
is dissolved. And nowhere are we closer to Goethe. Here quite
close—yes, in the same bed—rushes the deep stream of his
ideas. But it was the innate gesture of his spiritual being to
turn at this moment to the opposite side. The driving forces
of his nature were so powerful that they threatened to over-
whelm him. He had to oppose them with the Permanent, with
Nature, Laws, Ideas. The eye of his soul was fastened on
the changeless amidst the changes. This is how we see his
face; this is how the mask of the contemplative magician was
formed. Balzac's face we don't see as an Olympic mask enthroned above his work. Only in his books do we occasionally
think we see it appearing, like that of a seer, cast up by cha-

otic obscurities, by whirling lava, but it is not in our power to retain it. Each generation will see it differently; each as a titanic face, and after its fashion will make out of it a symbol of inexpressible inner experiences. We are surprised that we do not possess a likeness of this face by that hand which created the *Massacre of Chios* and *Dante's Barque*. He would have painted the thirty-year-old Balzac as the titan he was, as a demon of life, or he would have treated his face as a battlefield. It is a surprising hiatus that later the mask of the fifty-year-old man was not bequeathed to us by Daumier. His miraculous crayon and his equally miraculous brush would have made the faunlike quality of the man spring forth from the dark and would have ennobled it with the wild solitude of genius. But perhaps these generations were too close to him, and it required perspective for something like Rodin's creation to emerge—this completely symbolic, superhuman face wherein a terrible weight of matter is coupled with the dark, sultry quality of the demoniac, a face in which the synthesis of utterly opposite worlds has taken place, a face that reminds us of a fallen angel and simultaneously of the dim and boundless sadness emanating from primeval Greek demons of the earth and sea.

Each generation which, steeped in Balzac's work, conjures up this vision will create within this face a similar synthesis between the whole burden of life and the most secret urge towards the conquering of this burden, towards redemption, towards a transcendence of it. This Belonging to the dark, bulky burden of life (forever renewing itself) and at the same time the desire to transcend it, this deepest urge of the spirit for the spiritual: that is the signature of this great tragic face which, unlike Goethe's mask gazing up over our heads into eternity, looks through us, right through the burden of life. This enormous world constructed from our life

—the life of lust, of selfishness, of errors, of the grotesque, sublime and ridiculous passions—this world in whose medley the concepts Comedy and Tragedy are as dissolved as are Vice and Virtue, this world is fundamentally all movement, all urge, all love, all mystery. This apparent materialist is actually a passionate, ecstatic seer. The essence of his characters is aspiration. All forces of suffering, forces of love, all artistic exertion, all monomanias, these titanic powers, the great motors of his world, are aspirations: they all aim towards some highest ideal, towards something indefinable. Vautrin, the genius as criminal, and Steinbock the genius as artist, Goriot the father, Eugénie Grandet the virgin, Frenhofer the creator—they are all focused towards an Absolute which will reveal itself, as ships tossed about at night in a storm are focused on the existence of a polar star, even though darkness conceals it. In the depths of their cynicism, in the turmoil of their tortures, in the abyss of renunciation, they seek and find God, whether or no they call Him by name.

All these characters endowed with such physical presence are really nothing but the transitory embodiments of one nameless power. Through these infinite relativities breaks an Absolute; angels and demons look at us from the eyes of these people. All mythology, even the last, the most tenacious, that of words, is here dissolved. But a new, mysterious, most personalized mythology supplants all the others. Its conception is magnificent, so definite and yet vague that hundreds of thousands of people can adopt it and make out of it something like a myth of modern life. All these characters that force themselves on our imagination as "real" appear to us, in an almost supernatural light which descends from the summit of this work, as good and bad genii, beings in whom the earthly instincts are temporarily incarnate. But nothing in this conception is schematic. Here no dogmas are established, rather visions. Taine in his great essay on Balzac measures these intuitions, these floating truths—all of which are true only for the one moment and in the one place where they happen to be—by a yardstick which they do not allow. From a poet's work one cannot isolate details. Everything which within a world is truth—yes, more than truth, boundless premonition—becomes a miscarried phantasmagoria when taken out of context. We are concerned here with forms of vision. The thinker sees principles, abstractions, formulas, where the poet sees character, the human being, the demon.

Nevertheless, even when observed with the cold eye, the most grandiose synthesis has been accomplished. Here Novalis the magician encounters the titanic beginnings of true naturalism; here is the link between Swedenborg and Goethe or Lamarck. Here we find, to a certain degree, the last word of Catholicism, and at the same time an anticipation of Robert Mayer's discoveries breaks through the clouds like a star. The power of his work which is to subjugate more than one generation lies in his spirit's miraculous penetration of the reality of life, the *vraie vérité,* down to the most trivial human miseries. The spirituality of the nineteenth century, that whole enormous synthetic spirituality, is here compressed into the substance of life like a luminous vapour penetrating all fibres. When the precipitations of this vapour are strong and clearly crystallized as in *Louis Lambert,* in *La Recherche de l'absolu,* in *Le Chef-d'oeuvre inconnu,* there emerge concatenations of thoughts, forebodings, aphorisms, comparable only to the *Fragments* of Novalis. But whereas with Novalis these crystallizations are almost all that has reached us, in Balzac they are but a by-product of these psychophysical processes. Much more remarkable still is the phenomenon that develops when the compressed power of this spirituality drives the living substance forward, when characters result who thus driven make us feel the sway of spiritual forces in the very core of life. Hence Claës, the tireless searcher after the Absolute; hence Louis Lambert and Séraphita. And hence, above all, Balzac's conception of love. It is the most incomparable, most individual creation. All aspiration, it is at the same time the medium of the most mysterious synthesis between the spiritual and the sensual. It, this love, is a mysterious phenomenon which I have no desire to dilute with words. It does not occupy great space in this bulky work. And yet what warms and illuminates this work is just this love, and without it I could not imagine this immense weight, this dark world of human beings, as anything but terrible.

IN BALZAC we find a world teeming with characters. None among them is so powerfully conceived, so complete in himself, as to exist alone, divorced from his background in the immortal completeness of his gesture, like Don Quixote, King Lear, or Odysseus. The material is more brittle, the vision not of that radiant clarity that produces characters moulded in the purest, strongest light, like Homer's Achilles or Nausicaa, or in delicate twilight, like Mignon or Ottilie. In Balzac everything is interwoven, one thing conditions the other. It would be as impossible to isolate the single detail from his work as it would from a picture by Rembrandt or Delacroix. Here as there the grandiose consists of a stupendous wealth of colour value which up and down, *infinitis modis*, like Nature herself, produces an unbroken scale. Those figures appear as freely moving deities: how they may have come into existence is an inscrutable secret. Balzac's, on the other hand, are single notes in a titanic symphony. Their springing into existence seems to us more comprehensible; we believe we carry in our blood the elements out of which their sinister hearts are formed, and we believe we inhale them with the air of the great cities. Yet here also a last, higher truth pervades everything. Just as the scale from darkness to brightness in a painting by Rembrandt resembles the earthly light and earthly darkness only by being unbroken, convincing, and absolutely right, so there vibrates here, in the myriads of small features wherewith a teeming world is described, a barely definable ultimate truth. The plasticity of this world borders on the too weighty, its gloom on nihilism, the worldliness of its treatment on the cynical. But the colours with which they are painted are pure. A choir of angels by Fra Angelico is not painted with a cleaner brush than the characters in *La Cousine Bette*. To these colours, the truly fundamental elements of the soul, clings nothing dull, nothing sickly, nothing blasphemous, nothing base. They are imperishable; they cannot be harmed by any evil breath. Through them vibrates an absolute joyfulness that is untouched by the gloom of its theme, as the divine joyousness of the sounds in a symphony by Beethoven can at no moment be perturbed by the fearful nature of its musical expression.

On Characters in Novels and Plays

An imaginary conversation between Balzac and Hammer-Purgstall, the Orientalist, in a garden near Vienna, 1842.

HAMMER: You will permit me, dear sir, a question which for a long time has been burning on my tongue. Please excuse my liberty; you are aware that before you stands one of the most ardent admirers of your stupendous art of narration: but will you not now, in the prime of your creative imagination, present us with an equal, a similar series of works for the theatre?

You remain silent? You do not wish to answer me? Am I to presume that you do not love the dramatic form—that the theatre means nothing to you?

BALZAC: On the contrary, Baron.

HAMMER: Bravo! Bravo! I love the theatre boundlessly and, as a German, take the greatest delight in our own. But just imagine what could become of the French, were your genius to seize the reins and with mighty flicks of the whip drive the stranded cart on to a new road!

BALZAC, *obligingly:* I know. You have Schiller, you have the author of *The Ancestress*; above all, you have Raupach! Ah, the theatre! A beautiful dream.

HAMMER: Your dreams, dear sir, are in the habit of becoming reality. And what could hinder you in this instance? Contracts, agreements with publishers? These you tear to pieces, like the lion its net. The possibility of a failure?

A failure by Balzac? Balzac not the sovereign master of his audience? Balzac weaker than an audience of two or three thousand people? But are they not your creations? Do I not see in each row the physiognomies that have emerged from your retort? Do they not occupy all the boxes—the Duchess de Maufrigneuse and the Princess de Cadignan and the Grandlieus with their daughters and that dwarf, the Duke d'Hérouville, and the Baron de Nucingen and his wife, and the Rhétorés, and the Navarreins and the Lenoncourts? Do I not see in the semi-darkness, in Madame d'Espard's loge, the handsome Rubempré behind Madame de Bargeton, pale with jealousy and no longer young? Isn't that Rastignac, that genius of ambition and ruthlessness, standing in the stalls spying through his glasses upon Madame de Nucingen? Isn't that de Marsay approaching to shake his hand, that de Marsay who, like him, is one day to become Minister and Senator of France? And now Bianchon the doctor, and Claude Vignon the journalist, and Stidmann the sculptor, and the Polish emigrés, Laginski and Paz and Steinbock, are they not pointing out to one another the half-hidden stage-box in which the fabulous Esther, still known to very few, shrouded by the first shadows of the tragic life of a courtesan, is glancing across at Rubempré? Are there not, among the great ladies, other ladies displaying an exciting elegance—an elegance which seems permeated by the fever of our day? Do I not see the Bixiou and the de Lora visiting a Josepha, a Madame Schontz, a Jenny Cadine? And do I not recognize over there, with his beautiful daughter Victorine, the great industrialist Monsieur Taillefer, who has a murder on his conscience? And isn't that, seated down below, Vautrin the galley-slave, disguised as a Spanish priest—hair, beard, posture, voice, everything about him false save the alive,

indomitable eyes? In fact, what else do I see but these figures who, by some admirable magic, throw to one another
like hundred-faceted mirrors their whole lives, their
thoughts, their passions, their pasts, their futures a thousand times multiplied?

*At these sentences, at such unusual, genuine, enthusi-
astic admiration, which sent a livelier colour to the cheeks
of the great orientalist, at so ardent and unrestrained an
ovation given in private, Balzac could not suppress a smile.
It was the rare and beautiful smile of pure satisfaction
which does not vanish from the face with the speed of
lightning, not spasmodic but slowly fading, like the lovely
sunset of a peaceful summer's day. It was the same smile
that transfigured the mouth of Napoleon when, on the
afternoon of Austerlitz, he saw the effect which the mis-
siles, directed at his command, had on the icy lakes covered by thousands of fleeing Russians and Austrians. And
perhaps—yes, most probably—this smile had, in both
these outwardly so different cases, the same origin: on each
occasion it sprang from the soul of a great man destined
by nature for conquest, at the moment when the soul saw
quite clearly before it the possibility of breaking Europe's
obtuse resistance against its genius, like a bundle of dry
faggots over the knee. The tremendous energy of his soul
struggling with life itself was for one moment relaxed; his
eyes roamed with the casual gaze of the traveller over the
slopes of the Kahlenberg; in his attitude was the indefinable transformation, the repose of the one who, in a foreign atmosphere, under the fragrance and shade of foreign
trees, with foreign people whom perhaps he will never see
again, speaks amiably and untroubled: thus Balzac surrendered himself to the moment (which had in it something*

of the respite of a victor on the frontiers of distant conquered lands), surrendered himself to it so thoroughly that he missed several of the Baron's sentences, catching only this finale of a longish tirade:

What! Everything in the audience, the beautiful world of the loges and the stalls and the pit, all this is to show the traces of the lion's paw—all this except the stage?

BALZAC: Of course I love the theatre. The theatre as I understand it. The theatre where everything happens, everything. All vices, all absurdities, every manner of speech! How puny, how symmetrical in comparison is the theatre of Victor Hugo! Mine, the one I dream of, is the world, the chaos. And it did once exist, my theatre, it did exist. Lear on the heath, and the fool beside him, and Edgar and Kent and the voice of thunder mingled with their voices! Volpone, who worships his gold, and his servants—the dwarf, the eunuch, the hermaphrodite and the villain! And the legacy hunters, offering him their wives and daughters, dragging those wives and daughters by the hair into his bed! And the daemonic voices of beautiful things, of alluring possessions, of golden vessels, of cut stones, of glittering candelabra, mingling with the human voices just as did the thunder. Yes, there was a theatre once.

HAMMER: You mean in England around 1590?

BALZAC: Yes, they had it. And later still. There have been belated flashes of lightning. Do you know Otway's *Venice Preserved?*

HAMMER: I believe I saw it in Weimar.

BALZAC: My Vautrin considers it the best of all plays. I set great store by such a person's judgment.

HAMMER: Your lively interest in this subject is most gratifying to me. We will, I now see, have a *Comédie humaine* on the stage! We will see the wig fly from Vautrin's head and the convict's ghastly skull reveal itself. We will spy on Goriot while he, lonely in his ice-cold attic, conjures up the vision of his beautiful daughters. Why are you shaking your head, sir? From now on nothing can stand in your way.

BALZAC: Nothing, apparently nothing whatever. Not even in my intentions, apparently. Nor do I lack dramaturgic collaborators. You cannot walk from the Opéra to the Palais Royal without meeting one or two of them. For I have wanted to create collaborators for myself. I wanted to creep into someone else. But I was wrong. One cannot hide in the ass's skin. I wanted to find something which I did not carry in myself. I wanted to commit a dishonesty, one of the great secret dishonesties. It lies in the nature of most authors to commit quantities of such dishonesties, and to remain unpunished. They resemble the rider in the German ballad who, without knowing it, rides across the frozen Lake Constance. But such people don't realize it even afterwards and so do not drop dead, as did this rider. To make use of an art form and to do it justice: what an abyss lies between the two! The greater man is, the clearer he sees such things. Let others violate the forms; I, for my part, know that I am no dramatist, as little as——

Here M. de Balzac mentioned the names of all his compatriots who, in the preceding decade, had achieved a great, on occasion a European, reputation for their dramatic works, and continued:

The reason for this? The deepest reason? Perhaps I don't believe that characters exist. Shakespeare believed it. He was a dramatist.

HAMMER: You don't believe that human beings exist! That's good! You yourself have created between six and seven hundred of them, and given them life! And they've existed ever since.

BALZAC: I don't know whether these people could live on the stage. Are you familiar with what, in mineralogical science, is known as allotropy? The same matter appears twice in the realm of things, in completely different forms of crystallization, in quite unexpected shapes. The stage character is an allotropy of the corresponding real one. In the figure of Goriot I have the phenomenon of Lear; I have the chemical process of Lear, but I could not be further removed from the crystallization of Lear. — You, Baron, like all Austrians, are a born musician. You are, moreover, a learned musician. Let me tell you that characters in the theatre are nothing but contrapuntal necessities. The stage character is a contraction of the real one. What enchants me in the real one is precisely its breadth. Its breadth, which is the basis of its destiny. As I've said, I don't see people, I see destinies. And one must not confound destiny with catastrophe. Catastrophe as a symphonic composition, that's the business of the dramatist who is so closely related to the musician. The destiny of man—that is something whose reflection probably didn't exist before I wrote my novels. My people are nothing but litmus-paper which reacts by turning red or blue. The living, the great, the real, are the acids—the powers, the destinies.

HAMMER: You mean the passions?

BALZAC: You can use that word if you like, but you must give it a breadth such as it has never had, and then again narrow it down into the particular as has never been done before. I said "the powers." The power of the erotic for him who is the slave of love. The power of weakness for the weak. The power of glory for the ambitious. No, not just love, just weakness, just glory: but the love by which man is enslaved, his individual weakness, his specific glory. What I mean, Napoleon called his star: this is what compelled him to go to Russia, what compelled him to attach such importance to the notion of "Europe" that he could not rest until he had "Europe" lying at his feet. What I mean, unhappy people—glimpsing their lives in a flash of lightning—call their doom. For Goriot it is embodied in his daughters. For Vautrin, in human society, whose foundation he wants to blow up. For the artist, in his work.

HAMMER: And not in his experiences?

BALZAC: There are no experiences but the experience of one's own nature. This is the key which unlocks everyone's lonely prison-cell, whose impenetrably thick walls, to be sure, are hung with the phantasmagoria of the universe as with colourful carpets. No one can escape from his world. Have you ever taken a long journey by steamer? Do you remember seeing there an odd, almost pitiful figure emerging towards evening from a corner of the engine-room, to spend a quarter of an hour on deck for a breath of fresh air? The man was half-naked; he had a blackened face and red, inflamed eyes. You'd been told that he was a stoker. Each time he came up, he swayed; he greedily drank a large jug of water to its last drop, lay down on a heap of oakum and played with the ship's dog; he cast a few shy, almost idiotic glances at the gay and elegant first-class passengers assembled on deck to delight in the stars of the Southern sky; he breathed, this man, as greedily as he had drunk, the air which was moistened by a night-cloud dissolving in dew and the perfume of virgin palm-islands floating over the ocean; and he disappeared again into the belly of the ship without having so much as noticed the stars or the aroma of the mysterious islands. Such are the sojourns of the artist among men, when he emerges staggering and with dim-sighted eyes from the fiery belly of his work. But this creature is no poorer than those up on deck. Even if, among those fortunate ones up there, among those chosen by life, there were two lovers who, leaning against one another with intertwined fingers, oppressed by the flood of their emotions, were to experience the crashing down of immeasurably distant stars as the Southern sky lets fall in sheafs, in swarms and cataracts from the unfathomable to the unfathomable—if they were to experience this as the strongest pulse-beat of bliss resounding to the periphery of their existence—even measured by this, he would not be the poorer. The artist is no poorer than any other among living beings, no poorer than Timur the Conqueror, no poorer than Lucullus the Glutton, no poorer than Casanova the Seducer, no poorer than Mirabeau the Man of Destiny. But his destiny is nowhere but in his work. He should look nowhere else for his depths and his peaks: otherwise he will take a puny sand-hill for a Mont Blanc, will climb it breathlessly, will stand up there with arms akimbo and be the laughing-stock of all who live twenty years later. In his work he has everything; he has the nameless voluptuousness of conception, the rapturous ether-trance of inspiration, and he has the inexhaustible torment of execution. There he has experiences for which the language has no word and the most sinister dreams no comparison. Like the ghost from the bottle of Sindbad the Sailor, he will dilate like smoke, like a cloud, and cast a shadow over lands and seas. And the following hour will press him back into his bottle, where, suffering a thousand deaths, an imprisoned vapour suffocating itself, he will sense his limits, the merciless limits which fetter him, a despairing demon in a narrow glass prison, through whose invincible walls he sees with grinning torment the world spread out, the whole world over which but an hour ago he was hovering in meditation, a cloud, an immense eagle, a God.

But to such a point, so utterly is his work the whole destiny of the artist that in the entire world about him he can recognize only the counterparts of those conditions which he is accustomed to experience in the torments and delights of work. The poets have made a poet out of the highest being. And they are so clever at projecting into the ups and downs of all human souls the reflection of their own ecstasies and exhaustions that gradually—with the increase of the reading public and the sinister levelling of the classes from which we are suffering—the strangest phenomena will appear, and this, incidentally, not in isolated instances but in masses. Around 1890 the intellectual sicknesses of the poets, their excessively aggravated sensibility, the indescribable anxiety of their depressed hours, their disposition to succumb to the symbolic power even of insignificant things, their incapacity to remain content with existing words for the expression of their feelings—all this will be a common disease among the young men and women of the upper classes. For the artist resembles that Midas under whose hands everything turned to gold. The same curse fulfils itself, but always in an infinitely more subtle way. Benvenuto Cellini lies in the deepest dungeon of the Castel Sant' Angelo; he has a broken leg; his teeth are falling from his jaws; for days he has been left without nourishment; he's convinced he's dying: and then his agonizing deliriums condense into a lovely, comforting dream in which he sees the sun, but without blinding rays, as a bath of the purest gold. Its centre blows itself out and ascends into the heights: out of it there forms a Christ on the Cross of the same substance; at the side of the crucifix a beautiful Holy Virgin in the most pleasing position and seemingly smiling. On each side two heavenly angels, also of the same substance. All this he actually saw while continually thanking God in a loud voice. He lay in agony, but he was the greatest goldsmith of his century, and the vision in which Heaven sweetened his agony was the vision of a goldsmith's work. Twisting on the threshold of death, his dreams were of no other substance but that in which his hands were able to create a work of art. And do you know the painter, Frenhofer?

HAMMER: The hero of *Le Chef-d'oeuvre inconnu?* Yes, indeed.

BALZAC: He is Mabuse's only pupil. He received from his master the prodigious secret of form, of true form, that of the human body modelled by light and shade. He knows that contour does not exist. His sketches have the luminous power of Giorgione and the flesh tints of Titian; and he despises these sketches. Pourbus adores him, and Nicolas Poussin, who makes his acquaintance, trembles before him as before a demon. This man has worked for ten years on a nude female figure, and no one has set eyes on the picture. You remember how the story continues. Poussin is so roused, so overwhelmed by this demon of painting, that he offers him his mistress, an enchanting twenty-year-old creature, as his model. It is said that this Gillette had the most beautiful body on which the eyes of a painter had ever rested. To offer her to the old man was the most delirious sacrifice of love to art, to genius, to glory. It was a devilish attempt to surrender the most precious possession in order to buy one's way into the inhuman magnificence of creation. And the old man? He barely notices her. For ten years he has been living in his picture. In a delirium now almost continuous, he feels this painted body live, feels the air play round it, feels this nudity breathe, sleep, grow animated, come close to life. What could a living woman, a real body, give him? By now he sees this palpable body of a woman, he sees all forms and colours, all shadows and half-shadows, all harmonies of the world, only as a negative picture, in a secret relationship to his work, comprehensible only to himself. To him the world is the shell of an eaten egg. What exists of the world for his soul he has carried over into his picture. How vain to offer him a fruit, even were it the most enchanting on earth, against which the doors of his soul have closed themselves for ever! What a grotesque and vain sacrifice! Here you have the artist: when he's young, when he gives himself to art—Poussin. And when he is mature, when he is almost Pygmalion, when his statue, his goddess, the creation of his hands begins to walk towards him—Frenhofer. And Gillette—she is Experience, she is the fulness of Experience, she is the sweet fulness of life's possibilities: and one of them, the youth, is ready to hand her over, while the other no longer has eyes to see her.

Life! The world! The world is in his work, and his work is his life. Talk to a gambler, a real one, about the world at the moment he is going to lay his stake. Tell a collector that his wife has just been seized with convulsions, that his son has been arrested, that his house is on fire—tell him this at the moment when, in an antique shop, his eye has lighted on some Nardon Pénicaud enamel from Limoges, or on a screen of the genre that has begun to be known as Pompadour and whose bronze-work is modelled by Clodion. He will gaze at you with the expression with which Lear on the heath gazed at anyone who tried to convince him that it was not his ungrateful daughters who had caused Edgar's misery and the misery of every unfortunate creature. There are times when every eye finds the sublime expression of the soul which refuses to recognize that anything in the world exists beyond its own concern.

HAMMER, *humbly:* That is Lear in the Third Act. At this point he may be considered mad.

BALZAC: That, dear Baron, can be said of any man, and particularly in the beautiful, in the sublime, in the true moments of his life. I mean, of course, just as mad as Lear.

HAMMER: What, M. de Balzac! You want to set such narrow, such sad limits to your genius? The atmosphere of existences consuming themselves pathologically, the hideous, blind, devouring mania—are these the sinister and constricted subjects you want to choose as the topic of your narrative, instead of plunging into the colourful variety of human life? Have you not always known how to seize what is new, what is interesting?

BALZAC: My creating, Baron, has never known other laws than those which I am explaining here. But I have never felt the urge to explain them to myself. It would appear that the philosophic Germany has begun to infect me. But I fear, Baron, that you thoroughly misunderstand me when you assume that I consider anything between heaven and earth as lying outside my subject matter. I don't know what you call "pathological": but I know that every human existence worthy of presentation consumes itself, and that to maintain this flame it absorbs out of the whole world nothing but the elements expedient to its burning, as the candle devours the oxygen from the air. I know who brought into fashion the word "pathological" in relation to poetic creation: it was Herr von Goethe, a very great genius, perhaps the greatest your nation has ever produced, a man whose power of throwing armies of ideas and perceptions from one field of thought into another is not less surprising than that with which Napoleon threw armies of soldiers across the Po or the Vistula—save that his ideas could be as little handled by weaker hands as the bow of Odysseus. But I accept your word: "pathological," "maniacal"—I will tolerate them all. Yes, the world which I've fetched forth from my brain is peopled with madmen. They are all as mad, my creatures, as obsessed by their fixed ideas, as incapable of seeing anything in the world which they themselves do not project into it with their feverish eyes, as out of their senses as Lear when he takes a wisp of straw for Goneril. But they are so, because they are human. For them experiences do not exist, because there is no such thing as experience; because the inner core of man is a fire consuming itself, a fire of agony, a glass furnace in which the viscous liquid matter of life receives its forms, as graceful as flowers, like the stemmed vases from the isles of Murano, or hero-like, sparkling with metallic reflexes, like the potteries from Deruta and Rhodes; because each generation is more conscious than the preceding one; because a peculiar chemistry fulfilling itself with every breath will disintegrate life more and more until even disappointments, the loss of illusions, this inevitable experience, will not tumble down into the deep well of the soul like a single rock, but will be powdered to dust, into atoms, with each breath—so much so that around the year 1890 or 1900 it will no longer be possible to understand what we meant by the word "experience."

Pathological! Let us please conceive the notions in the broadest terms, and Heaven and Hell will find in them their place. I, at any rate, do not intend to renounce either of them. There is in everything the germ of a fetish, of a God, of an all-embracing God. Let us leave faith to him who has made faithfulness his god. I also have a vision of him who has made his god out of faithlessness. One must understand how to envisage Beethoven side by side with Casanova or Lauzun. The one who needed no woman next to him who needed all women. Everything is an empire, and each person is a Napoleon in his. They do not disturb one another, these empires, they are spiritual spheres: happy is he who can hear their music.

Yes, they are demons, all my creatures, and I have put the smouldering fire of madness into their heads. Admitted! But you must also admit, dear Baron, that your German Apollo, your Olympian, that your wizard of Weimar was a demon, and not one of the least awe-inspiring. I will not judge him by his *Werther:* he has repudiated this fever of his youth. But the whole man, the whole poet, the whole Being! I could imagine having known him: his eye must have been more uncanny than that of Klingsor the magician, than that of Merlin of whom they said that it reached down, like a bottomless pit, into the depths of hell; more uncanny than that of Medusa. He could kill, this prodigious man, with one glance, with one breath from his mouth, with one lift of his Olympian shoulders: he could turn a human heart to stone; he could kill a soul and then turn his back on it as if nothing had happened, and then walk off to his plants, to his stones, to his colours—which he called the sufferings and labours of light and with which he carried on conversations profound enough to cause the stars of the firmament to waver. There were times when men would have burned him, and there were other times when he would have been worshipped. He allowed his destiny, which was his nature, to bring to that nature—that is, his destiny—all the sacrifices demons require. What Napoleon called his star, he called the harmony of his soul. And this glittering enchanted castle which he fashioned out of immortal substance—do you imagine it had no dungeons where prisoners moaned their way towards a lingering death? But he deigned not to hear them, for he was great. Yes, who killed the soul of Heinrich von Kleist, who was it? Oh, I see him, the wizard of Weimar. I will paint his picture, I will recreate him completely. He is bigger and more sinister than the Trojan Horse, but I will break down the doorposts of my work and lead him in. Next to Séraphitus-Séraphita he will stand—as in the cemetery at Pisa the leaning tower beside the baptistry, gazing at one another, silent, immense, defying the centuries.

Oh, I see him, and what a shudder of delight to see him! There, I see him, where he lives, where his real life is—in the thirty or forty volumes of his work which he left behind him, not in the nonsense of his biographers. For all that matters is to be able to recognize destinies where they are stamped in divine substance. I know a woman, an obscure woman who will never be famous: she is the daughter of an enslaved country—a demon in imagination, a child in simplicity, a sage in experience, with the brain of a man, the heart of a woman; her love, her faith, her sufferings, her hopes, her dreams, are like chains strong enough to hold a world over the bottomless abyss: and her life, her destiny, her soul, are sometimes written in her face for him who can see it: thus Goethe's destiny can be seen in his works.

To read destinies where they are written—that is everything. To have the power to see them all as they consume

themselves, these living torches. To see them all at once
bound to the trees of the enormous garden which is illuminated by their blaze alone: and to stand on the uppermost terrace, to be the only spectator, and to search among
the strings of the lyre for those sounds which bind together heaven, hell, and this vision.

*At this moment, at the outer garden gate, a carriage
pulled up in which sat Madame Hanska, née Rzewuska.
Balzac, with a movement reminiscent of Mirabeau,
swung round to watch the newcomer make her appearance between the chestnut trees; and no one would have
dared attempt to resume a conversation which had been
broken off by so great a gesture.*

Sebastian Melmoth

THIS NAME was the mask behind which Oscar Wilde concealed his face, ravaged by gaol and the signs of approaching death, so as to live out a few more years of his life in the dark. It was the fate of this man to bear three successive names: Oscar Wilde, C 3 3, Sebastian Melmoth. The sound of the first suggests only splendour, pride, seduction. The second sounds terrifying, one of these marks which society brands with a fiery iron into the naked human shoulder. The third is the name of a ghost, a half-forgotten Balzacian character. Three masks, one after the other: the first with a fine brow, sensual lips, moist, magnificent, impudent eyes—a mask of Bacchus; the second a mask of iron with eye-holes through which gazes despair; the third a wretched costumier's domino hired to conceal a slow death from the eyes of mankind. Oscar Wilde glittered, enchanted, offended, seduced, betrayed and was betrayed, stabbed others' hearts and was himself stabbed in the heart. Oscar Wilde wrote his reflections upon *The Decay of Lying*, wrote *Lady Windermere's Fan* and *Salomé*. C 3 3 suffered. C 3 3 wrote *The Ballad of Reading Gaol* and that letter from Reading Gaol entitled *De Profundis*. Sebastian Melmoth wrote no more, dragged himself through the streets of Paris, died, and was buried.

And today Sebastian Melmoth, behind whose coffin five people walked, is exceedingly famous. Today all that he experienced, perpetrated, and endured is on everyone's lips. Today everyone knows that he sat in a kind of rabbit-hutch and with his fine fingers bleeding had to produce oakum by picking old ropes to pieces. Everyone knows the story of the foul bath he had to climb into, the dirty water into which the convicts had to climb one after the other, Oscar Wilde the last of all since he was the last in line. "Oscar Wilde," a man muttered behind him as they were being led round the prison yard, "I realize that you must suffer more than any of us." Even these words, muttered through the motionless lips of some convict, are very famous today. They form a detail of a legend that is full of wonder, as something wonderful invariably appears when life takes the trouble to treat fate poetically.

But people say, "What a transformation!" They say, "Oscar Wilde of the earlier phase, and Oscar Wilde of the later." They talk of an aesthete transformed into a new man, a believer, almost a saint. They have developed the habit of saying certain things about certain romanticists, and such things are too easily repeated. They should not be repeated. Firstly, because they were very likely incorrect in the first place; and secondly, because times change and it is senseless to pretend that things repeat themselves while in reality new, infinitely differentiated, infinitely surprising things are constantly rising to the surface. There's no point in trying to make out that Oscar Wilde's fate and Oscar Wilde's character were two different entities and that Fate had attacked him as a snarling mongrel attacks a harmless peasant child carrying a basket of eggs on its head. We should not always talk and think in clichés.

Oscar Wilde's character and Oscar Wilde's fate are one and the same. He walked towards his catastrophe with the same steps as Oedipus, the seeing-blind one. The aesthete was tragic. The dandy was tragic. He raised his hands in the air and drew the lightning towards him. People say, "He was an aesthete, and suddenly unfortunate entanglements overwhelmed him, a snare of unfortunate entanglements." We should not blanket everything with words. An aesthete! This signifies nothing. Walter Pater was an aesthete, a man who lived by the enjoyment and the re-creation of beauty, and towards life his attitude was one of reserve and reverence, full of propriety. An aesthete is, by nature, steeped in propriety. Oscar Wilde, however, was a figure of impropriety, tragic impropriety. His aestheticism had a convulsive quality. The jewels among which he professed voluptuously to delve were like death-dimmed eyes, petrified because they could not bear the sight of life. Incessantly he felt the threat of life directed towards him. He was forever surrounded by a tragic air of horror. He kept challenging life unceasingly. He insulted reality. And he sensed life lying in wait in order to spring upon him out of the darkness.

People say, "Wilde spoke in witty paradoxes while duchesses hung on his lips, while his fingers plucked an orchid to pieces and his feet lay among cushions of ancient Chinese silk; but then misfortune descended upon him and he was pushed into the bath ten convicts had used before him." Yet it is false to talk of life in such trite terms, wrong to drag everything down to the level of a case of disaster. The marvellously polished words, the sentences—their cynicism near to torture, their worldliness to vertigo—which fell from these beautifully curved, seductive, impudent lips were actually not meant for the ear of the lovely duchesses, but for the ear of an Invisible Listener who lured him with horror, like the Sphinx of whom he thought endlessly while all the time denying her, and whose name "Reality" passed his lips merely in order that he might jeer at and humiliate it. And his limbs which toyed with orchids and lounged among cushions of ancient silks were in reality filled with an awful longing for the ghastly bath from which, however, at its first touch, they shrank in nauseated repugnance.

This is why it must have been deeply moving to have seen Oscar Wilde at one moment of his life. I mean the moment when he (over whom no one but his fate had any power)— against the pleading of his friends and almost to the horror of his enemies—turned and denounced Queensberry. For then the mask of Bacchus with its full, beautifully curved lips must have been transformed in an unforgettable manner into the mask of the seeing-blind Oedipus or the raging Ajax. At that moment he must have worn round his magnificent brow the band of tragic fate, so rarely visible.

We must not make life more banal than it is, nor turn our eyes away so as not to behold this band when for once it can be seen on a brow.

We must not degrade life by tearing character and fate asunder and separating his misfortune from his fortune. We must not pigeonhole everything. Everything is everywhere. There are tragic elements in superficial things and trivial in the tragic. There is something suffocatingly sinister in what we call pleasure. There is something lyrical about the dress of a whore and something commonplace about the emotions of a lyric poet. Everything dwells simultaneously in man. He is full of poisons that rage against one another. There are certain islands whose savage inhabitants pierce the bodies of their dead relatives with poisoned arrows, to make sure that they are dead. This is an ingenious way of expressing metaphorically a profound thought and of paying homage to the profundity of Nature without much ado. For in truth the slowly killing poisons and the elixir of gently smouldering bliss all lie side by side in our living body. No one thing can be excluded, none considered too insignificant to become a very great power. Seen from the viewpoint of life, there is not one thing extraneous to the Whole. Everything is everywhere. Everything partakes of the dance of life.

In the words of Jalal-ud-din Rumi, "He who knows the power of the dance of life fears not death. For he knows that love kills."

6

An Episode in the Life of
the Marshal de Bassompierre

AT ONE TIME in my life I had, in the course of my service, to cross the little bridge (the Pont Neuf not yet being built) fairly regularly several times a week at the same hour, and as I did so, some labourers and others of the common people came to recognize and salute me. But the most insistent and regular greeting came from the very pretty shopkeeper whose shop bore the sign of the Two Angels. Every time I passed during those five or six months, she would drop me a low curtsey and watch me out of sight. Attracted by her behaviour, I returned her look and acknowledged her salutation with care. Once, towards the end of winter, I was riding from Fontainebleau to Paris, and as I mounted the little bridge, she came to the door of her shop and said, as I rode by, "Your servant, Sir." I returned her greeting and, looking back from time to time, saw that she had leaned yet farther out to keep me in sight as long as she possibly could. I had my man and a postillion behind me, whom I had meant to send back to Fontainebleau that evening with letters for certain ladies. On my order, my man now dismounted and approached the young woman, telling her in my name that I had remarked her eagerness to see and greet me, and that if she desired to make my closer acquaintance, I would wait upon her at any place she appointed.

She replied to my man that he could have brought her no more welcome message; she would herself come to any place I would name.

As we rode on, I asked my man if he knew where I could meet the woman. He replied that he could take her to a certain procuress's, but this man of mine, William of Courtrai, being a most careful and conscientious creature, he at once added that there was plague here and there in the city, and as it had already carried off not only men and women of the mean and dirty sort, but a doctor and a canon too, he would advise me to have my own mattresses and bed-clothes taken with me. I fell in with his proposal, and he promised to prepare me a good bed. Before we dismounted, I added that he should take to the place a proper wash-basin, a small bottle of sweet-smelling essence, and some cakes and apples; he should also see that the room was thoroughly warmed, for it was so cold that my feet were frozen stiff in the stirrups, and the sky was heavy with snow-clouds.

That evening, going to the appointed place, I found a very beautiful young woman, some twenty years of age, sitting on the bed, while the procuress, her head and bent old back muffled up in a black shawl, seemed to be urging something upon her. The door stood ajar; in the fireplace, big, fresh logs were blazing noisily. The women did not hear my approach, and I remained standing a moment in the doorway. The young woman was gazing steadily into the fire with wide open eyes, a single movement of her head seemed to have put miles between her and the old crone; in the movement, a few locks of her heavy dark hair had burst out from under the little nightcap she wore, and, twining in natural ringlets, had fallen over her shift between her shoulder and bosom.

She also wore a short petticoat of green woollen stuff, and slippers on her feet.

At that moment, I must have betrayed my presence by some noise; with a sudden movement of her head she turned towards me a face so haggard with expectation that it would have looked fierce but for the radiance of devotion which streamed from her wide-open eyes and burst like an invisible flame from her speechless mouth. She was inexpressibly beautiful. In a trice the old crone was banished from the room and I was with my mistress. When, in the first rapture of this unexpected possession, I ventured on a few liberties, she shrank from me with an unspeakably anxious pleading both in her look and in her rich, low voice. But in a moment her arms were about me again, and the upturned gaze of her fathomless eyes, straining upon me, clasped me yet more close than her lips and arms. Then again, she seemed to be struggling to speak, but her lips, quivering with kisses, formed no words, and from her pulsing throat there came no sound more distinct than a broken sob.

Now I had spent most of that day on horseback on freezing highroads; later, I had been party to a very annoying and violent scene in the King's antechamber, and then, to overcome my ill humour, I had both drunk wine and fenced vigorously with the two-handed sword, and so, in the midst of this lovely and mysterious adventure, as I lay with soft arms round my neck and perfumed hair pouring over me, I was overcome by a fatigue that was almost a swoon, so sudden and irresistible that I could no longer remember how I had come into this room. I even, for a moment, imagined the woman whose heart beat so close to mine to be a totally different one I had known earlier in life, and at once fell into a deep sleep.

When I awoke, the night was still dark, but I at once felt that my mistress was no longer by my side. I raised my head, and in the faint glow of the dying embers, saw her standing by the window. She had pushed open one of the shutters and was looking out through the crack. Then she turned round, saw that I was awake, and called (I can still see her raising the palm of her left hand to her cheek to toss back her fallen hair): "It is not day yet—not for a long time." Only now did I really see how tall and beautiful she was. I could hardly wait until one or two steady, long steps of her beautiful, glow-reddened feet had brought her to my side again. On her way, she moved to the fireplace, bent down, took the last heavy log lying in front of it in her shining bare arms, and flung it into the embers. And then she turned, her face sparkling with flames and joy; in passing, she snatched up an apple from the table, and was again in my arms, her limbs still bathed in the fresh heat of the fire, then dissolving, as it were, in the yet fierier flames which pulsed through them from within. Clasping me with her right hand, she bit into the cool fruit in her left, then held it to my mouth, offering the fruit, offering her face. The last log in the fireplace flamed higher than all the rest. With a shower of sparks it sucked in the flames, then hurled them up again in a furious blaze, and the firelight broke over us like a wave dashing against the wall, flinging our shadowed embrace up and down upon it. The great log crackled, feeding from its heart fresh flames which danced upward, dispelling the darkness with sheaves and fountains of glowing red. Then, all of a sudden, the flame sank; a breath of cold air pushed open the shutter like a hand and revealed the livid, hideous grey of dawn.

We sat up, knowing that day had come. But the light outside was like no day. This was no awakening of a world, and what lay outside was like no street. Things had no outlines. It was a world without form and void, where only shapeless, timeless things could move. From somewhere distant as a memory came the chime of a church clock, and a raw wind, which had no home in day or night, poured into the room till we clung together, shuddering. She leant back, her eyes fastened on my face; her throat quivered, something rose in her and surged to her lips, but no word came, no sigh and no kiss, but something which, unborn, was like all three. In the growing light the changing expressions flitting across her face grew yet more speaking. Suddenly, in the street outside, shuffling footsteps and voices approached the window so close that she bent and turned her face to the wall. Two men passed; for a moment, the light of a little lantern carried by one of them brightened the room; the other man was pushing a barrow whose wheel creaked and groaned. When the men had passed, I stood up, closed the shutters, and lit a candle. Half an apple was still lying there, we ate it together, and then I asked whether I could see her once more, as I was not to leave till Sunday, while this night had been the night from Thursday to Friday.

She replied that she certainly desired it more ardently than I, but unless I could stay over Sunday, she could not see me again, for she could only meet me in the night from Sunday to Monday.

A number of hindrances flashed through my mind, and I raised some objections to which she listened without a word, but with a most painful questioning in her eyes, while her face grew almost ghastly in its sombre hardness. Then, of course, I promised to stay over the Sunday, and added that I should come to the same place again on Sunday evening. She looked at me steadily and said, her voice quite harsh and broken, "I know very well that I have entered a house of shame for your sake, but I did it of my own free will, because I meant to be with you, because I would have done anything and gone anywhere. But now I should feel like the last and

lowest woman of the town if I brought myself to come here
again. I did it for your sake, because, for me, you are what
you are, because you are Bassompierre, because you are the
one human being in the world whose presence could make
this house my house of honour."

She said "house"; for a moment it seemed as if a more
contemptuous word were on her lips; as she said it, she cast
upon the walls, our bed, the bed-clothes that had slipped off
on to the floor, such a look that, in the sheaf of light that
flashed from her eyes, all these mean and ugly things seemed
to start and cringe away from her, as if the wretched room
had really grown bigger for a moment.

Then, in an inexpressibly gentle and solemn voice, she
added, "May I die a wretched death if I have ever known any
man but my husband and you, or desire any other in the
world," and bending forward a little, her whole life in the
breath of her parted lips, she seemed to be waiting for some
answer, some assurance of my faith, but not finding in my
face what she sought there, her eager, searching look clouded,
her lashes opened and closed, and in a moment she was at
the window, her back turned to me, her forehead pressed
against the shutter with all her might, her whole body so
shaken with noiseless but horribly violent weeping that speech
died in my mouth and I did not dare to touch her. In the end
I took one of her hands, which were hanging nerveless at her
sides, and with the most endearing words I could command,
I succeeded, after long effort, in soothing her until she turned
her tear-stained face to me again, and a smile broke out like a
light from her eyes and round her lips, instantly drying up
her tears and bathing her whole face in brightness.

And then it was the most delicious game to watch her
begin to speak to me again, with endless variations on the one
theme: "You will see me again! Then I will let you into my

aunt's house," speaking the first part in a dozen different ways, now with sweet insistence, then with a pretence of childish suspicion, then whispered in my ear as if it were the greatest secret in the world, then again thrown over her shoulder with a shrug and a pout as if she were making the most commonplace appointment in the world, and in the end caressingly reiterated as she clung to me, laughing up into my face. She described the house to me in long detail, like a mother telling her child the way when it must cross the road to the baker's alone for the first time. Then she drew herself up, turned serious, and bent her radiant eyes on me with such force that they could have raised the dead to life, and went on: "I shall be waiting for you from ten o'clock till midnight and even later, and yet later still, and the downstairs door will be open. First you walk along a little passage, but you must not stop there, for my aunt's door opens on to it. Then you come to a staircase leading to the upper storey, and there I shall be." And closing her eyes as if dazed, she threw back her head, spread out her arms, and embraced me—and a moment later was out of my arms, fully dressed, strange and grave, and out of the room, for now day had come.

I made my arrangements, sent some of my men ahead with my baggage, and by evening of the next day was a prey to such vehement restlessness that, soon after vespers had rung, I crossed the little bridge with my man William, whom I forbade to take a lantern, so that I might see my mistress in her shop or in the adjoining lodging and give her, at any rate, some sign of my presence, though I hoped for nothing more than perhaps to exchange a few words with her.

To avoid attracting attention, I stopped at the bridge, sending my man ahead to reconnoitre. He was away for some time, and on his return wore the moody and despondent look which always meant that he had failed to carry out one of my orders. "The shop is shut up," he said, "and there seems to be nobody in it. Indeed there is nobody to be seen or heard in any of the rooms looking on to the street. You can only get into the courtyard over a high wall, and there is a big dog growling in it. But there is a light in one of the front rooms, and you can see into the shop through a chink, though I fear it is empty."

I was put out by this and made up my mind to go home at once, but all the same crept slowly past the house again, while my man, in his eagerness, applied his eye to the chink, which let out a thin ray of light, and whispered to me that the woman was not in the shop, but that her husband was. I was anxious to get sight of this shopkeeper, whom I could not remember ever having seen in his shop, and whom I imagined by turns as fat and shapeless or withered and decrepit. I approached the window and, to my extreme surprise, saw walking about in the well-furnished, panelled room an uncommonly tall and well-built man, who was certainly a head taller than I and who, when he turned round, showed me a very handsome, very grave face with a brown beard, silvered here and there, and a forehead of almost rare sublimity, with temples more spacious than I had ever seen before in a human face. Though he was quite alone in the room, his eyes wandered, his lips moved, and as he paused from time to time in his pacing up and down, he seemed to be carrying on an imaginary conversation with some other person; once he made a gesture with his arm as if brushing aside some objection with half-indulgent authority. There was ease and an almost contemptuous pride in his every movement, and as he turned in his solitary pacing up and down the room, I could not but call vividly to mind a very illustrious prisoner whom I had had under guard in the King's service when he was held in an apartment in the tower of Blois Castle. The resemblance became still more complete when the man raised his right hand and looked down on his upturned fingers with a searching, even grim look.

For it was almost the same gesture as I had often observed my august prisoner make when gazing at a ring which he wore on the first finger of his right hand and never removed. The man in the room then approached the table, pushed the water-globe in front of the candle, and placed both his hands, with outstretched fingers, in the circle of light; he seemed to be examining his finger-nails. Then he blew out the candle and went out of the room, leaving me with a dull feeling of sullen, angry jealously, for my desire for his wife was rising steadily within me, feeding like a spreading fire on all it encountered, and fanned, in some bewildering fashion, by this unexpected vision as it was by every snow-flake that was blown by the raw wind to hang and melt, single, on my eyebrows and cheeks.

I idled away the next day, unable to bring my mind to bear on anything, bought a horse I really did not care for, waited after dinner on the Duke de Nemours and spent some time there at cards and in the silliest and most disagreeable conversation imaginable. For it all turned on the plague, which was spreading rapidly in the city, and there was not a word to be got out of any of these gentlemen but of the hasty burial of the bodies, the straw fire that must be lit in the room where anyone had died, to consume the pestilent vapours, and so on. But the silliest of all, in my opinion, was the Canon de Chandieu; fat and hearty as ever, he could not refrain from keeping one eye fixed on his finger-nails to see if there were to be seen there any trace of the suspicious blueness which was generally the first sign of the plague.

Disgusted with it all, I went home early and retired to bed, but could not sleep; in my impatience, I dressed again and resolved at all costs to go and see my mistress, even if I and my men had to force our way in. I went to the window to call them; the icy night air brought me to my senses and I realized that my plan would mean certain ruin to the whole affair. I threw myself fully dressed as I was on my bed and at last fell asleep.

I spent Sunday in similar fashion till evening came, and arrived in the street named long before my time, but forced myself to walk up and down a nearby alley till ten struck. Then I soon found the house and the door she had described; the door was open, as she had said, and the corridor and staircase were behind it. But upstairs, the second door at the head of the staircase was shut, though a thin streak of light shone from beneath it. So she was inside, waiting, standing perhaps with her ear to the inside of the door as I with mine to the outside. I scratched on the door with my finger-nail; then I heard a noise within which sounded like the shuffling, un-- steady steps of bare feet. For a time I stood breathless and then began to knock, but a man's voice replied, asking who was there. I pressed back into the shadow of the doorway without uttering a sound. The door remained shut, and I crept downstairs on silent feet, step by step, then along the passage out into the open air, and with beating temples and clenched teeth, afire with impatience, walked up and down a street or two. In the end, I could not resist returning to the house; I did not mean to go in yet. I felt, I knew, that she would get her husband away, she would, she must, succeed, and I should be able to go to her at once. The street was narrow, on the other side there were no houses, but only the wall of a convent garden; I stood flattened against it, trying to guess which was her window from the other side of the street. Suddenly, in one that stood open in the upper storey, a light flamed up and died down. I seemed to see it all before my eyes; she had thrown a big log on the fire, as on that other night. As on that other night, she was standing in the middle of the room, her limbs bathed in the firelight, or sitting on the bed, listening and waiting. I would see her from the doorway, with the shadow of her neck and shoulders rising and falling on that invisible wave on the wall. I was already in the corridor, on the stairs, the door had been opened. Standing ajar, it allowed the flickering light to pass out. I had stretched out my hands towards the doorhandle, when I seemed to hear the steps and voices of several persons inside. But I would not believe it, and took it for the pulsing of my blood in my temples, in my neck, and for the blazing of the fire within. That other night too, it had blazed noisily. My hand was on the doorhandle when it really came home to me that there were people in the room, several people. But now I cared no longer, for I felt, I knew, she was there too, and as soon as I had opened the door, I should see her, take her in my arms and, though I should have to wrench her out of the hands of others, hold her to me with one arm, cutting a way for her with my sword, with my dagger, through a melee of shouting men and women. The one thing that seemed quite intolerable was to wait longer.

I pushed the door open. This is what I saw.

In the middle of the empty room I saw a few people burning bed-straw, and in the flames whose light flooded the room, scaling walls whose plaster lay on the floor, while against one wall there was a table, on which two naked bodies lay stretched, one very big, with covered head, the other smaller, lying against the wall with the black shadow of its outline rising and falling beside it.

I reeled down the stairs, and in front of the house encountered two grave-diggers; one held his little lantern up to my face, asking me what I wanted, the other pushed his creaking, groaning barrow against the door. I drew my dagger to fend them off, and went home. There I at once drank three or four glasses of heavy wine and, having slept, set out on my journey to Lorraine.

All my efforts to discover something about the woman after my return were vain. I even went to the shop with the sign of the Two Angels, but the people who kept it did not know who had kept it before them.

A Tale of the Cavalry

O
N JULY 22, 1848, before six o'clock in the morning, the second squadron of Wallmoden cuirassiers, a troop of cavalry a hundred and seven strong under Captain Baron Rofrano, left the Casino San Alessandro and took the road to Milan. The wide, sunny landscape lay in untroubled peace; from distant mountain peaks, morning clouds rose like steady plumes of smoke into the radiant sky. Not a breath of air stirred the corn. Here and there, between clumps of trees fresh-bathed in the morning air, there was a bright gleam of a house or a church. Hardly had the troop left the foremost outposts of its own army about a mile behind them when they caught sight of a glint of weapons in the corn-fields, and the vanguard reported enemy infantry. The squadron drew up for the attack by the side of the highroad; over their heads cannon-balls flew, whizzing with a strangely loud, mewing noise; they attacked across country, driving before them like quails a troop of men irregularly armed. They belonged to the Manara Legion, and wore strange headgear. The prisoners were sent back in charge of a corporal and eight men. Outside a beautiful villa approached by an avenue of ancient cypresses, the vanguard reported suspicious figures. Anton Lerch, the sergeant, dismounted, took twelve men armed with carbines, whom he posted at the windows, and

captured eighteen students of the Pisan Legion, well-bred, handsome young men with white hands and long hair. Half-an-hour later the squadron stopped a wayfarer in the Berga-masque costume whose very guilelessness and insignificance aroused suspicion. Sewn into the lining of his coat he was carrying detailed plans of the greatest importance relating to the formation of irregular corps in the Giudicaria and their liaison with the Piedmontese army. About ten o'clock, a herd of cows fell into the squadron's hands. Immediately after-wards, they encountered a strong enemy detachment which fired on the vanguard from a cemetery wall. The front line, under Lieutenant Count Trautsohn, vaulted over the low wall and laid about them among the graves on the enemy, most of whom escaped in wild confusion into the church and through the vestry door into a dense thicket. The twenty-seven new prisoners reported themselves as Neapolitan irregulars under Papal officers. The squadron had lost one man. Cor-poral Wotrubek, with two men, Dragoons Holl and Haindl, riding round the thicket, captured a light howitzer drawn by two farm-horses by knocking the guard senseless, taking the horses by the bridles, and turning them round. Corporal Wotrubek was sent back to headquarters, slightly wounded, to report these skirmishes and the other successes of the day, the prisoners were also sent back, while the howitzer was taken on by the squadron which, deducting the escort, now numbered seventy-eight men.

Since the prisoners declared with one voice that the city of Milan had been abandoned by the enemy troops, regular and irregular, and stripped of artillery and ammunition, the captain could not deny himself and his men the pleasure of riding into the great, beautiful, defenceless city. Amid the ringing of noonday bells, under the march trumpeted into the steely, glittering sky by the four buglers, to rattle against a thousand windows and re-echo on seventy-eight cuirasses and seventy-eight upright, naked swords, with streets to right and left swarming like a broken anthill with gaping faces, watching pallid, cursing figures slipping into house-doors, drowsy windows flung wide open by the bare arms of unknown beauty, past Santa Babila, San Fedele, San Carlo, past the famous white marble cathedral, San Satiro, San Giorgio, San Lorenzo, San Eustorgio, their ancient bronze doors all opening wide on silvery saints and brocade-clad women with shining eyes, on candle-light and fumes of incense, on the alert for shots from a thousand attics, dark archways, and low shop-stalls, yet seeing at every turn mere half-grown girls and boys with flashing teeth and black hair, looking down on it all from their trotting horses, their eyes glittering in masks of blood-spattered dust, in at the Porta Venezia, out at the Porta Ticinese—thus the splendid squadron rode through Milan.

Not far from the Porta Ticinese, on a rampart set with fine plane-trees, it seemed to Sergeant Anton Lerch that he saw, at the ground-floor window of a new, bright-yellow house, a woman's face he knew. Curious to know more, he turned in his saddle; a slight stiffness in his horse's gait made him suspect a stone in one of its foreshoes, and as he was riding in the rear of the squadron, and could break file without disturbance, he made up his mind to dismount, even going so far as to back his horse into the entry of the house. Hardly had he raised the second white-socked hoof of his bay to inspect the shoe when a door leading straight into the front of the entry actually opened to show a woman, sensual-looking and still not quite past her youth, in a somewhat dishevelled bedgown, and behind her a sunny room with a few pots of basil and red pelargonium in the windows, while his sharp eyes caught in a pier-glass the reflection of the other side of the room, which was filled with a large white bed and a papered door, through which a stout, clean-shaven, elderly man was just withdrawing.

As there struggled back into the sergeant's mind the woman's name and a great many other things besides—that she was the widow or divorced wife of a Croat paymaster, that, nine or ten years before, he had on occasion spent the evening or half the night in Vienna with her and her accredited lover of the moment—he tried to distinguish, under her present stoutness, the full yet slender figure of those days. But standing there, she gave him a fawning Slav smile which sent the blood pulsing into his thick neck and under his eyes, and he was daunted by a certain archness in the way she spoke to him, by her bedgown and the furniture in the room behind. At the very moment, however, when with heavy eyes he was watching a big fly crawl over the woman's comb, when he had no thought in mind but of his hand on the warm, cool neck, brushing it away, the memory of the skirmishes and other lucky chances of the day came flooding back upon him, and he pressed her head forward with a heavy hand, saying: "Vuic"—he had not pronounced her name for ten years at least, and had completely forgotten her first name—"a week from now we shall occupy the town and these shall be my quarters," and he pointed to the half-open door of the room. Meanwhile he heard door after door slam in the house, felt his horse urging him to be gone, first by a dumb dragging at the bridle, then by loud neighing after the others. He mounted and trotted off after the squadron with no answer from Vuic save an evasive laugh and a toss of the head. But the word, once spoken, made him feel its power within him. Riding beside the main column of the squadron, his bay a little jaded, under the heavy, metallic glow of the sky, half blinded by the cloud of dust that moved with the riders, the sergeant, in his imagination, slowly took possession of the room with the mahogany furniture and the pots of basil, and at the same time entered into a life of peace still irradiated by war, an atmosphere of comfort and pleasant brutality with no officer to give him orders, a slippered life with the hilt of his sabre sticking through the left-hand pocket of his dressing-gown. And the stout, clean-shaven man who had vanished through the papered door, something between a priest and a pensioned footman, played an important part in it all, more important, even, than the fine, broad bed and Vuic's white skin. The clean-shaven man was now a somewhat servile companion who told court gossip and brought presents of tobacco and capons, now he was hard pressed and had to pay blackmail, was involved in many intrigues, was in the confidence of the Piedmontese, was the Pope's cook, procurer, owner of suspect houses with gloomy pavilions for political meetings, and swelled up into a huge, bloated figure from which, if it were tapped in twenty places, gold, not blood would pour.

There were no further surprises for the squadron that afternoon, and there was nothing to check the sergeant's musings. But there had awakened in him a craving for strokes of luck, for prize moneys, for ducats suddenly falling into his pockets. And the thorn which festered in his flesh, round which all wishes and desires clustered, was the anticipation of his first entrance into the room with the mahogany furniture.

When the squadron, its horses fed and half-rested, attempted towards evening to advance by a detour on Lodi and the Adda bridge, where there was every prospect of an encounter with the enemy, a village lying in a dark hollow off the high road with a half-ruined church spire looked enticing and suspicious enough to attract the sergeant's attention. Beckoning to two dragoons, Holl and Scarmolin, he broke away

from the squadron's route with them, and, so inflamed was
his imagination that it swelled to the hope of surprising in
the village some ill-defended enemy general, or of winning
some other great prize. Having arrived at the wretched and
seemingly deserted place, he ordered Scarmolin to reconnoitre the houses from the outside to the left, Holl to the
right, while he himself, pistol in hand, set off at the gallop
through the village. Soon, feeling under his feet hard flag-
stones which were coated with some slippery kind of grease,
he had to put his horse to the walk. Deathly silence reigned
in the village—not a child, not a bird, not a breath of air. To
right and left there stood foul hovels, the mortar scaling from
their walls, with obscene drawings in charcoal here and there
on the bare bricks. Between the naked doorposts the sergeant
caught sight from time to time of a dirty, half-naked figure
lounging on a bed or hobbling through the room as if on
broken hips. His horse advanced painfully, pushing its
haunches leadenly forward. As he turned and bent to look at
its hind shoe, shuffling footsteps issued from a house; he sat
upright, and a woman whose face he could not see passed
close in front of his mount. She was only half-dressed, her
ragged, filthy gown of flowered silk, half torn off her shoulders, trailed in the gutter, there were dirty slippers on her feet.
She passed so close in front of his horse that the breath from
its nostrils stirred the bunch of greasy curls that hung down
her bare neck under an old straw hat, yet she made no move
to hurry, nor did she make way for the rider. From a door-
step to the left, two rats, bleeding in their death-agony, rolled
into the middle of the street, the under one screaming so des-
perately that the sergeant's horse stopped, staring at the
ground, its head averted and its breathing audible. A pressure
on its flank sent it forward again, the woman having disappeared in an entry before the sergeant could see her face. A

dog ran out busily with upraised head, dropped a bone in the middle of the street and set about burying it between the paving-stones. It was a dirty white bitch with trailing teats; she scraped with fiendish intentness, then took the bone between her teeth and carried it away. As she began to dig again, three dogs ran up, two of them mere puppies with soft bones and loose skin; unable to bark or bite, they pulled at each others' muzzles with blunt teeth. The dog which had come with them was a pale yellow greyhound, its body so bloated that it could only drag itself along on its four skinny legs. The body was taut as a drum, so that its head looked far too small; there was a dreadful look of pain and fear in it restless little eyes. Two other dogs ran up at once, one thin and white, with black furrows running from its reddened eyes, and hideous in its avidity, the other a vile dachshund with long legs. This dog raised its head towards the sergeant and looked at him. It must have been very old. Its eyes were fathomlessly weary and sad. But the bitch ran to and fro in silly haste before the rider, the two puppies snapped soundlessly with their muzzles round the horse's fetlocks, and the greyhound dragged its hideous body close in front of the horse's hoofs. The bay could not advance a step. But when, having drawn his pistol to shoot one of the dogs, it misfired, the sergeant spurred his horse on both flanks and thundered away over the paving-stones. After a few bounds he was brought up short by a cow which a lad was dragging to the shambles at the end of a tight-stretched rope. But the cow, shrinking from the smell of blood and the fresh hide of a calf nailed to the doorpost, planted its hooves firm on the ground, drew the reddish haze of the sunset in through dilated nostrils and, before the lad could drag her across the road with stick and rope, tore away with piteous eyes a mouthful of the hay which the sergeant had tied on the front of his saddle.

He had now left the last house of the village behind him and, riding between two low and crumbling walls, could see his way ahead on the farther side of an old single-span bridge over an apparently dry ditch. He felt in his horse's step such an unutterable heaviness that every foot of the walls to right and left, and even every single one of the centipedes and wood-lice which housed in them, passed toilsomely before his eyes, and it seemed to him that he had spent eternity riding through the hideous village. But as, at the same time, he heard a great rasping breath from his horse's chest without at once realizing what it was, he looked above and beside him, and then ahead to see whence it came, and in doing so became aware, on the farther side of the bridge and at the same distance from it as himself, of a man of his own regiment, a sergeant riding a bay with white-socked forefeet. But as he knew that there was no other horse of the kind in the whole squadron but the one on which he was at that moment mounted, and as he still could not recognize the face of the other rider, he impatiently spurred his horse into a very lively trot, whereupon the other mended his pace in exactly the same way till there was only a stone's throw between them. And now, as the two horses, each from its own side, placed the same white-socked forefoot on the bridge, the sergeant, recognizing with starting eyes his own wraith, reined in his horse aghast, and stretched his right hand with stiffened fingers towards the being, while the wraith, also reining in its horse and raising its right hand, was suddenly there no longer; Holl and Scarmolin appeared from the dry ditch to left and right quite unperturbed, while loud and near at hand the bugles of the squadron sounded the attack.

Taking a rise in the ground at full speed, the sergeant saw the squadron already galloping towards a thicket from which enemy cavalry, armed with pikes, were pouring, and as he gathered the four loose reins in his left hand and wound the hand-strap round his right, he saw the fourth rank leave the squadron and slacken its pace, was already on the thundering earth, now in the thick smell of dust, now in the midst of the enemy, struck at a blue arm wielding a pike, saw close at hand the captain's face with starting eyes and savagely bared teeth, was suddenly wedged in among enemy faces and foreign colours, dived below whirling blades, lunged at the next man's neck and unseated him, saw Scarmolin beside him, laughing, hew off the fingers of a man's bridle hand and strike deep into the horse's neck, felt the thick of battle slacken, and was suddenly alone on the bank of a brook behind an enemy officer on an iron-grey horse. The officer put his horse to the jump across the brook, the horse refused. The officer pulled it round, turning towards the sergeant a young, very pale face and the mouth of a pistol, then a sabre was driven into his mouth with the full force of a galloping horse in its tiny point. The sergeant snatched back his sabre, and at the very spot where the fingers of the fallen rider had opened, laid hold of the snaffle of the iron-grey, which, light and airy as a fawn, lifted its hoofs across its dying master.

As the sergeant rode back with his splendid prize, the sun, setting in a thick mist, cast a vast crimson haze over the fields. Even on untrodden ground there seemed to lie whole pools of blood. A crimson glow lay on white uniforms and laughing faces, cuirasses and saddle-cloths sparkled and shone, and three little figtrees on which the men had wiped the grooves in their sabres glowed deepest of all. The captain came to a halt by the blood-stained trees, beside the bugler of the squadron, who raised his crimson-dripping bugle to his lips and blew. The sergeant rode from line to line and saw that the squadron had not lost a man, but had taken nine horses. He rode up to the captain to report, the iron-grey still beside him, capering with upraised head and wide nostrils, like the young, vain, beautiful horse it was. The captain hardly listened to the report. He made a sign to Lieutenant Count Trautsohn, who at once dismounted, unharnessed the captured light howitzer, ordered the gun to be dragged away by a detachment of six men and sunk in a swamp formed by the brook, having driven away the now useless draught-horses with a blow from the flat of his sabre, and silently resumed his place at the head of the first rank. During this time, the squadron, drawn up in two ranks, was not really restless, yet there was a strange feeling in the air; the elation of four successful skirmishes in one day found vent in outbursts of suppressed laughter and smothered shouts to each other. Even the horses were restless, especially those flanking the prizes. What with all these windfalls, the parade-ground seemed too small to hold them; in the pride of victory, the men felt they must scatter, swarm in upon a new enemy, fling themselves upon him, and carry off yet more horses.

At that moment Captain Baron Rofrano rose up to the front rank of his squadron and, raising his big eyelids from his rather sleepy blue eyes, gave, audibly but without raising his voice, the command "Release led horses." The squadron stood still as death. Only the iron-grey beside the sergeant stretched its neck, almost touching with its nostrils the forehead of the captain's mount. The captain sheathed his sabre, drew a pistol from its holster and, wiping a little dust from its shining barrel with the back of his bridle-hand, repeated the command, raising his voice slightly and beginning to count, "One . . . two. . . ." When he had counted "two," he fixed his veiled eyes on the sergeant, who sat motionless in his saddle, staring him full in the face. While Anton Lerch's steady, unflinching gaze, flashing now and then an oppressed, doglike look, seemed to express a kind of servile trust born

[330]

of many years of service, his mind was almost unaware of the huge tension of the moment, but was flooded with visions of an alien ease, and from depths in him unknown to himself there rose a bestial anger against the man before him who was taking away his horse, a dreadful rage against the face, the voice, the bearing, the whole being of the man, such as can only arise, in some mysterious fashion, through years of close companionship. Whether something of the same sort was going on in the captain's mind too, or whether he felt the silently spreading danger of critical situations coming to a head in this moment of mute insubordination, we cannot know. Raising his arm with a negligent, almost graceful gesture, he counted "three" with a contemptuous curl of his upper lip, the shot cracked, and the sergeant, hit in the forehead, reeled, his body across his horse's neck, then fell between the iron-grey and the bay. He had not reached the ground, however, before all the other non-commissioned officers and men had driven off their captured horses with a twist of the rein or a kick, and the captain quietly putting away his pistol, was able to rally his squadron, still twitching from the lightning stroke, against the enemy, who seemed to be gathering in the distant, shadowy dusk. The enemy, however, did not engage the new attack, and not long after, the squadron arrived unmolested at the southern outposts of its own army.

Lucidor

Characters for an Unwritten Comedy

IN THE LATE SEVENTIES, Frau von Murska took a small suite of rooms in an hotel in the Inner City. Her name, though not illustrious, was not entirely obscure, and she would drop hints of a family estate in the Russian part of Poland which belonged by rights to her and her children, but was, for the time being, sequestered or otherwise withheld from its rightful owners. Her circumstances seemed straitened, but, of course, only for the moment. With a grown-up daughter, Arabella, a half-grown son, Lucidor, and an elderly maid, she occupied three bedrooms and a drawing-room which looked out on to Kärntnerstrasse. There she had hung up some family portraits, engravings, and miniatures, spread a piece of old velvet embroidered with a coat of arms on an occasional table, set out on it some silver vases and baskets of good eighteenth-century French workmanship, and there she was at home. She had delivered letters and paid calls, and as she had an almost incredible number of "connections" all over the city, a kind of salon soon formed. It was one of those vague salons which are deemed "possible" or "impossible" according to the rigour of the critic. Yet Frau von Murska was decidedly neither dull nor ordinary, and her daughter was still more distinguished in temperament and bearing, and extremely beautiful. Anyone calling between four and six was sure to find the mother at home, and hardly ever alone. The daughter was not always present, and the thirteen- or fourteen-year-old boy, Lucidor, was known only to the intimates.

Frau von Murska's cultivation was genuine, and without any touch of the commonplace. In Viennese society, to which she vaguely assumed she belonged, though she moved on its outer fringe only, the reputation of a bluestocking would have given her much to contend with. But there was in her mind such a welter of memories, schemes, forebodings, misjudgments, enthusiasms, knowledge, and apprehensions that it was not worth while stopping to consider what she had acquired from books. Her conversation galloped from topic to topic by the most improbable bypaths; her restlessness was pitiful—no one hearing her talk needed to be told that she suffered from insomnia to the point of madness, and was consumed by anxiety, scheming, and thwarted hopes—yet to listen to her was an entertaining and most unusual experience, and though she did not wish to be indiscreet, her indiscretions were occasionally appalling. In short, she was a madwoman, though of the more amiable kind. She was extremely good-hearted, and at bottom a charming and unusual woman. But a difficult life, which she was quite unfitted to cope with, had so reduced her to confusion that, though only forty-two, she was already a fantastic figure. Most of her ideas and opinions were quite her own and very subtle, but utterly misapplied, whether to persons or circumstances. The closer her relationship to a person, the vaguer was her view of that person, and it would have been quite out of character for her to have anything but the most mistaken ideas about her two children and to follow them blindly. In her eyes, Arabella was an angel, Lucidor a rather heartless little creature. Arabella was a thousand times too good for this world, which suited Lucidor perfectly. In actual fact, Arabella was the image of her dead father, a proud, disappointed and irritable, very handsome man, prone to contempt but able to conceal it under excellent manners, respected or envied by men, loved by many women, and deficient in feeling. Little Lucidor, on the other hand, was feeling itself.

However, the time has now come to say that Lucidor was not a young gentleman, but a girl, whose name was Lucile. The idea that the younger daughter should wear boy's clothes during their season in Vienna was, like all Frau von Murska's ideas, a sudden inspiration springing from a tangle of motives. Its main object was to make a quite unprecedented move in connection with an old, mysterious, but fortunately real uncle who lived in Vienna and on whose account—all these hopes and schemes were extremely vague—she may possibly have chosen that city for the season. At the same time, however, the disguise had certain very real, very evident advantages. It was easier to live with one daughter than with two of not quite the same age, for there was, after all, nearly four years between them; it came cheaper. Besides, it was a still better, still more fitting position for Arabella to be the only daughter than the elder, and the very handsome little "brother," acting as a kind of groom, could set off her beauty.

A few chance circumstances fostered the plan. Frau von Murska's inspirations were never based on sheer fantasy; they were merely a strange combination of actual reality with what seemed possible or accessible to her imagination. Five years before, Lucile, then a child of eleven, had fallen ill with typhus; they had had to cut her beautiful hair short. Further, Lucile preferred to ride astride, a habit she had acquired when, with the peasant boys of Russian Poland, she had ridden the horses bareback into the horse-pond. Lucile submitted to the disguise as she would have submitted to a great many other things. She was patient by nature, and even the most absurd things can easily grow into a habit. At the same time, as she was painfully shy, she was delighted not to have to appear in the drawing-room in the guise of a girl at the awkward age. The only person in the secret was the maid: nobody else noticed anything. It is not so easy to be the first to notice something unusual, for, as a rule, it is not given to mankind to see things as they are. Besides, Lucile's hips were really boyishly slender, and there was little else to betray her as a girl. The disguise actually remained unknown and even unsuspected, and when matters took the turn which changed young Lucidor into a girl betrothed, or something still more womanly, everybody was exceedingly surprised.

It was only to be expected that a young lady of Arabella's distinction and beauty should soon be surrounded by a number of more or less professed admirers, the most outstanding of whom by far was Vladimir. His appearance was excellent, and he had particularly beautiful hands. He was more than well to do and without any encumbrances in the way of parents or family. His father had been an Austrian officer of the middle class, his mother a countess of a very well-known Baltic family. Of all those who seriously thought of Arabella, he was the one real match. There was a further point that completed the conquest of Frau von Murska. He alone was on any kind of real terms with the uncle who was so difficult to manage, so inaccessible, and so very important, the uncle on whose account they had really come to Vienna and on whose account Lucile had become Lucidor. This uncle, who occupied an entire floor of the Palais Buquoy, in Wallnerstrasse, and had, in his day, given rise to a good deal of gossip, had received Frau von Murska very badly. Although she was actually the widow of his nephew (or, to be more precise, of his father's brother's grandson), she had only succeeded in seeing him on her third call, and had never since been invited to so much as breakfast or a cup of tea. On the other hand, he had, with a somewhat bad grace, allowed them to send him Lucidor on one occasion. It was a peculiarity of this interesting old gentleman that he could not abide women, young or old. On the other hand, there was the vague hope that he might be moved to open his purse-strings for a boy who was, after all, a blood relation. And even that faint hope was infinitely precious in so precarious a situation.

Now Lucidor had actually driven there alone once at his mother's orders, but had not been received, to his own satisfaction and his mother's utter dismay, which was not diminished by the fact that nothing more came of it and the precious thread seemed broken. Vladimir, being in touch with both parties, now seemed to have been sent by heaven to pick it up again. With this end in view, Lucidor was, from time to time, unobtrusively brought to the drawing room when Vladimir was calling on his mother and sister, and by a most happy stroke of fate, Vladimir took a fancy to the boy and invited him, at their first meeting, to ride with him now and then, an invitation which was gratefully accepted after a swift exchange of glances between the mother and Arabella. It was perfectly natural for Vladimir to take to the brother of a lady with whom he was very much in love; besides, there are few things more delightful than the look of unconcealed admiration in the eyes of a nice boy of fourteen.

Frau von Murska's adoration of Vladimir grew steadily. This, like most of her mother's ways, irritated Arabella, and almost against her will, though she enjoyed Vladimir's society, she began to flirt with one of his rivals, Herr von Imfanger, a pleasant and rather elegant Tyrolese, a gentleman farmer, but quite out of the question as a match. Once, when her mother timidly ventured to charge Arabella with not behaving to Vladimir as he had a right to expect, Arabella answered very shortly, and spoke more coolly and slightingly of Vladimir than she really felt. Lucidor-Lucile happened to be present. A pang shot through her—a pang of anger, fear, and pain. She was utterly dismayed by her sister. She had never understood her, and at that moment felt for her something like horror, and could not have said whether she admired or hated her more. Then all feeling was blotted out in one overwhelming anguish. She went away and locked herself in her room. If she had been told that she was simply in love with Vladimir, she might even not have understood. She acted, as she could not help acting, mechanically, with tears whose real meaning she could not grasp pouring down her face. She sat down and wrote Vladimir a fervent love-letter. But it was in Arabella's name, not her own. She had often been annoyed that her handwriting was almost indistinguishable from Arabella's, and had been at great pains to acquire another, really ugly one. But she could at any time resume her own, which came readily to her hand; indeed, it caused her less trouble. Only someone who has ceased to think, who is literally beside himself, could write such a letter. It gave the lie to Arabella's whole being, but that was its sole purpose. It was utterly implausible, and yet again, in some way, plausible as the expression of a violent inner upheaval. If Arabella had been able to love with deep devotion, and had realized it in a sudden revulsion of feeling, she could certainly have written in these terms, and spoken of the Arabella whom everybody knew with the same boldness and burning contempt. The letter was strange, yet even for a cold, indifferent reader not quite incredible as written by a girl of unsuspected depth of feeling, if somewhat unaccountable. For that matter, the woman he loves always seems unaccountable to the lover. Finally, it was the kind of letter a man in that situation always hopes, in his heart of hearts, to receive, and believes that he may receive. I must anticipate here by saying that the letter was actually delivered to Vladimir not later than the following afternoon on the staircase, Lucidor stealing after him, calling him softly by name, whispering, and generally playing the part of an excited, gauche go-between for his lovely sister. There was, of course, a postscript urging, even imploring him not to be angry if no change should be immediately apparent in Arabella's behaviour, whether towards her lover or anyone else. And he was also besought not to betray by a word, or even a look, that he knew how tenderly he was loved.

A few days passed, during which Vladimir saw Arabella little, and never alone. He met her as she had told him to do, she met him as she had foretold. He was happy and unhappy. He only now knew how dear she was to him. The situation was infinitely tantalizing. Lucidor, with whom he was now riding daily, for he could hardly endure to be with anyone else, saw with delight and terror the change in his friend and the growing violence of his impatience. A second letter followed, almost more tender than the first, another touching plea not to disturb the precarious happiness of their suspense, to be satisfied with these confessions and to reply, if at all, in writing and through Lucidor. A letter passed every two or three days. Vladimir's days were happy, so were Lucidor's. The tone between them changed, they had an inexhaustible topic of conversation. When they had dismounted in some grove in the Prater and Lucidor had handed over his latest love-letter, he would watch with tremulous delight the features of his friend as he read the letter. At times he would put questions which verged on indiscretion, but the agitation of the boy who had been involved in this love-affair, his penetration, something about him which made him handsomer and tenderer every day, amused Vladimir, and he could not but admit to himself that, reserved and haughty though he was by nature, it would cost him a great deal not to talk to Lucidor about Arabella. At times Lucidor would be the woman-hater, the precocious and childishly cynical boy. What he said on such occasions was by no means commonplace, for he was always able to sprinkle his talk with what doctors call "introspective truths." But Vladimir, who had no small opinion of himself, made it clear that the love he inspired, and inspired in such a creature as Arabella, was of quite a peculiar kind, and not to be compared to anything else. Then Lucidor would feel Vladimir more admirable than ever, and himself a small and pitiable thing. They came to speak of marriage, and the subject was torture to Lucidor, for then Vladimir was almost entirely taken up with the Arabella of real life, not with the Arabella of the letters. And Lucidor lived in mortal dread of any decision, any drastic change. His one thought was to prolong the present state of affairs. The effort it cost the poor child to maintain that state of affairs, outwardly and inwardly so precarious, in some kind of balance, for days, for weeks—he had not the strength to think farther—is past telling. Since he had, after all, been charged to win his uncle's good graces for the family, he did what he could. Sometimes Vladimir accompanied him. The uncle was an odd old man, who took a frank pleasure in letting himself go in the company of younger men, and his conversation was of such a kind that an hour with him was, for Lucidor, a truly painful little ordeal. And nothing seemed farther from his uncle's mind than to do something for his relatives. Lucidor was incapable of lying, yet wished to reassure his mother. The lower the hopes his mother had set on the uncle sank, the greater her impatience that nothing seemed to announce a decision between Arabella and Vladimir. The wretched people on whom she was dependent for money began to write off both these brilliant prospects. Her fears, her painfully concealed impatience, infected everybody, most of all poor Lucidor, whose mind was so full of so many incompatible things. But he was to receive still more subtle and sterner lessons in the strange school of life which, after all, he had now entered.

Nothing definite had been said about Arabella's dual nature. But the idea arose of itself. The day-time Arabella was forbidding, coquettish, exacting, self-assured, worldly, and almost excessively unfeeling; the Arabella of the night, writing to her love by candlelight, knew no bounds in her self-surrender and longing. Now by chance, or by fate, this corresponded to a very mysterious split in Vladimir's own nature. He too, like every creature with a soul, had, more or less, his day and night sides. A somewhat chilling pride and an ambition which, though without meanness or self-seeking, was constant and soaring were balanced by impulses of a very different kind which withdrew into the dark, sought to hide, and were always on the point of vanishing beneath the hazy threshold of the subconscious mind. An imaginative sensuality, which could dream its way into an animal, a dog, a swan, had at times almost completely possessed his soul. He did not care to recall those years of transition from boyhood to young manhood, but they had left their mark on him, and a dark, mysterious light now fell upon this suppressed side of his nature, which no thought of his ever illuminated, and which he had laid waste by force of will. That light was his love for the invisible, other Arabella. If the Arabella of the day-time had happened to be his wife or become his mistress, he would always have remained somewhat *terre à terre* with her, and would never have permitted the forcibly suppressed fantasies of childhood to take any place in his life. Of her who lived in the darkness, he thought and wrote in very different fashion. What was Lucidor to do when his friend demanded something more, a sign more living than lines on white paper? Lucidor was alone with his fears, his confusion and his love. The Arabella of the day gave him no help. Indeed it was as if some evil demon was prompting her against him. The colder, more incalculable, worldly, and coquettish she grew, the more Vladimire hoped and prayed of the other. He was so good a suppliant that Lucidor could not bring himself to refuse. And even if he had wished to, his tender pen would not have found the words. A night came when Vladimir had every right to believe that Arabella had received him in Lucidor's room—and what a reception! Lucidor had managed so to curtain the windows that they could not see their hands before their eyes. It was only natural that they should subdue their voices to the most inaudible of murmurs, for only a single door separated them from the maid. No one inquired where Lucidor had spent the night, yet he could not be in the secret, and had been put off with some pretext. A strange thing was that Arabella wore her lovely hair bound closely up in a thick silk scarf, and gently but firmly prevented her lover's hand from unbinding it. But there was little else she refused him. Several nights passed which were not like this one, but another came which was, and Vladimir was very happy. These were perhaps the happiest days in his life. In the certainty of the joys the night would bring, his manner by day changed towards Arabella. He came to take a peculiar pleasure in the fact that the day-time Arabella was so incomprehensibly different. Her self-command, which she never betrayed by glance or gesture, ravished him. Week by week she seemed to grow cooler, the more tender her nights had been. He had no intention of being less adroit or self-controlled than she. By submitting without reserve to this mysteriously powerful womanly will, he imagined he was earning a certain right to the joys of his nights. He began to find the most exquisite enjoyment in the very duality of her nature. That she, who gave no sign of belonging to him, should yet belong to him, that she, who could abandon herself so utterly, could remain a presence so untouched, so untouchable—these things made him reel like repeated draughts from a magic cup. He knew that he must thank fate on his bended knees for a delight so peculiar, so fitted to the secret of his own nature. He poured it all forth in torrents to himself and Lucidor, and nothing could have more terrified poor Lucidor's very soul.

Meanwhile, the real Arabella had so openly turned away from Vladimir during these weeks that, without the oddest impulse to misinterpret everything he saw, he could not have failed to be aware of it every moment. Though he never betrayed himself, she felt that there was between them something that was not there before. They had always agreed, and still did so; their day sides were congenial, and they could have made an excellent if commonplace match of it. With Herr von Imfanger she did not agree, but she enjoyed his company. She began to understand more clearly that she did not enjoy Vladimir's society in that way. She was irritated by the mysterious vibration which seemed to radiate from him to her. It was neither courtship nor flattery; she did not understand it, and certainly did not relish it. Imfanger could not but realize that she was attracted by him. Vladimir, for his part, imagined that he had far better proofs on his side. The oddest situation arose between the two young men. Each imagined that the other had good grounds for being out of humour, or at any rate good reason to leave the coast clear. Each found the attitude, the imperturbable good humour of the other simply ridiculous. Neither knew what to make of the other, and each regarded the other as an arrant fop and fool.

The mother's situation was torture. Several resources dried up. Friends left her in the lurch. A loan offered under the mask of friendship was ruthlessly called in. Frau von Murska was at all times prone to hasty decisions. At a moment's notice she resolved to give up her home in Vienna, to take leave merely by letters, and seek a refuge elsewhere, if only in the agent's house on her sequestered estate. Arabella took the news with ill humour, but despair was not in her nature. Lucidor had anxiously to conceal a real and boundless despair. Several nights had passed without her summoning her lover. She made up her mind to do so that night. The conversation between Arabella and her mother, the decision to leave, her powerlessness to prevent the departure, stunned her. And even if she had wished to take to desperate remedies, cast everything overboard, confess to her mother, and above all, reveal to her lover who was the Arabella of his nights, she was held back by an icy pang of fear of his disappointment and anger. She felt like a criminal, but only towards him; she had no thought for anyone else. She could not see him that night. She knew that her own shame, fear, and confusion would betray her. Instead of embracing him, she wrote to him for the last time. It was the humblest, most touching of letters, and nothing could have been more remote from it than the name of Arabella with which she signed it. She had, she wrote, never hoped to become his wife. A few years, a single year, as his mistress would have been untold happiness to her, but that must and could not be. She besought him not to question her, not to press her. He was to come the next day, but not till the late afternoon. The day after they would probably have left. Perhaps, later, he would come to know and understand—she was on the point of adding, forgive, but the word was so incomprehensible in Arabella's mouth that she did not write it. She slept little, rose early, and sent the letter to Vladimir by the house porter. The morning was spent in packing. After dinner, without a word to anyone, she drove to her uncle's house. The idea had come to her in the night. She would find the words, the pleas, to soften this strange man. The miracle would happen and the fast-tied purse-strings be loosened. She did not think of the reality, only of her mother, the situation, her love. With the money or the letter in her hand she would fall at her mother's feet and implore, as her sole reward—what? her tormented, exhausted mind nearly failed her: of course—only that they should stay in Vienna, that there should be no change. She found her uncle at home. The details of this scene, which took the most peculiar course, cannot be given here. Thus much can be told—she actually softened him, he was on the point of taking the momentous step, when by some whim of age he changed his mind. He would do something later— when, he did not say. And that was all. She drove home, crept upstairs and, crouching on the floor among boxes and trunks, gave way to despair. Then it seemed to her that she could hear Vladimir's voice in the drawing-room. She crept on tiptoe to the door and listened. It was indeed Vladimir and Arabella, whose voices were raised in the strangest dialogue.

Vladimir had received Arabella's mysterious farewell letter in the morning. Nothing in his life had ever gone so deep. He sensed some dark secret between them, but not between heart and heart. He felt within him the power and love to bring it to light, to understand, to forgive, whatever it might be. The incomparable mistress of his nights had grown too dear for him to live without her. Oddly enough, he did not think of the real Arabella—he even felt some strangeness in the thought that it was she whom he was on his way to see, to soothe and sustain, to win for good and all. He arrived to find her mother alone in the drawing-room, agitated, distraught, and fantastic as never before. Nor had she ever seen him in his present state. He kissed her hands, he spoke, but with feeling and constraint. He asked to be allowed to speak to Arabella alone. Frau von Murska was delighted, and forthwith transported to the seventh heaven. The improbable was her element. She hurried to fetch Arabella, implored her not

to refuse the noble young man, now that everything was turning out so splendidly. Arabella was astounded. But I am not
on those terms with him," she replied frigidly. "You never
know what terms you are on with men," returned her mother,
and dispatched her to the drawing-room.

Vladimir was embarrassed, moved, and ardent. Arabella felt
more and more that Herr von Imfanger was right in thinking
Vladimir peculiar. Vladimir, in consternation at her coolness,
begged her at last to drop her mask. Arabella had no idea what
it was she had to drop. Vladimir was both loving and angry, a
mixture which Arabella found so distasteful that in the end
she rushed from the room, leaving him standing there. In his
utter bewilderment, Vladimir was the more inclined to believe
her unhinged, as she had just hinted that she thought the same
of him, and that her opinion was shared by a third party. At
that moment, Vladimir would have been reduced to a completely helpless soliloquy had not the other door opened and
the strangest figure darted towards him, embraced him, and
slid down at his feet. It was Lucidor, yet not Lucidor, but
Lucile, a lovely girl bathed in tears, in a dressing-gown of
Arabella's, with her short, boyish hair hidden under a thick
scarf. It was his friend and counsellor, and at the same time
his mysterious mistress, his beloved, his wife. Life may create
the dialogue which followed, comedy might imitate it, but a
story cannot.

Nor can we say whether Lucidor really became Vladimir's
wife or whether, by day and in another country, she remained
what she had been in the darkness of night, his happy mistress.

We are at liberty to doubt whether Vladimir was a sufficiently valuable being to deserve such devotion. But in any
case the whole beauty of a soul so devoted as Lucile's could
only have been revealed in circumstances as strange as these.

7

From the "Book of Friends"

I

MAN PERCEIVES in the world only what already lies within him; but to perceive what lies within him man needs the world; for this, however, activity and suffering are indispensable.

THE YOUNG suffer their powerful impressions, the mature produce them.

GROPING youth knows that the world is filled with strength; but it is not aware what role weakness, in its various forms, plays in the world.

IN EVERY man dwells a unique innocence.

AS A CHILD, man has participated in the memories of his grandparents; as an old man, he participates in the hopes of his grandchildren. Thus he spans five generations or a hundred to a hundred-and-twenty years.

MAN IS a manifold person as he is a manifold pupil.

YOUTH is as strong as it fancies itself and at the same time as delicate and weak as it behaves; these are its ambiguous and daemonic qualities.

THE NEXT of kin see in a person's attitude towards the world the intentions, which are usually the purer part; those more distant see the realization into which many impure, even evil things have often entered.

TO APPROVE is more difficult than to admire.

TO ATTEMPT to describe a person's life means—to say the least—putting oneself on the same level.

WE HAVE fewer friends than we imagine, but more than we know.

THE MOST important sense to develop in children is that of recognizing that the divine reveals itself in our immediate surroundings. Much that we do and allow to happen, however, aims at deadening this sense.

WHILE growing older we recognize that throughout all the vicissitudes of life we are not free of guilt; but in each of us there dwells our own form of innocence, which is what sustains us without our knowing how.

SITUATIONS are symbolic; it is the weakness of our time that we treat them analytically, and in so doing dissolve the magic.

CIRCUMSTANCES have less power than we think to make us happy or unhappy; but the anticipation of future circumstances has a gigantic one.

THE REASON old habits are so difficult to fight is because in them indolence, usually the enemy of activity, allies itself with a certain rhythmical sense of activity.

From the "Book of Friends"

WE ARE so eager to possess and are made so happy by any sign of fidelity that we can feel something like pleasure even in a regularly recurring fever.

PEOPLE in relation to people are almost invariably comic; the tragic arises when the fate of the single, solitary man moves in and hides behind the actors.

CASE histories recorded by Janet supply evidence that strength of faith decreases with decreasing will-power.—Here lies the root of higher existence.

A CERTAIN subtle transcendental vanity is an element without which we cannot live. Like a warped mirror it reflects for us a universe whose radiating centre we are; without it we feel that we would lose ourselves and fall into the void.

THE YARDSTICK of propriety is reality.

WITHOUT self-love not even the smallest decisions can be made; life, become nothing but despair and paralysis, is impossible.

A CERTAIN measure of conceit is a useful ingredient in genius.

WHAT is the basic element of dignity? Naïveté. Impressiveness without dignity is slightly disquieting. Napoleon's words, "Il n'y a qu'un pas du sublime au ridicule," are true, but only for him; his eminence was so constituted that it was continuously on the brink of collapse.

THERE'S a difference between genuinely having an attitude, whatever it may be, and making a pretence to others, or even to oneself, of having one.

[351]

CONTINUOUS indirect appreciation is a quality that should never be absent from social intercourse. Direct appreciation is more difficult to accept. He who expresses his appreciation directly shows that he is placing himself on our level, that he is at least in the position of judging us and our merit.

BETWEEN the fleeting fame of the actor and the allegedly lasting fame of the poet, there is but a small and specious difference.

THE ABILITY to recognize authority is a sign of a superior human being.

EGOTISM offends not so much by deeds as by lack of understanding.

APROPOS the notion "Experience," there exist two irritating kinds of people: those who lack experience and those who pride themselves too much on their experience.

IT'S AN unpleasant but necessary art to keep the vulgar at bay by coldness. "Only the cold," runs an Arabian proverb, "prevents dung from soiling your feet."

WHO TAKES social life as anything but symbolic errs.

ALLEGORY is a great medium which should not be despised. What friends really mean to one another can be demonstrated better by the exchange of a magic ring or a horn than by psychology.

REALITY is the *fable convenue* of Philistines.

THERE is something in us which is above and behind all ages and plays with all ages.

From the "Book of Friends"

AT THE beginning of life we are most subjective and least understand subjectivity in others.

WOMEN are fundamentally French by their sense of proportion and their inclination towards excess.

ONE FORM of self-education is to challenge a person who for us has authority to express himself on a subject about which we know he thinks otherwise than ourselves.

EACH new acquaintance causes a disintegration and a new integration.

WHEN treating the more subtle conditions of daily life—the essence of sociability—the Germans always waver between negligence and affectation.

WHO OBSERVES manners in social intercourse lives off his interest; who disregards them breaks into his capital.

THE HESITATION to speak to another of one's own personal concerns is a self-warning of the soul; into each confession, each account, distortion easily enters, turning in a trice the most delicate, most sacred, into something vulgar.

IT IS a fiction to speak of a European aristocracy in general; actually, an Austrian count, a German Junker, a *principe Romano,* a Polish nobleman, a lord, or a patrician from Berne are very different manifestations: but as a postulate one can and certainly should speak of a European aristocracy.

THE STRENGTH of patrician upbringing lies in refusing.

IN THE more refined forms of human relations, even in marriage, nothing should be taken for granted, nothing considered permanent, but everything considered a gift of each single world-encircling moment.

THE RULES of conduct, properly understood, are also signposts in the intellectual realm.

THERE are no two people on this earth who could not be turned into deadly enemies by a devilishly contrived indiscretion.

THE CONSOLER boasts easily.

NOTHING in the world is rarer than will-power, and yet the scanty measure vouchsafed mortal men suffices to distort all their judgments.

SOCIAL life should be taken only as an allegory. The whole social life of more modern times (beginning with Lessing and Madame de Sévigné) can be epitomized as one great mythology.

THE ABANDONMENT of a mistress suggests a flagging imagination.

EACH new significant acquaintance tears us down and builds us up anew; should it be of the greatest significance, then we undergo a regeneration.

CHILDREN are entertaining because they are easily entertained.

AMONG superior people there exists a creative and an uncreative indolence which merge, apparently without a distinct boundary, within a region concealed from sight.

From the "Book of Friends"

WHAT love requires from both is plastic energy: this is why there are in love, as in art, so many abortive sketches without sufficient energy for execution.

SINGING is near miraculous because it is the mastering of what is otherwise a pure instrument of egotism: the human voice.

UNDER certain circumstances a woman will tolerate a man's conversation about his love for another woman, but the whole emphasis must lie on love, not on the object of that love.

THE MEANING of marriage is mutual dissolution and palingenesis. Thus true marriage dissolves only in death—indeed, not even then.

AGREEMENT without sympathy produces a most disagreeable relationship.

MANNERS rest on a twofold foundation: to show the other every attention yet not to obtrude upon him.

THE DEFECTIVE in soul recognize and scent one another out.

SELF-LOVE and self-hate are the deepest of all earthly creative powers.

WE ALL possess certain virtues which never reveal themselves to us as a result of achievement, nor are we made aware of them in the reaction of the world; nevertheless they are the most valuable, and to be conscious of them would accelerate the course of our blood-stream: to gather and reflect these rays is the tenderest task of friendship.

MAN'S age, perceived from within, is everlasting youth.

JOY REQUIRES more surrender, more courage, than pain. As far as we surrender to joy, we challenge the unknown darkness.

TO GRASP proffered love requires the power of faith, hence genius.

THE PRESENT is the absolute suffering side of existence—but it is only transitory.

THE WHOLE soul is never one, save in ecstasy.

IN THE most extraordinary and most lonely manner of living and in the most miserable, most secret situation, we all have thousands of companions of whose existence we have never been aware.

THOUGHT of an aging man: that, if he but lived to see it, the rising generation could throw a revealing light upon him.

WHEN a man passes away he takes with him a secret: how it was possible for him, just for him, to have continued living —living in the profound sense of the word.

WHERE is your Self to be found? Always in the deepest enchantment that you have experienced.

II

EVERY truly great spiritual apparition is superhuman, making—for one who surrenders to it—everything else superfluous to the end of time. This is the source of the religions revealed by an individual and of their claim on orthodoxy.

From the "Book of Friends"

THOSE who feel little coherence in themselves talk about the adherence to ideas, but ideas are nothing to which one can adhere; they are something transcendent which reveals itself to us in sublime moments and then vanishes again.

MAN IS full of intentions; he is not aware of them but they are the hidden mainsprings of his actions.

ALL FANTASY in which you intensely participate is myth; in myth everything has a double and counter meaning: Death = Life, Snake-fight = Love-embrace. Hence in myth everything is balanced.

MAN'S soul finally becomes a labyrinth cut into a hard stone of which he believes that he alone knows the way out into the open. But this is only his belief.

IT CANNOT be expected that one knows everything, but that by knowing one thing he knows about all things.

THE SPIRIT seeks the real, the nonspirit clings to the unreal.

IN THE present which surrounds us there are no fewer fictitious elements than in the past, whose reflection we call history. Only by our interpreting one fictitious element through the other does something worth-while develop.

EVER-SURPRISING reality steps in where logic does not suffice to explain the necessity of an occurrence.

THE ONLY equality that stands the test of the deeply penetrating eye is the equality of opposites.

ALL HEAVENS and hells of all religions are fashioned from the human soul: what matters is the power of the projection to the outside.

[357]

Hugo von Hofmannsthal

THE EAGLE cannot take wing from flat ground; he has laboriously to jump on to a rock or tree-trunk: from there, however, he can soar to the stars.

EVERYTHING believed, and nothing else, exists.

MAN IS guided by five destinies: his mind, his body, his nation, his home, his language: to transcend all five is to approach the divine.

EVERY powerful impression brings freedom and bonds: this is why our impressions form us.

THERE is no point in the individual taking a modest attitude in the intellectual sphere; the whole contemporary world, all past included, is precisely the space he needs fully to exist.

EVERYTHING experienced tastes strange and dreadful, like brackish water: a mixture of life and death.

MAGIC is wisdom turned practical; unconscious wisdom can also turn practical. (As a rule, we perceive only reason turning practical.)

ALL SUPERIOR things require a combining. A superior person is the union of several people. The creation of superior poetry requires several poets in one.

IN OUR thoughts, Will has a greater share than Reason.

THE ABILITY to ask certain profound questions can develop in us by the presentiment that they might be answered, by encounters—even by the anticipation of encounters.

From the "Book of Friends"

THE WORLD wants to tear each person out of himself and restore him to himself again.

KNOWLEDGE is little; to know the right context is much, to know the right spot is everything.

THE MIND develops its greatest strength in contest with the sensual.

HE WHO grasps the highest unreality will create the highest reality.

SPIRIT conquers matter. Matter's strongest weapon in its battle with the spirit is its elusiveness.

THERE is nothing essential within which at the same time cannot be perceived without.

MAN CAN carry within himself a numb or keen sense of time as well as an acute or obtuse sense of space.

ALTHOUGH a great nation continues to produce new poets and thinkers who represent its intellectual essence, most of them are objects, not subjects, of that life.

THE WITTY and the dull scholar are both dangerous. The latter increases the bulk of material in the world under the pretext of making an intellectual contribution. The former easily sacrifices the best to the mediocre.

WHEN I think of myself and anything else at the same time —be it only the map of Greece—then I look into myself as through a window.

Hugo von Hofmannsthal

POWERFUL imaginations are conservative.

To GROW more mature is to separate more distinctly, to connect more closely.

PERHAPS the strangest contact between the real and the unreal is the actual damage which false notions cause.

THE MEDIOCRE person stops short too soon after the right thought, which is why there are so many half-truths in the world.

JUDGING by the innumerable pamphlets and ephemeral books that appear, "unspiritualized intellectualism" is quite a good description of the contemporary mental condition.

EMBRYOS have the form but not the strength of giants.

WHAT is culture? To know what concerns one, and to know what concerns one to know.

A MAN should be allowed to occupy himself with his own intellectual personality if his incentive is real curiosity.

PERCEPTION of the strange is hindered by strangeness; recognition of the familiar is prevented by familiarity.

THE PAST has been incorporated into our memory so that we shall overestimate it.

RECOGNIZE the moments of creative conception as the real Present.

THE QUESTIONS in human faces are of the spirit; the assertions are manifestations of matter.

From the "Book of Friends"

EVEN in the highest sublimation it is still the naïveté, still the irrational physical, that provides permanence to the spirit.

THE NEARER the scholar or thinker approaches (without becoming) the artist, the more dubious a phenomenon he becomes.

THE MOST dangerous form of stupidity is a sharp intellect.

SIMILARITIES exist only in the sphere of Non-Being—the Non-Human in men, and so on. Being is always unique.

SPIRIT is transcended reality. What absents itself from reality is not spirit.

IN ORDER to see at all we have to free our eyes of the dust which the present is continually throwing into them.

NOT TO know many things but to bring many things into contact with one another is a first step toward the creative.

BY SAYING anything conclusive about reality we already bring it nearer to the dream, or rather to poetry.

THE FULNESS of human existence is built out of any number of vacuums.

THE BEST moments are those in which the individual grasps his role in life; this feeling can be intensified to the point of magic and it is without any egotism, without striving.

THE MAN of imagination needs a lifetime to resolve himself into his elements; the genius builds of these a new world.

EVENTS are waves which threaten the spirit but also buoy it up.

WHAT is inner freedom? To recognize simultaneously the general and the necessary in the particular.

BELIEF, like Unbelief, has but one aim. Both strive for the whole.

TO CONSIDER himself as material for higher things is the last resort of a man who repudiates himself.

DEPTH must be hidden. Where? On the surface.

THE WORLD tolerates the infamous, but only the exceptional gives it satisfaction. Those between have much to contend with and are prone to a bad conscience.

IT IS the simple not the complex characters which are difficult to understand.

THE MOST dangerous of our prejudices reign in ourselves against ourselves. To dissolve them is a creative act.

THE MOST dangerous opponent of strength is weakness.

FORMS animate and kill.

TO RECOGNIZE the difference between ourselves and others calls for a moment of illumination.

IF LOVE had a "goal," transcendentally speaking, it would have to be this: love's ardour would weld into unity man who is continually disintegrating.

WHAT distinguishes the one who enters the temple of culture from the one remaining in the outer sanctum is that the wealth of the morally possible represents itself to him in forms, not in concepts.

WHERE the will is awakened, something is already near achieved.

FIERY air amidst burning logs looks like crystal-clear moving water.

A FEATHER can whet a pebble round provided it is held by the hand of love.

CEREMONY is the spiritual manifestation of the body.

A WORK of art is a detailed and extended action by which a character becomes recognizable.

THE BEAUTIFUL, even in art, is inconceivable without chastity.

III

THE PRESENT urges forms upon us. To break out of this magic circle and produce new forms is the creative act.

THERE is more freedom within the narrowest limits, within the most specialized task, than in the limitless vacuum which the modern mind imagines to be the playground for it.

AT EVERY moment of the present there is always a hidden element whose emergence could alter everything: this is a dizzy-making thought, but one which gives us comfort.

A THOUGHT at which one does not easily arrive and which is yet the key to many problems is this: that in each epoch the particularly weak might be hidden once more under the guise of the specially powerful.

IF THE Germans wish to incorporate intellectual values into politics, they must learn above all to make a sharp distinction between two concepts, one of which is concerned with the Nearest, the other with the Highest: immediate purpose and ultimate aim.

PAST events (history) appear as something present when all circumstances (all aspects of a character) are grasped—i.e., conjured up.

WHAT drives us into contemplation of the past is the similarity between it and our own lives, which are somehow one. By the grasp of this identity we can transport ourselves even into the purest of all regions, into death.

THE DESPAIR of an epoch would express itself by deeming it no longer worthwhile to show interest in the past.

IN THE present confusion of mind we find elements of every German folly since the sixteenth century.

WE ARE as poorly and unprecisely informed about our own nation as about our own bodies.

A NATION exercises at times a kind of ostracism by making certain ranks and classes objects of accusation; but by so doing it points toward a more profound truth: only the totality of productive individuals form a nation.

ALL NATIONAL politics lead finally into an incommunicable element, into *idioteia*, using that word in its original meaning.

From the "Book of Friends"

NATIONS speak such different languages that they can neither offend nor do justice to one another.

THE ANTHROPOCENTRIC is also a form of chauvinism.

FRENCH wit is a pleasant and startling way of expressing a truth with precision. (The Germans make a great mistake in assuming that the French supplant truth by wit, that their wit conceals untruth or nothing.) This was the point of Voltaire's jests about God and the Church; so must Rodin be understood when he answered that what the German barbarians did to Rheims Cathedral was no different from what the French restorers did, year after year, to all the cathedrals of France.

GERMANS pride themselves highly upon their profundity, which is simply another word for unrealized form. According to them, Nature would have us wander about without skin, nothing but viscera and vertebrae.

A PHILOSOPHER—in the sense employed by antiquity and the eighteenth century—has a good position in a great as well as in a miserable epoch: he will stand out from both. But an epoch which annihilates itself annihilates him, too.

IN THE national sphere idiosyncrasy prevails; everyone believes he knows the last truth about his nation as he believes he knows it about himself. Should he be asked what this truth is, however, he would answer as Augustine did to the question concerning the nature of time: If I'm not asked I know it; if I am, I don't.

MINOR intellects—the so-called brilliant ones—stir up, but do not dominate, the ideas of their time.

[365]

Hugo von Hofmannsthal

IN BYGONE epochs it was the sentimental affectations which prevailed; in ours it is the realistic.

POLITICS is the art of social intercourse on a higher level.

POLITICS is agreement on reality.

THE GERMAN has an enormous objectivity and a very poor relationship to facts.

EACH epoch has its own sentimentality, its specific way of overemphasizing strata of emotion. The sentimentality of the present is egotistical and unloving; it exaggerates not the feeling of love but that of the Self.

THE GERMANS have little talent for acting, but much theatrical affectation; little sense and taste for rhetoric, but great exaggeration; little aptitude for the social, but endless social inhibitions.

THE FRENCH view sociability, the world of reflexes, as absolute reality which no one would be absurd enough to question.

IF A CLASS which has ruled a nation is not annihilated and reduced to a mere shadow of itself, it will do harm.

THE INDESTRUCTIBLE foundation upon which the self-confidence of the English rests is the great consistency in their history.

THAT a man like Wagner, essentially a theatrical temperament of the highest calibre, could provoke a conflict which split a whole culture and has not yet calmed down reveals a strong side of the German mind; it shows that to them, as to the Greeks, divisions and departments mean nothing in the world of ideas.

THE FRENCH have made their most spiritual contribution on the frontier zone between Catholicism and heresy.

IT IS hard to struggle with a ruling society, but harder to have to represent one that doesn't exist.

IT IS just possible to imagine what past epochs included in their thinking, but not what they excluded.

OWING to the poverty of their social life, the vanity of the Germans has been perverted into self-righteousness and sentimentality.

POLITICS is magic. The powers will obey him who knows how to summon them.

IV

EACH true work of art is the blue print for the only temple on earth.

AS A BASIS for education Goethe can replace a national culture.

WE HAVE no literature of modern times. We have Goethe, and attempts.

IT IS the paradox of literary existence that the public of one age show a desire for a different kind of literary nourishment than the public of all ages.

Hugo von Hofmannsthal

ANY DESCRIPTION of anything existing is already indiscretion; to atone for this inherent defect by a counter-action (which we cannot help calling religious) is the meaning of any higher striving in art.

A KIND of religious function is attributed to the greatest poetic works; the different ways in which this can be achieved can be seen in Goethe's symbolic poems and Dostoevski's novels.

PAINTING transforms space into time, music time into space.

HUMAN beings expect a poetic work to appeal to them, speak to them, place itself on their level. The loftier works of art do this as little as Nature places herself on a level with human beings; she is there and leads man beyond himself—when he is self-composed and ready.

WHOEVER wants to fathom the great style of a Dante or of a Raphael must evoke for himself the worlds of doubt and weakness, the false powers and the terror which the intensity of these works posits as non-existing. This is the cleansing and constructive power that emanates from the works of great style, and it is in this sense that we should consider Molière as a master of great style, even in his buffooneries, and understand what quality emanates even from them.

THE WRITER'S task is to cleanse, to organize, to articulate the substance of life. Throughout life there prevails a ghastly absurdity, a frightful raging, of Matter—such as heredity, inner compulsion, stupidity, malice, profound wickedness. Throughout the intellectual sphere confusion, an almost unbelievable inconsistency, prevails: here we have the Augean stable which needs to be cleansed over and over again and transformed into a temple.

AN AUTHOR, whether he wishes it or not, is always at war with the age he lives in. He experiences every resistance of the epoch, but during his lifetime he will never learn whether the weights that threatened to smother him were made of iron or paper.

THE DIFFICULTY in life is that in man reason and passion live side by side and that he must, so far as he can, make them both harmonize within himself. A similar difficulty exists in the creation of poetry: to achieve a good transition from the passionate to the rational.

KINSHIP of forms: Dostoevski's novels and the Greek tragedy; calculation in Kleist and Poe; Novalis's intuition about the identity between Body and Soul, and the same intuition in Tolstoy and Dostoevski.

IN A WORK of art spirit and creative process mutually substantiate one another.

WHAT prevented Ibsen from making comedies out of his material was a Nordic-Protestantic stiffness and shyness.

THE FAMOUS author lives merely in a different form of obscurity from the author of whom no one speaks.

EACH subject-matter at each point leads to the Infinite.

IS NOT the despair of the present age due to the lost faith in form?

IN HIS work and human contacts the artist offers most substance where he offers most form and nuance.

WE SHOULD emulate Nature in her way of not considering anything as intermediate, of minor importance, or as provisional, and in her way of treating all things as of paramount importance.

WHAT in poetry is called the plastic, the actual process of creation, has its roots in justice.

WHAT the inferior writer knows least how to appreciate in the superior—because he is not aware of it, indeed, cannot even divine it—is perseverance: the real tenacious drive.

IN DILETTANTISM lies the germ of moral depravity.

THE MAIN difference between living people and fictitious characters is that the writer takes great pains to give the characters coherence and inner unity, whereas the living people may go to extremes of incoherence because their physical existence holds them together.

MODERN psychological poets give depth to what should be lightly passed over, and take superficially what should be treated profoundly.

TALENT is no achievement, limbs are no dance.

ON THE highest level of art nakedness and self-exposure prevail; their counterweight is profound seriousness and complete dedication. When this condition is suspended, when an eye winks at the audience, then it is shameless.

From the "Book of Friends"

EVERY spoken word presupposes a listener, every written word a reader; to create its audience is the hidden but more important aspect of literary achievement.

CHARACTERS without action are lame, action without characters blind.

THE TRULY poetic is as far removed from the heartless as from the sentimental.

NOWADAYS, perhaps, there is more to be learned from Goethe's aphorisms than from all the German universities put together.

NOT EVEN a section of a form's surface can be created save from its innermost centre.

TRUE love of language is not possible without sacrifice of language.

THE AVERAGE raconteur relates how something might occur. The good raconteur makes something occur before our eyes as though it were occurring. The master raconteur relates his story as though something which occurred long ago were occurring again.

FLAUBERT is a very distinguished author. Compare him, however, with Goethe or Dostoevski, and irony appears to be too predominant an element in his writing.

FRENCH prose at its highest level is more sensual in the intellectual field and in the sensual more intellectual than the German at its present level.

[371]

GOOD taste is the ability continuously to counteract exaggeration.

GOLDONI was a man with a poetic hand, but the guts of a Philistine.

WERE I asked to name two books which, while not in the class of major poetry, represent the infinitude of human substance, I would choose La Bruyère's *Caractères* and Goethe's autobiography. A third would be Boswell's *Life of Johnson*.

ANY SURRENDER to the descriptive leads to exaggeration.

PLASTICITY develops not through observation, but through identification.

THE DEEPER a man's solitude the more powerful his language; conversely, the most sociable of men should be silent and watch.

GOETHE is not the source of this and that in our more recent literature, but he is a mountain range, and the source-region of all and everything in it.

WE CAN educate ourselves on Goethe provided we don't let ourselves be confused; German literature in general cannot educate, only confuse.

THE WORST style develops when a man imitates something while pretending to feel superior to the object of his imitation.

THE BLENDING of the descriptive with the enthusiastic produces an intolerable style.

From the "Book of Friends"

NATURE permeates everything with the secret of not-understanding, which exists even between the intellectual product and its producer.

ALLUSION is an inferior rhetorical form which cannot occur in superior modes of speech because these are in themselves nothing but allusion to the incommunicable.

CAN COMEDY be palatable without a breath of mysticism?

OF THOSE for whom the theatre is their real destiny, the heroic and tragic actors are in flight from the I, the comic in flight from the world.

ONE ADVANTAGE of the French language is that it can form spontaneously the plural of sensual *abstracta: les fatigues, les vides, les noirs.*

ONLY he who can create the tenderest can create the strongest.

THE GENIUS creates harmony between the world he lives in and the world that lives in him.

GOETHE'S works combine sociability and solitude.

POETRY on the highest level points towards an element whereon all events are based and which is more secret than causality; why Hector and Achilles do not clash with one another save in the one decisive battle cannot be substantiated; it can only be represented.

EMINENT Germans always seem to be swimming under water; only Goethe, like a lonely dolphin, moves on the sparkling surface.

Hugo von Hofmannsthal

THE WORLD has lost its innocence, and without innocence no one creates or enjoys a work of art.

TO YOUTH the so-called Interesting is remarkable, to a more mature age the Good.

NATURALISM distorts Nature because by copying the surface it has to neglect the wealth of inner relatedness—Nature's real mysterium.

IN A WORK of art of a higher order, as much as in an organic formation, it is not the isolated form which is so magical, but the emergence of one form from another.

THE PUREST poesy is a state of being completely out of one's own self, the most perfect prose a complete returning to one's own self. The latter is perhaps even rarer than the former.

ONLY from the apparently Evident and Palpable can emanate the powerful effect of a secret.

NOTES

Biographical Note

HUGO VON HOFMANNSTHAL was born in Vienna on February 1, 1874, the only child of a family of Austrian, south German-Jewish, and Lombard antecedents. When he entered the University of Vienna, in 1892, he was already famous as a poet—as "Loris," his *nom de plume*. Hofmannsthal first studied law; after military service, in 1894–95, he turned to romance philology and took the Ph.D. in 1898. Nearly all of his lyrical poetry was written during the nineties, as well as most of the short lyrical plays later collected as "little dramas" (the most famous is *Death and the Fool*, 1893) and a few tales and essays. He married in 1901 and settled in Rodaun, a village near Vienna. He had three children. Occasionally he travelled—the Continent; England twice, briefly; Greece, Morocco, Sicily once. In 1899, Hofmannsthal had begun to write for the stage. From about 1908 until his death, he collaborated with both the composer Richard Strauss and the producer Max Reinhardt. His drama *Elektra* (1904), an adaptation from Sophocles, became the libretto in 1909 of an opera of Strauss. There followed the operas *Der Rosenkavalier* (1911), *Ariadne in Naxos* (1912), *The Woman without a Shadow* (1919), *The Egyptian Helen* (1928), and *Arabella* (staged in 1933). Reinhardt produced Hofmannsthal's rendering of *Oedipus Rex* (1909), his morality play *Everyman* (1911), and his comedy *The Man Who Was Difficult* (1922). During all these years, Hofmannsthal continued to write essays. He began two works of prose fiction: *Andreas* (1912–13) and *The Woman with-*

out a Shadow (1919); only the latter was completed. During the first World War, he dedicated his efforts to his country, imperial Austria, and after the war to the new Austrian republic and to the idea of the European community. He was the guiding spirit behind the Salzburg Festival; his *Everyman* became one of its central pieces. For the Festival he wrote the *Salzburg Great World Theatre* (1922); that and his last tragedy, *The Tower* (1925; second version, 1927), had their starting points in plays of Calderón. Hofmannsthal died suddenly on July 15, 1929, at Rodaun.

Textual Notes

THE COLLECTING of Hofmannsthal's entire works was not undertaken until 1945, when the S. Fischer Verlag, now of Frankfurt a/M, began the publication of all that he had got into print (some of it almost unknown) and all that has been published posthumously. The Fischer edition, edited by Herbert Steiner, will ultimately consist of about fourteen volumes; four volumes of Hofmannsthal's letters and important papers will also be published under the same editorship. The selections in this book can be found in three of the Fischer volumes (*Die Erzählungen, Prosa II,* and *Prosa IV*) and in the *Buch der Freunde* (Insel-Verlag, now of Wiesbaden, 1922).

INTRODUCTION, *by Hermann Broch.* One of his last writings, completed at the end of 1950; Broch died in May, 1951, at New Haven, Connecticut.

    x. Bekenntnis-Lyrik, a term frequently used in German literature, here contrasted with *Erkenntnis-Lyrik.* It goes back to Goethe's often misinterpreted comment that all his works are one great confession.

    xii. *Tat tvam asi:* "Thou Art That (i.e., the Universal Self)," the "great formula" of Hinduism.

    xxviii. The poem is Hofmannsthal's "Reiselied" ("Travel Song"), written in 1898. (Translated by Willard Trask.)

ANDREAS. The author put as a sub- or alternative title "The United." The internal headings may have been other tentative titles.

Textual Notes

1. The motto is from *Orlando Furioso,* Book VIII, lines 1–2. In the translation of John Hoole (1783):

> What strange enchanters in our times abound!
> What strange enchantresses alike are found!

3–73. This fragment, not more than one fourth, perhaps, of the intended novel, was written in 1912 and 1913; though gone over by the author it is, as small inconsistencies and repetitions denote, not in a final state. It was first published in 1930, after Hofmannsthal's death.

10. Wieden: a district of Vienna, at the time of the story outside the walls.

> *Mandoletti:* wafers made with honey and almonds.

74–125. These notes and drafts for *Andreas,* written approximately 1910–17, were arranged in this order by the author's son-in-law, Heinrich Zimmer, for the book publication of the novel (1932). A few lines Zimmer omitted have been restored.

79. What a spectacle . . . : quoted from Faust's first monologue.

83. I have neglected nothing: this remark of Poussin's at the end of his life Hofmannsthal admired and quoted at the end of the *Book of Friends.*

84. Human beings are the sufferings and acts of the spirit: cf. Goethe: "Colours are the sufferings and acts (or labours) of light." — And cf. also page 298, four lines from the end.

> *Goethe's "Note":* to his translation of Diderot's *Neveu de Rameau.*

85. identity: in Keats's sense; cf. his letters (Translator's note).

> *pointe acérée de l'infini:* Hofmannsthal continued to use this quotation from Baudelaire years later.

87. silent fall of distant stars: from one of his own poems (1895): "I cannot ward off from my frightened eyelids the silent fall of distant stars."

88. Princess in "Tasso": Hofmannsthal wrote an essay on the vestal-like Princess.

> *Yesterday* was his earliest play, written at 17.

89. Galiani: the Abbé Fernando Galiani, eighteenth-century Italian writer and economist.

91. *Moreau horrors:* cf. H. G. Wells's novel *The Island of Dr. Moreau* (1896).

    Key of his life: magic diagram, horoscope, or the like.

94–95. Welsberg Castle and Bruneck: in eastern Tirol, near Carinthia and the Italian border. Also pages 114–15.

95. *Pyramid of Life:* a motif frequent in old prints and pictures, showing the stages of man's life—the child and young man climbing steps, the elderly and old man stepping down toward the grave.

    Hebbel's epigram: that of Friedrich Hebbel on the fate of philosophers reads, in Mrs. Hottinger's translation: "We believe we hold the Key of Solomon in our hands, and can unlock heaven and earth with it, but it dissolves in figures, and, to our horror, we see the alphabet renew itself. Yet let us take comfort, it has in the meantime grown more august."

96. *Jung-Stilling:* Goethe's contemporary, a Pietist and author of famous recollections.

    Tabula smaragdina Hermetis: the "Emerald Tablet of Hermes," an ancient anonymous alchemical work.

99. *Ramakrishna:* the nineteenth-century Hindu Tantrist saint and teacher. Cf. "Colours," pages 150–51.

103. *Sette Communi:* "Seven Communes," a region in the Venetian Alps.

    Terra ferma: the Venetian mainland.

    in a raving way: originally in English.

105. *imp of the perverse:* originally in English.

115. *the sieve of the Danaides, the rock of Sisyphus:* quoted from Goethe, *Wilhelm Meisters Lehrjahre.*

117. *Grillparzer's relationship to Kathi:* Kathi Froehlich was the "eternal fiancée" of the Austrian poet and playwright, author of *The Ancestress* (cf. page 285).

118. *the grasp to get it:* originally in English.

120. *Hafiz:* in Goethe's *Westöstlicher Diwan.*

121. *Allomatic:* a translation of "allomatisch," a word taken over from Greek *allomatos,* "occurring because of another's influence." The word here means "transformation through the influence of another individual."

122. *Tale of the Six-Hundred-and-Seventy-Second Night, The*

Textual Notes

Wedding of Sobeide, Death and the Fool: works of Hofmannsthal's youth.

124. *Saïs:* ancient capital of Lower Egypt. The "image of Saïs" was a recurrent symbol in German literature; cf. Schiller's "The Veiled Image at Saïs" and Novalis's "The Disciples of Saïs."

THE LETTER OF LORD CHANDOS. Written in 1901 or 1902, published in 1902.

COLOURS. Written in 1907, published in 1908, fifth and last of the uncompleted Letters of a Man Who Returned, supposedly written in 1901 by an Austrian (or German) who after many years abroad has come back to Europe.

FEAR. Written and published in 1907. Hofmannsthal was deeply interested in the revival of dance. He wrote on Ruth St. Denis and on Nijinsky and composed librettoes for his friend the Viennese dancer Grete Wiesenthal and for Diaghilev's Russian Ballet (e.g., *Legend of Joseph,* libretto by Count Harry Kessler and Hofmannsthal, choreography by Fokine, music by Richard Strauss, 1914).

MOMENTS IN GREECE. Part I, written and published in 1908; Part II, written in 1912, published in 1917; Part III, date of writing unknown, published in 1917. The author had travelled in Greece in 1908, with his friend Count Kessler and the French sculptor Maillol.

174–75. The meetings with Rimbaud (died 1891) were imaginary.

184–86. The statues in the Acropolis Museum are the Korai, the "Maidens."

JOURNEY IN NORTHERN AFRICA: FEZ. One of two essays on the north African journey, written and published in 1925, the year of the author's visit. He was received by Marshal Lyautey.

A MEMORY OF BEAUTIFUL DAYS. Written and published in 1908. It probably refers to the time ten years before when Hofmannsthal, in Venice, wrote his play *The Adventurer and the Singer.*

ENCOUNTERS. Written and published in 1907. The words of Agur are quoted from Proverbs 30 : 18, 19.

Textual Notes

TWILIGHT AND NOCTURNAL STORM. A fragment written in 1911 or 1912 and posthumously published. It was to be the beginning of the story of Euseb's night of destiny and of his way into life.

THE WOMAN WITHOUT A SHADOW. This tale, published in 1919, is a fuller and deeper treatment of the theme of Hofmannsthal's libretto for Strauss's opera of the same name, produced in 1919. Chapter Four (one of seven), probably written in 1918, relates the Vision of the Unborn.

SHAKESPEARE'S KINGS AND NOBLEMEN. Published in 1905. In 1916, for the tercentenary of Shakespeare's death, Hofmannsthal wrote an essay "Shakespeare and Ourselves."

255–56. The dance at the end of Sir Herbert Beerbohm Tree's production of *Twelfth Night,* a Masque of Life, reminded Hofmannsthal of one of his own principal motifs, the Dance of Death.

267. *glowing key . . . Mothers . . . neither Space, still less Time:* from *Faust,* Part II.

BALZAC. Written half a century after Taine's essay (see page 282), in 1908, and published the same year, as an introduction to the German twelve-volume edition of Balzac brought out by the Insel-Verlag.

275. *the one famous book we have on the same subject:* Stendhal's *De l'amour* (1822).

280. Hofmannsthal did not know we have a drawing of Balzac by Daumier, made at the artist's studio early in his career (though not one by Delacroix).

ON CHARACTERS IN NOVELS AND PLAYS. Written and published in 1902.

285. *The Ancestress:* see note for page 117.

288. *Venice Preserved:* Hofmannsthal's own adaptation of Otway's tragedy was published in 1905.

Vautrin considers it . . . : His words, at his first meeting with Rubempré, are found toward the end of *Les Illusions perdues.*

SEBASTIAN MELMOTH. Written and published in 1905.

Textual Notes

AN EPISODE IN THE LIFE OF THE MARSHAL DE BASSOMPIERRE. Written and published in 1900. Goethe, in his *Conversations of German Émigrés* (1795), took this episode from the *Mémoires du Maréchal de Bassompierre* (Cologne, 1665). Hofmannsthal, at the end of his tale based on the Goethe anecdote, cited both titles.

A TALE OF THE CAVALRY. Written and published in 1899. In 1848, Lombardy and Venice were Austrian.

321. *Rofrano:* the name appears much later, in *Der Rosenkavalier*, as the family name of Octavian.

LUCIDOR. Written and published in 1910. The last libretto that Hofmannsthal wrote for Strauss, *Arabella* (produced in 1933), is an unfolding of the Lucidor motif.

FROM THE "BOOK OF FRIENDS." The *Book of Friends*, compiled from Hofmannsthal's notebooks of 1917–22 and from quotations, was published in 1922. It may be compared to the aphorisms of the French *moralistes* and, more so, to Goethe's *Maxims and Reflections* and to Novalis's *Fragments*.